當代中文課程

A Course in Contemporary Chinese

Textbook 課本

③

國立臺灣師範大學國語教學中心 策劃
Mandarin Training Center National Taiwan Normal University

主編／鄧守信　編寫教師／王瓊淑、盧翠英、盧德昭

序 Foreword

　　臺灣師範大學國語教學中心成立於 1956 年，是臺灣歷史最悠久、規模最完備、教學最有成效的華語文教學機構。每年培育三千名以上的外籍學生，學生來自世界一百二十餘國，至今累計人數已達五萬餘人，在國際間享譽盛名。

　　本中心自 1967 年開始編製教材，迄今共計編寫五十餘本教材，在華語教學界具有舉足輕重之地位。而現今使用之主教材已有十五年之久，不少學生及教師認為現行教材內容需要更新，應新編配合時代需求的新教材。因此，本中心因應外在環境變遷、教學法及教學媒體的創新與進步，籌畫編寫《當代中文課程》6 冊，以符合海內外華語教學的需求，並強化臺灣華語文教學教材之品牌。

　　為了讓理論與實務結合，並落實發揚華語文教學的精神與理念，本中心邀請了華語教學界的大師——鄧守信教授擔任主編，率領 18 位極富教學經驗的第一線老師進行內容編寫，並由張莉萍副研究員、張黛琪老師及教材研發組成員蔡如珮、張雯雯擔任執行編輯，進行了這項《當代中文課程》的編寫計畫。

　　這是本中心歷經數十年深厚教學經驗後再次開發的全新主教材，更為了確保品質，特別慎重；我們很榮幸地邀請到美國的 Claudia Ross 教授、白建華教授及陳雅芬教授，擔任顧問，也邀請了臺灣的葉德明教授、美國的姚道中教授及大陸的劉珣教授，擔任審查委員，並由本校英語系李櫻教授和畢永峨教授分別協助生詞和語法的翻譯。此教材在本中心及臺灣其他語言中心，進行了一年多的試用；經過顧問的悉心指導、審查委員的仔細批閱，並參考了老師及學生提出的寶貴意見，再由編寫老師做了多次修改，才將版本定稿。對於所有在編寫過程中，努力不懈的編輯團隊、給予指教的教授、配合試用的老師及學生，我們都要致上最高的謝意。

　　在此也特別感謝聯經出版事業股份有限公司，願意投注最大的心力，以專業的製作出版能力，協助我們將這套教材以最佳品質問世。

　　我們希望，《當代中文課程》不只提供學生們一套實用有效的教材，亦讓老師得到愉快充實的教學經驗。歡迎老師在使用後，給予我們更多的指教與建議，讓我們不斷進步，也才能為海內外的華語教學，做更多更好的貢獻。

國立臺灣師範大學國語教學中心主任　陳浩然

2015 年 6 月

The Mandarin Training Center (MTC) at National Taiwan Normal University (NTNU) was established in 1956, and is the oldest, most comprehensive, and most pedagogically effective educational institute of its kind in Taiwan. Every year over 3,000 international students are trained at MTC, and to the present day over 50,000 students representing more than 120 countries have walked through its doors, solidifying international renown.

MTC started producing teaching material in 1967, and has since completed over 50 textbooks, making it a frontrunner in the field of teaching Chinese as a second language. As the core books have been in circulation for 15 years already, many students and teachers agree that updates are in order, and that new materials should be made to meet the modern demand. Changes in the social landscape, improved teaching methods, and innovations in educational media are what prompted the production of MTC's six-volume series, *A Course in Contemporary Chinese*. The project responds to Chinese teaching needs both at home and abroad, and bolsters Taiwan's brand of teaching material for Chinese as a second language.

With the goal of integrating theory and practice, and carrying forward the spirit of teaching Chinese as a second language, MTC petitioned one of the field's most esteemed professors, Shou-Hsin Teng, to serve as chief editor. *A Course in Contemporary Chinese* has been compiled and edited under his leadership, together with the help of 18 seasoned Chinese teachers and the following four executive editors: Associate Research Fellow Liping Chang, Tai-chi Chang, and Ru-pei Cai and Wen-wen Chang of the MTC teaching material development division.

MTC is presenting this brand new core material after half a century's worth of educational experience, and we have taken extra care to ensure it is of uncompromised quality. We were delighted to have American professors Claudia Ross, Jianhua Bai , and Yea-fen Chen act as consultants, Professor Teh-Ming Yeh from Taiwan, Professor Tao-chung Yao from the U.S., and Professor Xun Liu from China on the review committee, and professors Ying Cherry Li and Yung-O Biq of NTNU's English department help with the respective translation of vocabulary and grammar points. The material was first trialed at MTC and other language centers around Taiwan for a year. The current version underwent numerous drafts, and materialized under the careful guidance of the consultants, a sedulous reading from the review committee, and feedback from teachers and students. As for the editorial process, we owe the greatest thanks to the indefatigable editorial team, the professors and their invaluable input, and the teachers and students who were willing to trial the book.

An additional and special thanks is due to Linking Publishing Company, who put forth utmost effort and professionalism in publishing this set of teaching material, allowing us to deliver a publication of superior quality.

It is our hope that *A Course in Contemporary Chinese* is not merely a practical set of teaching materials for students, but also enriching for teachers and the entire teaching experience. We welcome comments from instructors who have put the books into practice so that we can continue improving the material. Only then can we keep furthering our contribution to the field of teaching Chinese as a second language, both in Taiwan and abroad.

Hao Jan Chen

Director of the Mandarin Training Center
National Taiwan Normal University
June, 2015

From the Editor's Desk

Finally, after more than two years, volume one of our six-volume project is seeing the light of day. The language used in *A Course in Contemporary Chinese* is up to date, and though there persists a deep 'generation gap' between it and my own brand of Chinese, this is as it should be. In addition to myself, our project team has consisted of 18 veteran MTC teachers and the entire staff of the MTC Section of Instructional Materials, plus the MTC Deputy Director.

The field of L2 Chinese in Taiwan seems to have adopted the world-famous 'one child policy'. The complete set of currently used textbooks was born a generation ago, and until now has been without predecessor. We are happy to fill this vacancy, and with the title 'number two', yet we also aspire to have it be number two in name alone. After a generation, we present a slightly disciplined contemporary language as observed in Taiwan, we employ Hanyu Pinyin without having to justify it cautiously and timidly, we are proud to present a brand-new system of Chinese parts of speech that will hopefully eliminate many instances of error, we have devised two kinds of exercises in our series, one basically structural and the other entirely task-based, each serving its own intended function, and finally we have included in each lesson a special aspect of Chinese culture. Moreover, all this is done in full color, the first time ever in the field of L2 Chinese in Taiwan. The settings for our current series is in Taipei, Taiwan, with events taking place near the National Taiwan Normal University. The six volumes progress from basic colloquial to semi-formal and finally to authentic conversations or narratives. The glossary in vocabulary and grammar is in basically semi-literal English, not free translation, as we wish to guide the readers/learners along the Chinese 'ways of thinking', but rest assured that no pidgin English has been used.

I am a functional, not structural, linguist, and users of our new textbooks will find our approaches and explanations more down to earth. Both teachers and learners will find that the content resonates with their own experiences and feelings. Rote learning plays but a tiny part of our learning experiences. In a functional frame, the role of the speaker often seen as prominent. This is natural, as numerous adverbs in Chinese, as they are traditionally referred to, do not in fact modify verb phrases at all. They relate to the speaker.

We, the field of Chinese as a second language, know a lot about how to teach, especially when it comes to Chinese characters. Most L2 Chinese teachers world-wide are ethnically Chinese, and teach characters just as they were taught in childhood. Truth is, we know next to nothing how adult students/learners actually learn characters, and other elements of the Chinese language. While we have nothing new in this series of textbooks that contributes to the teaching of Chinese characters, I tried to tightly integrate teaching and learning through our presentation of vocabulary items and grammatical structures. Underneath such methodologies is my personal conviction, and at times both instructors' and learners' patience is requested. I welcome communication with all users of our new textbooks, whether instructors or students/learners.

Shou-hsin Teng

Series Introduction

This six-volume series is a comprehensive learning material that focuses on spoken language in the first three volumes and written language in the latter three volumes. Volume One aims to strengthen daily conversation and applications; Volume Two contains short essays as supplementary readings; Volume Three introduces beginning-level written language and discourse, in addition to extended dialogues. Volume Four uses discourse to solidify the learner's written language and ability in reading authentic materials; Volumes Five and Six are arranged in topics such as society, technology, economics, politics, culture, and environment to help the learner expand their language utilizations in different domains.

Each volume includes a textbook, a student workbook, and a teacher's manual. In addition, Volume One and Two include a practice book for characters.

Level of Students

A Course in Contemporary Chinese 《當代中文課程》 is suitable for learners of Chinese in Taiwan, as well as for high school or college level Chinese language courses overseas. Volumes One to Six cover levels A1 to C1 in the CEFR, or Novice to Superior levels in ACTFL Guidelines.

Overview

- The series adopts communicative language teaching and task-based learning to boost the learner's Chinese ability.

- Each lesson has learning objectives and self-evaluation to give the learner a clear record of tasks completed.

- Lessons are authentic daily situations to help the learner learn in natural contexts.

- Lexical items and syntactic structures are presented and explained in functional, not structural, perspectives.

- Syntactic, i.e. grammatical, explanation includes functions, structures, pragmatics, and drills to guide the learner to proper usage.

- Classroom activities have specific learning objectives, activities, or tasks to help fortify learning while having fun.

- The "Bits of Chinese Culture" section of the lesson has authentic photographs to give the learner a deeper look at local Taiwanese culture.

- Online access provides supplementary materials for teachers & students.

目次 **Contents**

Contents

An Introduction to the Chinese Language

China is a multi-ethnic society, and when people in general study Chinese, 'Chinese' usually refers to the Beijing variety of the language as spoken by the Han people in China, also known as Mandarin Chinese or simply Mandarin. It is the official language of China, known mostly domestically as the Putonghua, the lingua franca, or Hanyu, the Han language. In Taiwan, Guoyu refers to the national/official language, and Huayu to either Mandarin Chinese as spoken by Chinese descendants residing overseas, or to Mandarin when taught to non-Chinese learners. The following pages present an outline of the features and properties of Chinese. For further details, readers are advised to consult various and rich on-line resources.

Language Kinship

Languages in the world are grouped together on the basis of language affiliation, called language-family. Chinese, or rather Hanyu, is a member of the Sino-Tibetan family, which covers most of China today, plus parts of Southeast Asia. Therefore, Tibetan, Burmese, and Thai are genetically related to Hanyu.

Hanyu is spoken in about 75% of the present Chinese territory, by about 75% of the total Chinese population, and it covers 7 major dialects, including the better known Cantonese, Hokkienese, Hakka and Shanghainese.

Historically, Chinese has interacted highly actively with neighboring but unaffiliated languages, such as Japanese, Korean and Vietnamese. The interactions took place in such areas as vocabulary items, phonological structures, a few grammatical features and most importantly the writing script.

Typological Features of Chinese

Languages in the world are also grouped together on the basis of language characteristics, called language typology. Chinese has the following typological traits, which highlight the dissimilarities between Chinese and English.

A. Chinese is a non-tense language. Tense is a grammatical device such that the verb changes according to the time of the event in relation to the time of utterance. Thus 'He talks nonsense' refers to his habit, while 'He talked nonsense' refers to a time in the past when he behaved that way, but he does not necessarily do that all the time. 'Talked' then is a verb in the past tense. Chinese does not operate with this device but marks the time of events with time expressions such as 'today' or 'tomorrow' in the sentence. The verb remains the same regardless of time of happening. This type of language is labeled as an atensal language, while English and most European languages are tensal languages. Knowing this particular trait can help European learners of Chinese avoid mistakes to do with verbs in Chinese. Thus, in responding to 'What did you do in China last year?' Chinese is 'I teach English (last year)'; and to 'What are you doing now in Japan?' Chinese is again 'I teach English (now)'.

B. Nouns in Chinese are not directly countable. Nouns in English are either countable, e.g., 2 candies, or non-countable, e.g., *2 salts, while all nouns in Chinese are non-countable. When they are to be counted, a measure, or called classifier, must be used between a noun and a number, e.g., 2-piece-candy. Thus, Chinese is a classifier language. Only non-countable nouns in English are used with measures, e.g., a drop of water.

Therefore it is imperative to learn nouns in Chinese together with their associated measures/classifiers. There are only about 30 high-frequency measures/classifiers in Chinese to be mastered at the initial stage of learning.

C. Chinese is a Topic-Prominent language. Sentences in Chinese quite often begin with somebody or something that is being talked about, rather than the subject of the verb in the sentence. This item is called a topic in linguistics. Most Asian languages employ topic, while most European languages employ subject. The following bad English sentences, sequenced below per frequency of usage, illustrate the topic structures in Chinese.

*Senator Kennedy, people in Europe also respected.

*Seafood, Taiwanese people love lobsters best.

*President Obama, he attended Harvard University.

Because of this feature, Chinese people tend to speak 'broken' English, whereas English speakers tend to sound 'complete', if bland and alien, when they talk in Chinese. Through practice and through keen observations of what motivates the use of a topic in Chinese, this feature of Chinese can be acquired eventually.

D. Chinese tends to drop things in the sentence. The 'broken' tendencies mentioned above also include not using nouns in a sentence where English counterparts are 'complete'. This tendency is called dropping, as illustrated below through bad English sentences.

Are you coming tomorrow? ----- *Come!

What did you buy? ----- *Buy some jeans.

*This bicycle, who rides? ----- *My old professor rides.

The 1st example drops everything except the verb, the 2nd drops the subject, and the 3rd drops the object. Dropping happens when what is dropped is easily recoverable or identifiable from the contexts or circumstances. Not doing this, Europeans are often commented upon that their sentences in Chinese are too often inundated with unwanted pronouns!!

Phonological Characteristics of Chinese

Phonology refers to the system of sound, the pronunciation, of a language. To untrained ears, Chinese language sounds unfamiliar, sort of alien in a way. This is due to the fact that Chinese sound system contains some elements that are not part of the sound systems of European languages, though commonly found on the Asian continent. These features will be explained below.

On the whole, the Chinese sound system is not really very complicated. It has 7 vowels, 5 of which are found in English (i, e, a, o, u), plus 2 which are not (-e,); and it has 21 consonants, 15 of which are quite common, plus 6 which are less common (zh, ch, sh, r, z, c). And Chinese has a fairly simple syllable shape, i.e., consonant + vowel plus possible nasals (n or ng). What is most striking to English speakers is that every syllable in Chinese has a 'tone', as will be detailed directly below. But, a word on the sound representation, the pinyin system, first.

A. Hanyu Pinyin. Hanyu Pinyin is a variety of Romanization systems that attempt to represent the sound of Chinese through the use of Roman letters (abc…). Since the end of the 19th century, there have been about half a dozen Chinese Romanization systems, including the Wade-Giles, Guoyu Luomazi, Yale, Hanyu Pinyin, Lin Yutang, and Zhuyin Fuhao Di'ershi, not to mention the German system, the French system etc. Thanks to the consensus of media worldwide, and through the support of the UN, Hanyu Pinyin has become the standard worldwide. Taiwan is probably the only place in the world that does not support nor employ Hanyu Pinyin. Instead, it uses non-Roman symbols to represent the sound, called Zhuyin Fuhao, alias BoPoMoFo (cf. the symbols employed in this volume). Officially, that is. Hanyu Pinyin represents the Chinese sound as follows.

b, p, m, f   d, t, n, l   g, k, h   j, q, x   zh, ch, sh, r   z, c, s

a, o, -e, e   ai, ei, ao, ou   an, en, ang, eng   -r, i, u, ü

B. Chinese is a tonal language. A tone refers to the voice pitch contour. Pitch contours are used in many languages, including English, but for different functions in different languages. English uses them to indicate the speaker's viewpoints, e.g., 'well' in different contours may indicate impatience, surprise, doubt etc. Chinese, on the other hand, uses contours to refer to different meanings, words. Pitch contours with different linguistic functions are not transferable from one language to another. Therefore, it would be futile trying to learn Chinese tones by looking for or identifying their contour counterparts in English.

Mandarin Chinese has 4 distinct tones, the fewest among all Han dialects, i.e., level, rising, dipping and falling, marked ˉ ˊ ˅ ˋ, and it has only one tone-change rule, i.e., ˅ ˅ → ˊ ˅, though the conditions for this change are fairly complicated. In addition to the four tones, Mandarin also has one neutral(ized) tone, i.e., ˙, pronounced short/unstressed, which is derived, historically if not synchronically, from the 4 tones; hence the term neutralized. Again, the conditions and environments for the neutralization are highly complex and cannot be explored in this space.

C. Syllable final –r effect (vowel retroflexivisation). The northern variety of Hanyu, esp. in Beijing, is known for its richness in the –r effect at the end of a syllable. For example, 'flower' is 'huā' in southern China but 'huār' in Beijing. Given the prominence of the city Beijing, this sound feature tends to be defined as standard nationwide; but that –r effect is rarely attempted in the south. There do not seem to be rigorous rules governing what can and what cannot take the –r effect. It is thus advised that learners of Chinese resort to rote learning in this case, as probably even native speakers of northern Chinese do.

D. Syllables in Chinese do not 'connect'. 'Connect' here refers to the merging of the tail of a syllable with the head of a subsequent syllable, e.g., English pronounces 'at' + 'all' as 'at+tall', 'did' +'you' as 'did+dyou' and 'that'+'is' as 'that+th'is'. On the other hand, syllables in Chinese are isolated from each other and do not connect in this way. Fortunately, this is not a serious problem for English language learners, as the syllable structures in Chinese are rather limited, and there are not many candidates for this merging. We noted above that Chinese syllables take the form of CV plus possible 'n' and 'ng'. CV does not give rise to connecting, not even in English; so be extra cautious when a syllable ends with 'n' or 'g' and a subsequent syllable begins with a V, e.g., MǐnÀo 'Fujian Province and Macao'. Nobody would understand 'min+nao'!!

E. Retroflexive consonants. 'Retroflexive' refers to consonants that are pronounced with the tip of the tongue curled up (-flexive) backwards (retro-). There are altogether 4 such consonants, i.e., zh, ch, sh, and r. The pronunciation of these consonants reveals the geographical origin of native Chinese speakers. Southerners do not have them, merging them with z, c, and s, as is commonly observed in Taiwan. Curling up of the tongue comes in various degrees. Local Beijing dialect is well known for its prominent curling. Imagine curling up the tongue at the beginning of a syllable and curling it up again for the –r effect!! ! Try 'zhèr-over here', 'zhuōr-table' and 'shuǐr-water'.

On Chinese Grammar

'Grammar' refers to the ways and rules of how words are organized into a string that is a sentence in a language. Given the fact that all languages have sentences, and at the same time non-sentences, all languages including Chinese have grammar. In this section, the most salient and important features and issues of Chinese grammar will be presented, but a summary of basic structures, as referenced against English, is given first.

A. Similarities in Chinese and English.

	English	Chinese
SVO	They sell coffee.	Tāmen mài kāfēi.
AuxV+Verb	You may sit down!	Nǐ kěyǐ zuòxià ō!
Adj+Noun	sour grapes	suān pútáo
Prep+its Noun	at home	zài jiā
Num+Meas+Noun	a piece of cake	yí kuài dàngāo
Demons+Noun	those students	nàxiē xuéshēng

B. Dissimilar structures.

	English	Chinese
RelClause: Noun	the book that you bought	nǐ mǎi de shū
VPhrase: PrepPhrase	to eat at home	zài jiā chīfàn
Verb: Adverbial	Eat slowly!	Mànmār chī!

Set: Subset	6th Sept, 1967	1967 nián 9 yuè 6 hào
	Taipei, Taiwan	Táiwān Táiběi
	3 of my friends…	wǒ de péngyǒu, yǒu sān ge…

C. Modifier precedes modified (MPM). This is one of the most important grammatical principles in Chinese. We see it operating actively in the charts given above, so that adjectives come before nouns they modify, relative clauses also come before the nouns they modify, possessives come before nouns (tāde diànnǎo 'his computer'), auxiliary verbs come before verbs, adverbial phrases before verbs, prepositional phrases come before verbs etc. This principle operates almost without exceptions in Chinese, while in English modifiers sometimes precede and some other times follow the modified.

D. Principle of Temporal Sequence (PTS). Components of a sentence in Chinese are lined up in accordance with the sequence of time. This principle operates especially when there is a series of verbs contained within a sentence, or when there is a sentential conjunction. First compare the sequence of 'units' of an event in English and that in its Chinese counterpart.

Event: David /went to New York/ by train /from Boston/ to see his sister.

English: 1   2   3   4   5

Chinese: 1   4   2   3   5

Now in real life, David got on a train, the train departed from Boston, it arrived in New York, and finally he visited his sister. This sequence of units is 'natural' time, and the Chinese sentence 'Dàwèi zuò huǒchē cóng Bōshìdùn dào Niǔyuē qù kàn tā de jiějie' follows it, but not English. In other words, Chinese complies strictly with PTS.

When sentences are conjoined, English has various possibilities in organizing the conjunction. First, the scenario. H1N1 hits China badly (event-1), and as a result, many schools were closed (event-2). Now, English has the following possible ways of conjoining to express this, e.g.,

Many schools were closed, because/since H1N1 hit China badly. (E2+E1)

H1N1 hit China badly, so many schools were closed. (E1+E2)

As H1N1 hit China badly, many schools were closed. (E1+E2)

Whereas the only way of expressing the same in Chinese is E1+E2 when both conjunctions are used (yīnwèi… suǒyǐ…), i.e.,

Zhōngguó yīnwèi H1N1 gǎnrǎn yánzhòng (E1), suǒyǐ xǔduō xuéxiào zhànshí guānbì (E2).

PTS then helps explain why 'cause' is always placed before 'consequence' in Chinese.

PTS is also seen operating in the so-called verb-complement constructions in Chinese, e.g., shā-sǐ 'kill+dead', chī-bǎo 'eat+full', dǎ-kū 'hit+cry' etc. The verb represents an action that must have happened first before its consequence.

There is an interesting group of adjectives in Chinese, namely 'zǎo-early', 'wǎn-late', 'kuài-fast', 'màn-slow', 'duō-plenty', and 'shǎo-few', which can be placed either before (as adverbials) or after (as complements) of their associated verbs, e.g.,

Nǐ míngtiān zǎo diǎr lái! (Come earlier tomorrow!)

Wǒ lái zǎo le. Jìnbúqù. (I arrived too early. I could not get in.)

When 'zǎo' is placed before the verb 'lái', the time of arrival is intended, planned, but when it is placed after, the time of arrival is not pre-planned, maybe accidental. The difference complies with PTS. The same difference holds in the case of the other adjectives in the group, e.g.,

Qǐng nǐ duō mǎi liǎngge! (Please get two extra!)

Wǒ mǎiduō le. Zāotà le! (I bought two too many. Going to be wasted!)

'Duō' in the first sentence is going to be pre-planned, a pre-event state, while in the second, it's a post-event report. Pre-event and post-event states then are naturally taken care of by PTS. Our last set in the group is more complicated. 'Kuài' and 'màn' can refer to amount of time in addition to manner of action, as illustrated below.

Nǐ kuài diǎr zǒu; yào chídào le! (Hurry up and go! You'll be late (e.g., for work)!)

Qǐng nǐ zǒu kuài yìdiǎr! (Please walk faster!)

'Kuài' in the first can be glossed as 'quick, hurry up' (in as little time as possible after the utterance), while that in the second refers to manner of walking. Similarly, 'màn yìdiǎr zǒu-don't leave yet' and 'zǒu màn yìdiǎr-walk more slowly'.

We have seen in this section the very important role in Chinese grammar played by variations in word-order. European languages exhibit rich resources in changing the forms of verbs, adjectives and nouns, and Chinese, like other Asian languages, takes great advantage of word-order.

E. Where to find subjects in existential sentences. Existential sentences refer to sentences in which the verbs express appearing (e.g., coming), disappearing (e.g., going) and presence (e.g., written (on the wall)). The existential verbs are all intransitive, and thus they are all associated with a subject, without any objects naturally. This type of sentences deserves a mention in this introduction, as they exhibit a unique structure in Chinese. When their subjects are in definite reference (something that can be referred to, e.g., pronouns and nouns with definite article in English) the subject appears at the front of the sentence, i.e., before the existential verb, but when their subjects are in indefinite reference (nothing in particular), the subject appears after the verb. Compare the following pair of sentences in Chinese against their counterparts in English.

Kèrén dōu lái le. Chīfàn ba! (All the guests we invited have arrived. Let's serve the dinner.)

Duìbùqǐ! Láiwǎn le. Jiālǐ láile yí ge kèrén. (Sorry for being late! I had an (unexpected) guest.)

More examples of post-verbal subjects are given below.

Zhè cì táifēng sǐle bù shǎo rén. (Quite a few people died during the typhoon this time.)

Zuótiān wǎnshàng xiàle duōjiǔ de yǔ? (How long did it rain last night?)

Zuótiān wǎnshàng pǎole jǐ ge fànrén? (How many inmates got away last night?)

Chēzi lǐ zuòle duōshǎo rén a? (How many people were in the car?)

Exactly when to place the existential subject after the verb will remain a challenge for learners of Chinese for quite a significant period of time. Again, observe and deduce!! Memorising sentence by sentence would not help!!

The existential subjects presented above are simple enough, e.g., people, a guest, rain and inmates. But when the subject is complex, further complications emerge!! A portion of the complex subject stays in front of the verb, and the remaining goes to the back of the verb, e.g.,

Míngtiān nǐmen qù jǐge rén? (How many of you will be going tomorrow?)

Wǒ zuìjìn diàole bù shǎo tóufǎ. (I lost=fell quite a lot of hair recently.)

Qùnián dìzhèn, tā sǐle sān ge gēge. (He lost=died 3 brothers during the earthquake last year.)

In linguistics, we say that existential sentences in Chinese have a lot of semantic and information structures involved.

F. A tripartite system of verb classifications in Chinese. English has a clear division between verbs and adjectives, but the boundary in Chinese is quite blurred, which quite seriously misleads English-speaking learners of Chinese. The error in *Wǒ jīntiān shì máng. 'I am busy today.' is a daily observation in Chinese 101! Why is it a common mistake for beginning learners? What do our textbooks and/or teachers do about it, so that the error is discouraged, if not suppressed? Nothing, much! What has not been realized in our profession is that Chinese verb classification is more strongly semantic, rather than more strongly syntactic as in English.

Verbs in Chinese have 3 sub-classes, namely Action Verbs, State Verbs and Process Verbs. Action Verbs are time-sensitive activities (beginning and ending, frozen with a snap-shot, prolonged), are will-controlled (consent or refuse), and usually take human subjects, e.g., 'chī-eat', 'mǎi-buy' and 'xué-learn'. State Verbs are non-time-sensitive physical or mental states, inclusive of the all-famous adjectives as a further sub-class, e.g., 'ài-love', 'xīwàng-hope' and 'liàng-bright'. Process Verbs refer to instantaneous change from one state to another, 'sǐ-die', 'pò-break, burst' and 'wán-finish'.

The new system of parts of speech in Chinese as adopted in this series is built on this very foundation of this tripartite verb classification. Knowing this new system will be immensely helpful in learning quite a few syntactic structures in Chinese that are nicely related to the 3 classes of verbs, as will be illustrated with negation in Chinese in the section below.

The table below presents some of the most important properties of these 3 classes of verbs, as reflected through syntactic behaviour.

	Action Verbs	State Verbs	Process Verbs
Hěn- modification	✗	✓	✗
Le- completive	✓	✗	✓
Zài- progressive	✓	✗	✗
Reduplication	✓ (tentative)	✓ (intensification)	✗
Bù- negation	✓	✓	✗
Méi- negation	✓	✗	✓

Here are more examples of 3 classes of verbs.

Action Verbs: mǎi 'buy', zuò 'sit', xué 'learn; imitate', kàn 'look'

State Verbs: xǐhuān 'like', zhīdào 'know', néng 'can', guì 'expensive'

Process Verbs: wàngle 'forget', chén 'sink', bìyè 'graduate', xǐng 'wake up'

G. Negation. Negation in Chinese is by means of placing a negative adverb immediately in front of a verb. (Remember that adjectives in Chinese are a type of State verbs!) When an action verb is negated with 'bu', the meaning can be either 'intend not to, refuse to' or 'not in a habit of', e.g.,

Nǐ bù mǎi piào; wǒ jiù bú ràng nǐ jìnqù! (If you don't buy a ticket, I won't let you in!)

Tā zuótiān zhěng tiān bù jiē diànhuà. (He did not want to answer the phone all day yesterday.)

Dèng lǎoshī bù hē jiǔ. (Mr. Teng does not drink.)

'Bù' has the meaning above but is independent of temporal reference. The first sentence above refers to the present moment or a minute later after the utterance, and the second to the past. A habit again is panchronic. But when an action verb is negated with 'méi(yǒu)', its time reference must be in the past, meaning 'something did not come to pass', e.g.,

Tā méi lái shàngbān. (He did not come to work.)

Tā méi dài qián lái. (He did not bring any money.)

A state verb can only be negated with 'bù', referring to the non-existence of that state, whether in the past, at present, or in the future, e.g.,

Tā bù zhīdào zhèjiàn shì. (He did not/does not know this.)

Tā bù xiǎng gēn nǐ qù. (He did not/does not want to go with you.)

Niǔyuē zuìjìn bú rè. (New York was/is/will not be hot.)

A process verb can only be negated with 'méi', referring to the non-happening of a change from one state to another, usually in the past, e.g.,

Yīfú méi pò; nǐ jiù rēng le? (You threw away perfectly good clothes?)

Niǎo hái méi sǐ; nǐ jiù fàng le ba! (The bird is still alive. Why don't you let it free?)

Tā méi bìyè yǐqián, hái děi dǎgōng. (He has to work odd jobs before graduating.)

As can be gathered from the above, negation of verbs in Chinese follows neat patterns, but this is so only after we work with the new system of verb classifications as presented in this series. Here's one more interesting fact about negation in Chinese before closing this section. When some action verbs refer to some activities that result in something stable, e.g., when you put on clothes, you want the clothes to stay on you, the negation of those verbs can be usually translated in the present tense in English, e.g.,

Tā zěnme méi chuān yīfú? (How come he is naked?)

Wǒ jīntiān méi dài qián. (I have no money with me today.)

H. A new system of Parts of Speech in Chinese. In the system of parts of speech adopted in this series, there are at the highest level a total of 8 parts of speech, as given below. This system includes the following major properties. First and foremost, it is errors-driven and can address some of the most prevailing errors exhibited by learners of Chinese. This characteristic dictates the depth of sub-categories in a system of grammatical categories. Secondly, it employs the concept of 'default'. This property greatly simplifies the over-all framework of the new system, so that it reduces the number of categories used, simplifies the labeling of categories, and takes advantage of the learners' contribution in terms of positive transfer. And lastly, it incorporates both semantic as well as syntactic concepts, so that it bypasses the traditionally problematic category of adjectives by establishing three major semantic types of verbs, viz. action, state and process.

Adv	Adverb (dōu 'all', dàgài 'probably')
Conj	Conjunction (gēn 'and', kěshì 'but')
Det	Determiner (zhè 'this', nà 'that')
M	Measure (ge, tiáo; xià, cì)
N	Noun (wǒ 'I', yǒngqì 'courage')
Ptc	Particle (ma 'question particle', le 'completive verbal particle')
Prep	Preposition (cóng 'from', duìyú 'regarding')
V	Action Verb, transitive (mǎi 'buy', chī 'eat')
Vi	Action Verb, intransitive (kū 'cry', zuò 'sit')
Vaux	Auxiliary Verb (néng 'can', xiǎng 'would like to')
V-sep	Separable Verb (jiéhūn 'get married', shēngqì 'get angry')
Vs	State Verb, intransitive (hǎo 'good', guì 'expensive')
Vst	State Verb, transitive (xǐhuān 'like', zhīdào 'know')
Vs-attr	State Verb, attributive (zhǔyào 'primary', xiùzhēn 'mini-')
Vs-pred	State Verb, predicative (gòu 'enough', duō 'plenty')
Vp	Process Verb, intransitive (sǐ 'die', wán 'finish')
Vpt	Process Verb, transitive (pò (dòng) 'lit. break (hole)' , liè (fèng) 'lit. crack (a crack))

Notes:

Default values: When no marking appears under a category, a default reading takes place, which has been built into the system by observing the commonest patterns of the highest frequency. A default value can be loosely understood as the most likely candidate. A default system results in using fewer symbols, which makes it easy on the eyes, reducing the amount of processing. Our default readings are as follows.

Default transitivity. When a verb is not marked, i.e., V, it's an action verb. An unmarked action verb, furthermore, is transitive. A state verb is marked as Vs, but if it's not further marked, it's intransitive. The same holds for process verbs, i.e., Vp is by default intransitive.

Default position of adjectives. Typical adjectives occur as predicates, e.g., 'This is *great*!' Therefore, unmarked Vs are predicative, and adjectives that cannot be predicates will be marked for this feature, e.g. zhǔyào 'primary' is an adjective but it cannot be a predicate, i.e., *Zhètiáo lù hěn zhǔyào. '*This road is very primary.' Therefore it is marked Vs-attr, meaning it can only be used attributively, i.e., zhǔyào dàolù 'primary road'. On the other hand, 'gòu' 'enough' in Chinese can only be used predicatively, not attributively, e.g. 'Shíjiān gòu' '*?Time is enough.', but not *gòu shíjiān 'enough time'. Therefore gòu is marked Vs-pred. Employing this new system of parts of speech guarantees good grammar!

Default wordhood. In English, words cannot be torn apart and be used separately, e.g. *mis- not –understand. Likewise in Chinese, e.g. *xǐbùhuān 'do not like'. However, there is a large group of words in Chinese that are exceptions to this probably universal rule and can be separated. They are called 'separable words', marked -sep in our new system of parts of speech. For example, shēngqì 'angry' is a word, but it is fine to say *shēng tā qì* 'angry at him'. Jiéhūn 'get married' is a word but it's fine to say *jiéguòhūn* 'been married before' or *jiéguò sān cì hūn* 'been married 3 times before'. There are at least a couple of hundred separable words in modern Chinese. Even native speakers have to learn that certain words can be separated. Thus, memorizing them is the only way to deal with them by learners, and our new system of parts of speech helps them along nicely. Go over the vocabulary lists in this series and look for the marking –sep.

Now, what motivates this severing of words? Ask Chinese gods, not your teachers! We only know a little about the syntactic circumstances under which they get separated. First and foremost, separable words are in most cases intransitive verbs, whether action, state or process. When these verbs are further associated with targets (nouns, conceptual objects), frequency (number of times), duration (for how long), occurrence (done, done away with) etc., separation takes pace and these associated elements are inserted in between. More examples are given below.

Wǒ jīnnián yǐjīng *kǎo*guò 20 cì *shì* le!! (I've taken 20 exams to date this year!)

Wǒ *dào*guò *qiàn* le; tā hái shēngqì! (I apologized, but he's still mad!)

Fàng sān tiān *jià*; dàjiā dōu zǒu le. (There will be a break of 3 days, and everyone has left.)

Final Words

This is a very brief introduction to the modern Mandarin Chinese language, which is the standard world-wide. This introduction can only highlight the most salient properties of the language. Many other features of the language have been left out by design. For instance, nothing has been said about the patterns of word-formations in Chinese, and no presentation has been made of the unique written script of the language. Readers are advised to search on-line for resources relating to particular aspects of the language. For reading, please consult a highly readable best-seller in this regard, viz. Li, Charles and Sandra Thompson. 1982. Mandarin Chinese: a reference grammar. UC Los Angeles Press. (Authorised reprinting by Crane publishing Company, Taipei, Taiwan, still available as of October 2009).

Highlights of Lessons

Lessons	Topic & Themes	Learning Objectives
❶ School Starts	School Life	1. Learning to discuss topics frequently encountered on campus. 2. Learning to discuss in detail learning experiences. 3. Learning to try to persuade others. 4. Learning to discuss school-related services and procedures.
❷ Up to 20% off	Shopping	1. Learning to talk about shopping. 2. Learning to understand simple regulations and contracts. 3. Learning to refute arguments. 4. Learning to offer clear reasons for why you like or dislike certain things.
❸ Did You Bring Your Coat?	Climate and Holidays	1. Learning to describe changes in climate and weather. 2. Learning to talk about the seasons and activities particular to each. 3. Learning to talk about traditional Chinese New Year, Dragon Boat Festival, and Mid-Autumn Moon Festival customs. 4. Learning to read about the origins of important festivals.
❹ I Love Taiwanese Hospitality	Social Environment	1. Learning to discuss with your friends leisure activities that you enjoy. 2. Learning to tell others about Taiwan's culture and provide travel information for different destinations. 3. Learning to emphasize, give examples, and provide further information. 4. Learning to talk about the unique characteristics and culture of small towns.

Grammar	Bits of Chinese Culture
1. …的話 *if, supposing* 2. 不到 *less than* 3. 差一點（就）… *almost* 4. 恐怕… *probably* 5. 好不容易 *finally managed to* 6. Instantly without Prior Warning with 說…就… 7. 不管…都… *regardless of whether or not*	Wrap Zongzi to Bring Good Luck to Examinees 包粽包中（bāozòng-bāozhòng）
1. 一般來說 *generally speaking* 2. General Verb 弄 3. 再說 *besides, moreover* 4. V + 成 *to become, to turn into* 5. Contrary to Expectation with 並 6. 尤其是 *especially* 7. Concession with 只好 *could only, have no choice but to*	Six of One, a Half Dozen of the Other 半斤八兩 （bànjīn bāliǎng）
1. 受到（…的）影響 *to be influenced by, affected by* 2. 幸虧… *fortunately...* 3. 算是… *can be considered...* 4. 是… *it is indeed true that...* 5. 難怪 *no wonder* 6. A Post-verbal Intensifier 死了 *terribly* 7. 幾乎 *almost* 8. 多少 *somewhat* 9. 再…也… *no matter how..., still...*	Ghost Month Taboos
1. 不但…，還… *not only..., but also...* 2. Speak 說 vs. Talk 談 3. …不是…，而是… *not...; rather...* 4. 從來 + Negation *never* 5. Various Meanings of the Verb 上 6. 非…不可 *it is imperative that...* 7. 對…來說 *as far as...is concerned, for* 8. 對…講究 *to be discerning, discriminating, particular about*	Ghost Money

Lessons	Topic & Themes	Learning Objectives
5 What Are the Trends Now?	Popular Culture	1. Learning to talk about trends. 2. Learning to explain in detail the merits of your hobbies and activities. 3. Learning to provide various reasons refuting the views of others. 4. Learning to describe a live concert.
6 Spending the Night in the Countryside	Taiwan's Agricultural Industry	1. Learning to discuss the cultivation of agricultural crops. 2. Learning to explain your reasons for choosing something. 3. Learning to talk about changes in society, including values and lifestyle. 4. Learning to discuss food safety issues with friends.
7 My Closest "Family"	Family	1. Learning to talk about the merits and shortcomings of different family makeups. 2. Learning to describe in detail the various family makeups of your friends and relatives. 3. Learning to state reasons and arguments methodically and sum up your thoughts. 4. Learning to talk about the relationship between people and pets in modern society.
8 I Just Want to Be Myself	Education	1. Learning to explain in detail classes that you are currently taking and your future plans. 2. Learning to talk about study and work experience. 3. Learning to discuss differences in traditional and modern ideas and values. 4. Learning the names of university departments and graduate school programs.

Grammar	Bits of Chinese Culture
1. Verb Plus Complement V + 滿 *crowded with* 2. Verb Particle 出 *to have emerged* 3. 不如 *not as good as* 4. Urgent Conditional with 再不⋯就⋯了 5. Verb Particle 掉 *separated from* 6. 居然 *to one's surprise* 7. Concession with 既然⋯（就）⋯ *since... (then)...* 8. V + 個不停 *keep on...*	Japanese Words Borrowed into Chinese
1. 因為⋯才⋯ *only because...* 2. Complaining with ⋯S_1⋯不說，S_2 也⋯ *not merely, but also* 3. 再加上 *furthermore* 4. 什麼都⋯，就是⋯ *everything but...* 5. 寧可⋯，也要⋯ *would rather..., in order to...* 6. 像⋯的 + noun *such (nouns) as* 7. 一方面⋯，一方面⋯ *on the one hand, ..., on the other* 8. 隨著 S_1⋯，S_2 也⋯ *as a consequence of...*	Hu, Fan, and Yang
1. 亂 + V *to do something in an irresponsible manner, risking undersirable consequences* 2. 各 V 各的 *each doing her/his own...* 3. 就算⋯，也⋯ *even if... (S_1)..., would...(S_2)...* 4. 因為 NP，S⋯ *because of NP, S...* 5. 一來⋯，二來⋯ *on the one hand..., and on the other...; first..., second...* 6. Repetitively, Back and Forth with V 來 V 去 7. 不再⋯了 *not...any more*	Visiting the Parents
1. 不是⋯就是⋯ *if it's not..., then it's...* 2. 算了 *forget it, drop it* 3. 這樣一來 *that being the case, that way* 4. 早就⋯了 *long since...* 5. 從⋯起 *starting from...* 6. 卻 *however* 7. 因為⋯而⋯ *therefore, consequently* 8. 經過 *after*	How Children Are Named

Grammar	Bits of Chinese Culture
1. 靠 *to rely on, by means of* 2. 既…又… *not merely..., but...as well* 3. …以內 *within...* 4. 占 *to constitute* 5.（在）NP 上 *regarding NP* 6. 給…帶來 *to bring... to...* 7. 結果 *consequently, in the end*	The Abacus
1. Introducing a New Topic with 至於… *as to, as far as... is concerned* 2. 看 *depends on* 3. 一向 *all along, has always...* 4. 拿…來說 *take...as an example* 5. Passive Sentences with 受 6. 動不動就… *to do something impetuously*	Cold, Balanced, and Hot Food
1. 到底 *after all? how on earth...?* 2. 甚至 *even* 3. 這麼說 *that being the case, in that case* 4. 跟 B 有關的 A *A is related to B* 5. 不得不 *have no choice but to* 6. 以及 *as well as*	Origins of Geographical Names in Taiwan
1. 只不過…（而已） *merely...; nothing more than...* 2. Introducing an Agent with 由 3. 難道… *how could it possibly be true* 4. To Reach a Ceiling with 滿 5. Beneficiary marker 為 6.（在）…方面 *with respect to; regarding*	Elections and Numbers

Parts of Speech in Chinese

List of Parts of Speech in Chinese

Symbols	Parts of speech	八大詞類	Examples
N	noun	名詞	水、五、昨天、學校、他、幾
V	verb	動詞	吃、告訴、容易、快樂,知道、破
Adv	adverb	副詞	很、不、常、到處、也、就、難道
Conj	conjunction	連詞	和、跟,而且、雖然、因為
Prep	preposition	介詞	從、對、向、跟、在、給
M	measure	量詞	個、張、碗、次、頓、公尺
Ptc	particle	助詞	的、得、啊、嗎、完、掉、把、喂
Det	determiner	限定詞	這、那、某、每、哪

Verb Classification

Symbols	Classification	動詞分類	Examples
V	transitive action verbs	及物動作動詞	買、做、說
Vi	intransitive action verbs	不及物動作動詞	跑、坐、睡、笑
V-sep	intransitive action verbs, separable	不及物動作離合詞	唱歌、上網、打架
Vs	intransitive state verbs	不及物狀態動詞	冷、高、漂亮
Vst	transitive state verbs	及物狀態動詞	關心、喜歡、同意
Vs-attr	intransitive state verbs, attributive only	唯定不及物狀態動詞	野生、公共、新興
Vs-pred	intransitive state verbs, predicative only	唯謂不及物狀態動詞	夠、多、少
Vs-sep	intransitive state verbs, separable	不及物狀態離合詞	放心、幽默、生氣
Vaux	auxiliary verbs	助動詞	會、能、可以
Vp	intransitive process verbs	不及物變化動詞	破、感冒、壞、死
Vpt	transitive process verbs	及物變化動詞	忘記、變成、丟
Vp-sep	intransitive process verbs, separable	不及物變化離合詞	結婚、生病、畢業

Default Values of the Symbols

Symbols	Default values
V	action, transitive
Vs	state, intransitive
Vp	process, intransitive
V-sep	separable, intransitive

XXIV

Classroom Phrases

1. 上課了。
   Shàngkè le.
   Let's begin the class.

2. 請打開書。
   Qǐng dǎkāi shū.
   Open your book.

3. 請看第五頁。
   Qǐng kàn dì wǔ yè.
   Please see page 5.

4. 我說，你們聽。
   Wǒ shuō, nǐmen tīng.
   I'll speak, you listen.

5. 請跟我說。
   Qǐng gēn wǒ shuō.
   Please repeat after me.

6. 請再說／念一次。
   Qǐng zài shuō/niàn yí cì.
   Please say it again.

7. 請回答。
   Qǐng huídá.
   Please answer my question.

8. 請問，這個字怎麼念／寫？
   Qǐngwèn, zhè ge zì zěnme niàn/xiě?
   How do you pronounce/spell this word?

9. 對了！
   Duì le!
   Right! Correct!

10. 不對。
    Bú duì.
    Wrong. Incorrect.

11. 請念對話。
    Qǐng niàn duìhuà.
    Read the dialogue, please.

12. 請看黑板。
    Qǐng kàn hēibǎn.
    Look at the board, please.

13. 懂不懂？
    Dǒng bù dǒng?
    Do you understand?

14. 懂了！
    Dǒng le!
    Yes, I/we understand.

15. 有沒有問題？
    Yǒu méi yǒu wèntí?
    Any question?

16. 很好！
    Hěn hǎo!
    Very good!

17. 下課。
    Xiàkè.
    The class is over.

何雅婷

Hé Yǎtíng

Taiwanese.
Female.

She just completed her first year of study in college, and changed her major from Accounting to International Relation. She met Lǐ Wényàn through language exchange, and she came to know many of Wényàn's friends.

安德思

Ān Désī

Honduran.
Male.

He is studying in a language center and is in the same class with Luó Shāndì, Chén Mǐnxuān, and Gāoqiáo Jiàntài.

He is awarded scholarship for the duration of 5 years. He wants to pursue a degree in the field of Science and Technology, and he plans to attend college in Taiwan after studying Chinese for one year.

羅珊蒂

Luó Shāndì

Indonesian.
Female.

She is studying in a language center and is in the same class with Ān Désī, Chén Mǐnxuān, and Gāoqiáo Jiàntài. She took a leave of absence from college to study Chinese in Taiwan. She plans to help her parents with their business after returning home.

陳敏萱

Chén Mǐnxuān

Dutch.
Female.

She is studying in a language center and is in the same class with Ān Désī, Luó Shāndì, and Gāoqiáo Jiàntài. She is an exchange student. She majors in Chinese and minors in Business.

高橋健太

Gāoqiáo Jiàntài

Japanese.
Male.

He is studying in a language center and is in the same class with Ān Désī, Luó Shāndì, and Chén Mǐnxuān. He met Lǐ Wényàn when working out in a gym.

He is an expatriate of a Japanese company. His company sponsors him to take Chinese classes twice a week.

李文彥

Lǐ Wényàn

An American-born Chinese.
Male.

He is a friend of Ān Désī and Luó Shāndì's. He is also Hé Yǎtíng's language exchange partner.

He just graduated from college, and is not sure what to do next. So, he decided to learn Chinese first.

LESSON 1

第一課

開學了

School Starts

學習目標 Learning Objectives

Topic: 學校生活 School Life

- Learning to discuss topics frequently encountered on campus.
- Learning to discuss in detail learning experiences.
- Learning to try to persuade others.
- Learning to discuss school-related services and procedures.

LESSON 1

開學了
School Starts

對話 Dialogue 01-01

安德思：羅珊蒂，下課啦！怎麼樣？你們班上有我們上個學期的同學嗎？

羅珊蒂：沒有，都沒有。你們班怎麼樣？

安德思：都是新生，我一個也不認識，而且只有我一個男的。

羅珊蒂：老師呢？老師怎麼樣？

安德思：老師很嚴。他說我們這學期除了每一課的口試、筆試以外，還要做兩次口頭報告。我覺得壓力好大。你們班呢？

羅珊蒂：老師的說明很清楚，同學也很熱情。我們今天就一起去吃中飯了。

安 德 思：聽起來不錯。還有位子嗎？有位子的話，我想去旁聽。

羅 珊 蒂：你想換班啊？你不是打算在台灣上大學嗎？老師嚴才學得快，學得好啊。

安 德 思：可是我是獎學金學生。要是成績不到80分，拿不到獎學金，就得回國了。

羅 珊 蒂：我真羨慕你有獎學金。不像我休學來台灣，花的都是父母的錢，一定得用功念書才行。

（何雅婷走過來）

安 德 思：何雅婷，聽說妳轉系了？

何 雅 婷：是啊，這個學期我轉到國際關係系去了。

安 德 思：妳原來念的會計系不是很熱門嗎？怎麼不念了？

何 雅 婷：我念不下去了。我每天熬夜念書，可是還是差一點被當。這樣下去，四年恐怕沒辦法畢業。

羅 珊 蒂：念國際關係很適合妳。妳的英文那麼流利，口才又好，以後可以當外交人員。

何 雅 婷：謝謝妳這麼說。我真想多跟你們聊聊。可惜我得走了，我跟教授約好了討論選課的事，不能遲到。再見。

課文簡體字版 Text in Simplified Characters

安 德 思：罗珊蒂，下课啦！怎么样？你们班上有我们上个学期的同学吗？

罗 珊 蒂：没有，都没有。你们班怎么样？

安 德 思：都是新生，我一个也不认识，而且只有我一个男的。

罗 珊 蒂：老师呢？老师怎么样？

安 德 思：老师很严。他说我们这学期除了每一课的口试、笔试以外，还要做两次口头报告。我觉得压力好大。你们班呢？

罗 珊 蒂 ： 老师的说明很清楚，同学也很热情。我们今天就一起去吃中饭了。

安 德 思 ： 听起来不错。还有位子吗？有位子的话，我想去旁听。

罗 珊 蒂 ： 你想换班啊？你不是打算在台湾上大学吗？老师严才学得快，学得好啊。

安 德 思 ： 可是我是奖学金学生。要是成绩不到 80 分，拿不到奖学金，就得回国了。

罗 珊 蒂 ： 我真羡慕你有奖学金。不像我休学来台湾，花的都是父母的钱，一定得用功念书才行。

（何雅婷走过来）

安 德 思 ： 何雅婷，听说妳转系了？

何 雅 婷 ： 是啊，这个学期我转到国际关系系去了。

安 德 思 ： 妳原来念的会计系不是很热门吗？怎么不念了？

何 雅 婷 ： 我念不下去了。我每天熬夜念书，可是还是差一点被当。这样下去，四年恐怕没办法毕业。

罗 珊 蒂 ： 念国际关系很适合妳。妳的英文那么流利，口才又好，以后可以当外交人员。

何 雅 婷 ： 谢谢妳这么说。我真想多跟你们聊聊。可惜我得走了，我跟教授约好了讨论选课的事，不能迟到。再见。

课文英译 Text in English

An Desi : Luo Shandi, class is out. How was it? Did your class have any of our classmates from last semester?

Luo Shandi : No, none at all. How is your class?

An Desi : They're all new students. I don't know any of them and I'm the only guy.

Luo Shandi : And the teacher? How was the teacher?

An Desi : The teacher is strict. He said that this semester, in addition to an oral test and a written test every chapter, we also have to give two oral reports. I feel the pressure is really great. How about your class?

Luo Shandi : The teacher's instructions were clear and the students in the class are warm and friendly. Today, we even had lunch together.

An Desi : Sounds good. Are there any more seats? If there are seats, I'd like to go sit in on the class.

Luo Shandi : You want to change classes? Aren't you planning to go to university in Taiwan? You can only learn quickly and well if you have a strict teacher.

An Desi : But I'm a scholarship student. If my grades aren't up to 80 points, I won't get a scholarship and I'll have to go home.

Luo Shandi : I really envy you having a scholarship. Unlike me, I took a break from school to come to Taiwan and I'm spending my parents' money. I have to study. There's no other way.

(He Yating walks over.)

An Desi : He Yating, I heard you changed majors.

Luo Shandi : Yes, this semester I changed to the international relations department.

An Desi : Isn't the accounting department, which you originally studied in, really popular? How come you stopped studying?

He Yating : I cannot go on like this any more! Every day, I stayed up late studying, but I still was almost flunked. That way, I'm afraid there's no way I can graduate in four years.

Luo Shandi : Studying in the department of international relations suits you. You speak English fluently and you are very eloquent. In the future, you can be a diplomat.

He Yating : Thank you for saying that. I would really love to keep chatting with you. Unfortunately, I have to go. I made an appointment with the professor to discuss the issue of selecting classes and I can't be late. See you.

生詞一 Vocabulary I 01-02

People in the Dialogue

1	安德思	Ān Désī	ㄢ ㄉㄜˋ ㄙ		a man from Honduras
2	羅珊蒂	Luó Shāndì	ㄌㄨㄛˊ ㄕㄢ ㄉㄧˋ		a woman from Indonesia
3	何雅婷	Hé Yǎtíng	ㄏㄜˊ ㄧㄚˇ ㄊㄧㄥˊ		a woman from Taiwan

Vocabulary

4	開學	kāixué	ㄎㄞ ㄒㄩㄝˊ	(Vp)	(school) to start
5	班	bān	ㄅㄢ	(N)	class, i.e., the students (not the classroom or the course)

6	新生	xīnshēng	ㄒㄧㄣ ㄕㄥ	(N)	new student
7	嚴	yán	ㄧㄢˊ	(Vs)	strict, stern
8	口試	kǒushì	ㄎㄡˇ ㄕˋ	(N)	oral test
9	筆試	bǐshì	ㄅㄧˇ ㄕˋ	(N)	written test
10	以外	yǐwài	ㄧˇ ㄨㄞˋ	(N)	except, other than
11	口頭	kǒutóu	ㄎㄡˇ ㄊㄡˊ	(Vs-attr)	verbal, oral
12	報告	bàogào	ㄅㄠˋ ㄍㄠˋ	(N)	report
13	壓力	yālì	ㄧㄚ ㄌㄧˋ	(N)	pressure, stress
14	說明	shuōmíng	ㄕㄨㄛ ㄇㄧㄥˊ	(N)	instructions, explanation
15	清楚	qīngchǔ	ㄑㄧㄥ ㄔㄨˇ	(Vs)	clear(ly)
16	位子	wèizi	ㄨㄟˋ ㄗ˙	(N)	seat, place
17	旁聽	pángtīng	ㄆㄤˊ ㄊㄧㄥ	(V)	to audit, to sit in (on a class)
18	分	fēn	ㄈㄣ	(N)	points
19	羨慕	xiànmù	ㄒㄧㄢˋ ㄇㄨˋ	(Vst)	to envy
20	休學	xiūxué	ㄒㄧㄡ ㄒㄩㄝˊ	(Vp-sep)	to take a break from school
21	用功	yònggōng	ㄩㄥˋ ㄍㄨㄥ	(Vs)	diligent, conscientious (as a student)
22	行	xíng	ㄒㄧㄥˊ	(Vs)	to be all right
23	轉	zhuǎn	ㄓㄨㄢˇ	(V)	to transfer (to a different major)
24	原來	yuánlái	ㄩㄢˊ ㄌㄞˊ	(Adv)	originally
25	會計	kuàijì	ㄎㄨㄞˋ ㄐㄧˋ	(N)	accounting, an accountant
26	熱門	rèmén	ㄖㄜˋ ㄇㄣˊ	(Vs)	highly popular
27	熬夜	áoyè	ㄠˊ ㄧㄝˋ	(V-sep)	to stay up all night, to burn the midnight oil
28	當	dàng	ㄉㄤˋ	(V)	to fail a course
29	恐怕	kǒngpà	ㄎㄨㄥˇ ㄆㄚˋ	(Adv)	(I am) afraid that, probably
30	口才	kǒucái	ㄎㄡˇ ㄘㄞˊ	(N)	speaking skills

| 31 | 事 | shì | ㄕˋ | (N) | issue, matter, event, thing |
| 32 | 遲到 | chídào | ㄔˊ ㄉㄠˋ | (Vp) | to be late (in arrival) |

Phrases

33	差一點	chà yì diǎn	ㄔㄚˋ ㄧˋ ㄉㄧㄢˇ		barely, nearly, almost
34	這樣下去	zhèyàng xiàqù	ㄓㄜˋ ㄧㄤˋ ㄒㄧㄚˋ ㄑㄩˋ		if it goes on like this
35	沒辦法	méi bànfǎ	ㄇㄟˊ ㄅㄢˋ ㄈㄚˇ		there's no way, there's nothing that can be done

短文 Reading 🎧 01-03

何雅婷要轉系

何雅婷是家裡的獨生女。從小父母讓她念私立小學,下了課還去學西班牙文、書法、游泳跟網球。何雅婷也沒讓父母失望,成績一直都很好,還考上了理想的大學,念的是熱門的會計系。沒想到才念了一個學期,她就發現跟她的興趣不合,念起來非常痛苦。她想了很久,決定跟媽媽討論轉系的事。

媽媽聽到何雅婷打算轉到國際關係系,非常生氣。她覺得何雅婷好不容易才考上這麼好的科系,怎麼可以說放棄就放棄?而且,念會計系工作機會比較多。跟興趣比起來,將來的發展當然更重要。如果她真的對別的課有興趣,利用時間去旁聽就好了。不管何雅婷怎麼說,她都反對。

不過何雅婷告訴媽媽,她個性活潑,而且外語能力不錯,如果念國際關係,會有更好的成績,請媽媽不必擔心她的將來。這一次就請媽媽讓她自己決定吧。媽媽想了又想,捨不得女兒念得這麼痛苦,最後還是同意了。何雅婷聽了非常高興,她立刻上網填表辦轉系的手續,申請上學期的成績單,然後還請教授幫她寫推薦信。

7

課文簡體字版 Text in Simplified Characters

何雅婷要转系

何雅婷是家里的独生女。从小父母让她念私立小学，下了课还去学西班牙文、书法、游泳跟网球。何雅婷也没让父母失望，成绩一直都很好，还考上了理想的大学，念的是热门的会计系。没想到才念了一个学期，她就发现跟她的兴趣不合，念起来非常痛苦。她想了很久，决定跟妈妈讨论转系的事。

妈妈听到何雅婷打算转到国际关系系，非常生气。她觉得何雅婷好不容易才考上这么好的科系，怎么可以说放弃就放弃？而且，念会计系工作机会比较多。跟兴趣比起来，将来的发展当然更重要。如果她真的对别的课有兴趣，利用时间去旁听就好了。不管何雅婷怎么说，她都反对。

不过何雅婷告诉妈妈，她个性活泼，而且外语能力不错，如果念国际关系，会有更好的成绩，请妈妈不必担心她的将来。这一次就请妈妈让她自己决定吧。妈妈想了又想，舍不得女儿念得这么痛苦，最后还是同意了。何雅婷听了非常高兴，她立刻上网填表办转系的手续，申请上学期的成绩单，然后还请教授帮她写推荐信。

课文英译 Text in English

He Yating Wants to Change Majors

He Yating is the only child in her family. Ever since she was young, her parents had her study at a private elementary school, and she even took extracurricular Spanish, calligraphy, swimming, and tennis classes. He Yating didn't disappoint her parents either; she always maintained good grades and even got into a competitive program–accounting–at a good university. Unexpectedly, after studying only one semester, she found that she had no interest in accounting, and her studies became a chore. After putting much thought into it, she decided to discuss the matter of changing majors with her mother.

When her mom heard that He Yating was planning to transfer to the department of international relations, she was very angry. He Yating worked hard to test into such a good department. How could she simply give it up? There are more job opportunities for those who study accounting, she thought, and career prospects should always take precedence over personal interests. If she really wanted to take other courses, she should just audit them on her own time. No matter what He Yating said, her mother objected.

He Yating explained to her mom that she is outgoing and proficient at foreign languages. If she studied international relations, her grades would be even better than they were now. She told her mom not to worry about her future, and that she could decide this for herself. Her mom thought about it long and hard. She would hate to see her daughter struggle, and so in the end she agreed. Hearing this, He Yating was ecstatic. She immediately went online, filled out the forms required to change majors, applied for her previous semester's transcripts, and requested that her professor write a letter of recommendation for her.

生詞二 Vocabulary II 01-04

Vocabulary

1	獨生女	dúshēngnǚ	ㄉㄨˊ ㄕㄥ ㄋㄩˇ	(N)	only child (girl)
2	私立	sīlì	ㄙ ㄌㄧˋ	(Vs-attr)	private
3	理想	lǐxiǎng	ㄌㄧˇ ㄒㄧㄤˇ	(Vs)	ideal, aspired
4	合	hé	ㄏㄜˊ	(Vst)	to tally with, to match
5	痛苦	tòngkǔ	ㄊㄨㄥˋ ㄎㄨˇ	(Vs)	painful
6	科系	kēxì	ㄎㄜ ㄒㄧˋ	(N)	(academic) department
7	放棄	fàngqì	ㄈㄤˋ ㄑㄧˋ	(V)	to give up
8	不管	bùguǎn	ㄅㄨˋ ㄍㄨㄢˇ	(Conj)	no matter, regardless of
9	反對	fǎnduì	ㄈㄢˇ ㄉㄨㄟˋ	(Vst)	to oppose, to be against
10	個性	gèxìng	ㄍㄜˋ ㄒㄧㄥˋ	(N)	personality
11	活潑	huópō	ㄏㄨㄛˊ ㄆㄛ	(Vs)	lively, bubbly, vivacious
12	外語	wàiyǔ	ㄨㄞˋ ㄩˇ	(N)	foreign language
13	擔心	dānxīn	ㄉㄢ ㄒㄧㄣ	(Vst)	to worry about, to fret over with
14	填	tián	ㄊㄧㄢˊ	(V)	to fill out (a form)
15	表	biǎo	ㄅㄧㄠˇ	(N)	a form
16	辦	bàn	ㄅㄢˋ	(V)	to deal with
17	手續	shǒuxù	ㄕㄡˇ ㄒㄩˋ	(N)	procedures
18	申請	shēnqǐng	ㄕㄣ ㄑㄧㄥˇ	(V)	to apply for

| 19 | 成績單 | chéngjī dān | ㄔㄥˊ ㄐㄧ ㄉㄢ | (N) | report card, transcripts |

Phrases

| 20 | 考上 | kǎoshàng | ㄎㄠˇ ㄕㄤˋ | | to test into |
| 21 | 推薦信 | tuījiàn xìn | ㄊㄨㄟ ㄐㄧㄢˋ ㄒㄧㄣˋ | | a letter of recommendation |

文法 Grammar

I. …的話 *if, supposing* 🎧 01-05   英譯 p.16

Function: The pattern …的話, appears at the very end of the 'if' part, while the 'consequence' part appears in the second clause.

❶ 酸辣湯太辣的話，你就別喝了。

❷ 你想轉系的話，最好先跟父母討論。

❸ 學生要參加社團的話，得先上網填申請表。

❹ 我覺得外語能力不錯的話，念國際關係系比較適合。

❺ 美美說拿到獎學金的話，就請我們看電影。

Usage: Conjunctions 如果 or 要是 can be used together with the pattern above. In such cases, 的話 can be omitted。…的話 is more colloquial, while 如果／要是…（的話）is more formal.

❶ 如果你覺得這裡太吵的話，我們可以換一個地方繼續聊。

❷ 要是爸爸給我的生活費不夠的話，我就得去打工。

練習 Exercise

Use the pattern （如果／要是）…的話 to answer the following questions.

❶ A：你明天要不要跟我們一起去參觀故宮博物院？

B： 念書完了的話，就跟你們一起去吧 我 。

❷ A：大學畢業以後，你考不考慮去義大利念研究所？

B：ICLP太難的話,會考慮去(✓)的課 我 。

❸ A：你打算去旁聽王教授的課嗎？

B：＿＿＿＿＿＿＿＿＿＿＿＿＿＿＿＿＿＿。

❹ A：下個學期我打算選林教授的課，你呢？

B：＿＿＿＿＿＿＿＿＿＿＿＿＿＿＿＿＿＿。

❺ A：她說的那個公寓就在捷運站旁邊，你租不租？

B：＿＿＿＿＿＿＿＿＿＿＿＿＿＿＿＿＿＿。

II. 不到 *less than* 🎧 01-06　　　　🔍 英譯 p.17

Function: 不到 is often followed by a number, meaning 'less than...'.

❶ 博物院的人說不到 6 歲的小孩子，不可以進去參觀。

❷ 這支手機不到五千塊，真便宜。

❸ 老師說成績不到 85 分，不可以申請獎學金。

❹ 安德思來台灣還不到半年，就認識了不少台灣朋友。

❺ 昨天的作業那麼多，可是羅珊蒂不到一個小時就寫完了。

練習 Exercise

Please fill in the blanks after 不到… with a number expression.

❶ 這裡離捷運站不到＿＿＿＿＿＿，走路去只要五分鐘。

❷ 她的小孩不到＿＿＿＿＿＿，還沒念小學。

❸ 林美美上個月才來台灣，所以會寫的漢字不到＿＿＿＿＿＿。

❹ 他一個月的生活費不到＿＿＿＿＿＿，得節省一點。

❺ 他學中國話不到＿＿＿＿＿＿，就說得很流利了。

III. 差一點（就）… *almost* 🎧 01-07

Function: 差一點（就）… means 'almost ... (but did not)'. The … part usually indicates a situation that--from the speaker's perspective--was not expected to take place. 就 in this pattern is optional.

❶ 前天的演講真沒意思，我差一點睡著了。
❷ 上次我哥哥去爬山的時候，差一點迷路。
❸ 為了健康，他差一點就搬到鄉下去住。
❹ 上個星期他在圖書館念書，背包差一點被偷走。
❺ 王月文的生日，我差一點就忘了送她禮物。

Usage: 差一點（就）… indicates that some situation almost took place but did not. 差不多, on the other hand, means 'about, close to'. The emphasis is on the small difference between two things that are compared with each other. For example,

❶ 外面的雨很大，我差一點來不了。
❷ 他昨天告訴我的事情，我差不多都忘了。

練習 Exercise

Please complete the following sentences by using 差一點 to describe events that would have happened.

❶ 你做的蛋糕，差一點被_____。
❷ 我跟何教授約好了，可是公車一直沒來，我差一點就
_____。
❸ 還好你告訴我，我差一點_____明天要考試。
❹ 他的成績不好，差一點_____。
❺ 沒想到這個城市的路那麼複雜，我差一點_____。

IV. 恐怕… *probably* 🎧 01-08 英譯 p.17

Function: The adverb 恐怕 introduces a situation that is likely to take place from the speaker's perspective. Usually the situation is a non-favorable one. Similar to 'I am afraid that' in English.

                                      effect

1. 壓力太大，恐怕會影響身體健康。 *(yā lì / yǐng xiǎng)*
2. 網路雖然把世界變小了，但是人跟人的關係恐怕更遠了。 *(though / wǎng lù suī rán bǎ shì jiè biàn xiǎo)*
3. 我租的房子，合約快到期了，恐怕得搬家。 *(contract)*
4. 走快一點吧。去晚了，恐怕小陳會生氣。 *(chén)*
5. 明天的報告，我還沒準備好，今天恐怕得熬夜。 *(bào gào / report)*

Usage:

1. 大概 'approximately, about' and 可能 'probably' are also used to express an estimate. However, these expressions are neutral and don't usually suggest that the situation is non-favorable. For example: 我家離學校大概五百公尺。 'My house is around 500 meters from school.' 我大概等了十分鐘就走了。 'I waited about 10 minutes, and then I left.' 明天大概不會下雨。 'It probably won't rain tomorrow.' 今天晚上可能會下雨。 'It might rain tonight.'

2. 恐怕 is used to indicate the speaker's conjecture. When the conjecture is from someone other than the speaker (and the situation is non-favorable), 怕 is used, rather than 恐怕. For example, 他怕熬夜會影響身體健康。 'He's afraid that staying up late at night will affect (his) health.' 你怕下雨的話，就帶傘吧。 'If you're afraid that it'll rain, go ahead and take an umbrella with you.'

練習 Exercise

Please complete the following sentences by using 恐怕 to describe a highly likely unfavorable situation.

1. 捷運站附近的房子這麼貴，他<u>恐怕買不起</u>。
2. 這課的語法又多又難，<u>恐怕成績越來越低</u>。
3. 他從小在鄉下長大，<u>恐怕不知道怎麼用捷運</u>。
4. 你準備的豬肉餡兒不夠多，<u>恐怕沒辦法吃飽</u>。
5. 如果薪水太低，<u>恐怕不能看醫生</u>。

V. 好不容易　*finally managed to*　 01-09　 英譯 p.17

Function: 好不容易 indicates the hard-won realization of a favorable situation. It means roughly 'finally managed to...'.

1 爸爸好不容易才答應讓我去美國念書，我一定要更用功。
dā yìng promise

2 好不容易拿到獎學金，怎麼就要回國了？ *scholarship*
jiǎng xué jīn

3 下了兩個星期的雨，今天好不容易才停。
didn't expect

4 好不容易看到一雙（shuāng, pair）喜歡的鞋子，沒想到這麼貴。

5 他做了一大碗豬腳麵線，我好不容易才吃完。
zhū jiǎo miàn xiàn
pork noodles?

練習 Exercise

Please complete the following sentences by using 好不容易 to describe a hard-won accomplishment.

1 最近經濟不太好，小王好不容易買得起房子。
jīng lì economy

2 這個語法，我說明了半天，他好不容易懂　。

3 包餃子看起來很容易，可是我學了好久，好不容易包好　。
make jiǎo zi

4 這個星期的垃圾很多，我好不容易丟垃圾。（垃圾分類）
lè sè

5 孩子好不容易上電杆　，你就讓他休息一下吧。

爬電線桿

VI. Instantly without Prior Warning with 說⋯就⋯　 01-10　 英譯 p.17

Function: This pattern means that something unexpected happens, without prior warning, or happens faster than expected (from the speaker's perspective). The pattern is roughly equivalent to 'just like that' and 'and before you know it' in English.

1 你不喜歡你的班嗎？怎麼說換班就換班？

2 台北的天氣真奇怪，說下雨就下雨。

3 小明怎麼了？怎麼說走就走？

4 美美上個月剛來台灣，怎麼說回國就回國？

5 李老師很嚴，常常說考試就考試，學生都覺得壓力很大。

練習 Exercise

Please re-write the following sentences with 說…就….

❶ 我們聊得很高興，你怎麼要離開了？有什麼事嗎？
→ ___你怎麼~~要~~說離開就離開？___ ?

❷ 我才聽說她打算搬家，怎麼已經搬走了？
→ ___怎麼說搬走就搬走？___ ?

❸ 這件事很急，我們現在就開始做吧。
→ ___我們說開始就開始做吧___ 。

❹ 你念得好好的，為什麼忽然決定休學？
→ ___為什麼說休學就休學？___ ?

❺ 他很容易生氣，所以沒有人喜歡他。
→ ___他說生氣就生氣，___ 。

VII. 不管…都… *regardless of whether or not* 01-11   英譯 p.18

Function: This pattern indicates that the consequence (following 都) remains the same no matter whether the condition (following 不管) is or is not met.

❶ 我爸爸不管工作忙不忙，天天都去健身房運動。
❷ 不管那裡的環境怎麼樣，他都要搬去那裡。
❸ 不管蒸魚還是炸魚，我都不吃。
❹ 不管上幾點的課，他都會遲到。
❺ 不管媽媽同不同意，我都要去美國念書。

Structure: Note that whatever comes after 不管 is basically a question in concept, e.g., 忙不忙 (❶ above), 怎麼樣 (❷) and 蒸魚還是炸魚 (❸).

Usage: The following expressions often appear after 不管 :

❶ Interrogative pronouns like 什麼, 誰, 哪

要是你有問題，不管什麼時候都可以打電話給我。

2 A-not-A question

不管父母同不同意，他都要念會計系。

3 Choice question

老師說不管天氣好（還是）壞，學生都不可以遲到。

練習 Exercise

Please answer the following questions with the pattern 不管…，…都….

1 A：李明珊的父母不答應她去西班牙念書的話，她還去嗎？

B：不管父母同不同意都 她會去 。

2 A：聽說李教授很嚴，你還要選他的課嗎？

B：不管嚴不嚴，我都要選 。

3 A：這家餐廳的生意總是這麼好嗎？

B：不管是不是週末，都這麼好 。

4 A：捷運站附近的房租都很貴，你還要租嗎？

B：住在捷運站附近很方便，不管租子都要租 。

5 A：中文這麼難學，我真想放棄。

B：學中文對找工作有很大的幫助，不管難不難學 。

語法例句英譯
Grammar Examples in English

I. …的話 *if, supposing*

Function:

1 If the hot and sour soup is too spicy, don't drink it.

2 If you want to change majors, it would be best if you discuss it with your parents first.

3 If students want to take part in school clubs, they have to first go online and fill out a form.

4 I believe that if one's foreign language skills are pretty good, it would be more suitable to study international relations.

5 Meimei said that if she gets a scholarhip, she will treat us to a movie.

Usage:

1 If you think it's too noisy here, we can continue our conversation somewhere else.

2 If Dad doesn't give me enough allowance money, I'll have to go work part time.

II. 不到 *less than*

Function:.

❶ The museum staff say that children less than 6-years old cannot go inside (and visit).

❷ This cell phone is less than NT$5,000. That's really cheap.

❸ The teacher said that students with grades of less than 85 cannot apply for a scholarship.

❹ An Desi has been in Taiwan for less than half a year and he already has lots of Taiwanese friends.

❺ There was all that homework yesterday, but Luo Shandi finished it in less than an hour.

III. 差一點（就）… *almost*

Function:

❶ The speech yesterday was really boring. I almost fell asleep.

❷ The last time my brother went hiking in the mountains, he almost got lost.

❸ For the sake of his health, he nearly moved to the countryside.

❹ Last week, he was studying in the library and his backpack almost got stolen.

❺ On Wang Yuewen's birthday, I almost forgot to give her a present.

Usage:

❶ It's pouring outside. I almost couldn't get here.

❷ I've forgotten just about everything he told me yesterday.

IV. 恐怕… *probably*

Function:

❶ I'm afraid that too much stress will affect your physical health.

❷ Although the internet has made the world smaller, I'm afraid that relationships between people are drifting further and further apart.

❸ The contract on the apartment I'm renting is almost up. I'm afraid I'll have to move.

❹ Let's move faster. If we're late, Xiao Chen will probably get angry.

❺ I haven't prepared the report for tomorrow. I'm afraid I'll have to burn the midnight oil tonight.

V. 好不容易 *finally managed to*

Function:

❶ After a great deal of effort (on somebody's part), Dad finally agreed to let me study in the US, so I'm going to make a point of working even harder.

❷ You finally managed to get a scholarship. How come you're going back home?

❸ After two weeks of rain, it finally managed to stop today.

❹ I finally managed to find a pair of shoes that I like. I had no idea it'd be so expensive.

❺ He made a huge bowl of pork knuckle rice threads that I barely managed to finish.

VI. Instantly without Prior Warning with 說…就…

Function:

❶ You didn't like your class? Why did you change classes just like that?

❷ The weather in Taipei is really strange. Rain can come at any moment.

❸ What's up with Xiaoming? Why did he just up and leave?

❹ Meimei came to Taiwan just last month. How come she's going back home already?

❺ Our teacher, Mr. Li, is very strict. He often gives tests without prior warning. The students are under a lot of stress.

VII. 不管…都… *regardless of whether or not*

Function:

❶ Regardless of whether or not he's busy at work, my dad goes to the gym every day to work out.

❷ Regardless of what the conditions will be like, he's going to move there.

❸ Whether it's steamed fish or fried fish, I won't eat it.

❹ No matter when his classes are, he's always late.

❺ I am going to go study in the US, no matter what my mom says.

Usage:

❶ If you have a question, no matter when, you can call me.

❷ Regardless of whether or not his parents agree, he is going to major in accounting.

❸ The teacher says that whether the weather is good or bad, students are not allowed to be late.

課室活動 Classroom Activities

I. The Ideal Major/Program

Goal: Learning to describe my major/program in university.

Task: Interview three classmates. Ask them to tell you what majors/programs they consider ideal and why. After the interviews, report your findings to the class.

	同學	理想的科系	為什麼？
❶			
❷			
❸			

II. My Good Friends

Goal: Learning to describe good friends and talk about information about them.
Task: Interview three classmates. Ask them to talk about their good friends. After interviews, report your findings to the class.

同學	怎麼認識的	個性	特別的能力	興趣	學歷	專長
1						
2						
3						

學歷：xuélì, educational background
專長：zhuāncháng, speciality

III. Persuading Others

Goal: Learning to provide ample information to persuade others.
Task: You want to do something, but your parents or friends are against it. How would you persuade them? Pair up and role play.

Examples of things that might cause opposition for your reference:

1 Working (in a dangerous job, a bar).

2 Choosing a university, department, or changing majors.

3 Opening a small restaurant or a café.

Try to use the following sentence patterns and vocabulary words:

除了…以外，還…	…的話	不管…都…	好不容易

IV. Application Procedures

Goal: Learning to ask for instructions on application procedures for something.

Task: After class, go to the office and ask about applying for a scholarship or a work permit.

Sample Questions

How do I apply? What documents and qualifications do I need?

文化 *Bits of Chinese Culture*

Wrap Zongzi to Bring Good Luck to Examinees
包粽包中（**bāozòng-bāozhòng**）

Even though the Dragon Boat Festival might have been a while ago, you can sometimes still see families wrapping that Dragon Boat Festival speciality-- 粽子（zòngzi）. Is this because these families make their livings selling zongzi? Of course not. It's because

▲ Wenchang Temple

▲ Test takers bring a copy of their exam admission slips to the Wenchang Temple.

▲ Parents wrap zongzi to bring good luck to their kids when they take exams.

there are children in the families that are preparing to take the entrance exam for high school or college. Parents in these families hope to use wrapping zongzi to bring a little luck for their kids. This is because the sound for "wrap zongzi" 包粽（bāozòng）sounds similar to that for 包中（bāozhòng）, i.e., guaranteed to hit the mark or to pass the test.

In addition, before their children take entrance examinations, some families offer uncooked green onions, celery, garlic, salad oil, and daikon at Wenchang Temple（文昌帝君廟 Wénchāng Dìjūn miào）. They do this because 文昌帝君（Wénchāng Dìjūn）is the God of Test Venues, so a great many students look to him during test times. The reason they bring these various items to the temple is because in Mandarin, "green onions" 蔥（cōng）sounds like "intelligent" 聰（cōng）, "celery" 芹（qín）is the same sound as "hardworking" 勤（qín）, "garlic" 蒜（suàn）is identical in sound to "calculate" 算（suàn）, and "salad oil" 沙拉油（shālā yóu）which is similar in sound to the phrase "keep up the good work" 加油（jiāyóu）. So together, parents hope that their children will be smart, diligent, do their math well, and will keep up the good work. In Taiwanese (i.e., Southern Min dialect), the word for daikon radishes 白蘿蔔（baí luóbo）is pronounced 菜頭（càitóu）which is similar to "good fortune" 好彩頭（hǎo cǎitóu）and they offer it in the hope that their kids will have good luck and pass their examinations.

These offerings for Wenchang Dijun are then brought home and cooked and given to the individual preparing to take the test. But when cooking these items, they have to make sure not to add meat balls 丸子（wánzi）or eggs 蛋（dàn）, because they are round foods in the shape of a "0" suggesting that they could get a "0" 零分（língfēn）on their test. An additional reason for this is because the first character in 丸子 and the character for 蛋 placed together 丸蛋（wándàn）become a homophone for 完蛋（wándàn）which can be translated in a number of ways, including "to be doomed", "to be done for", or "to crash and burn".

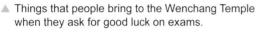

▲ Things that people bring to the Wenchang Temple when they ask for good luck on exams.

▲ Things people shouldn't put in the food to bring to the Wenchang Temple.

Self-Assessment Checklist

I can discuss topics frequently encountered on campus.

20%   40%   60%   80%   100%

I can discuss in detail learning experiences.

20%   40%   60%   80%   100%

I can try to persuade others.

20%   40%   60%   80%   100%

I can discuss school-related services and procedures.

20%   40%   60%   80%   100%

第二課

八折起

Up to 20% off

. . . .

學習目標 Learning Objectives

Topic: 購物 Shopping

- Learning to talk about shopping.
- Learning to understand simple regulations and contracts.
- Learning to refute arguments.
- Learning to offer clear reasons for why you like or dislike certain things.

LESSON

2

八折起

Up to 20% off

對話 Dialogue 🎧 02-01

（在百貨公司裡）

羅 珊 蒂 ：謝謝妳陪我來買外套。沒想到今天人這麼多。

何 雅 婷 ：現在百貨公司週年慶。一般來說，週年慶的時
候大部分的商品都會有不錯的折扣。很多人趁
這時候來買需要的東西，可以省不少錢。這個
牌子品質不錯，選擇也多，我們進去看看吧。

（何雅婷指著一件衣服要羅珊蒂看）

何 雅 婷 ：妳看，這件黃色的樣子不錯，摸起來也很舒服。
妳覺得怎麼樣？

羅 珊 蒂 ：我比較喜歡那件咖啡色的。

何 雅 婷 ：妳還是兩件都拿去試穿吧。有時候得穿上才知
道好看不好看。

店　　員：小姐，這件外套妳穿起來真漂亮。大小、長短都很合適，顏色也好看，而且是羊毛的，又輕又暖和。

何　雅　婷：這件打完折多少錢？

店　　員：原價 3,900，現在九折，打完折 3,510，算妳3,500。

何　雅　婷：廣告上不是寫八折嗎？

店　　員：不好意思，是八折起。那件八折，可是這件打九折。

何　雅　婷：羊毛外套 3,500，雖然不便宜，可是品質不錯，樣子也好，值得買。

羅　珊　蒂：好吧。我就買這件。

店　　員：刷卡還是付現金？今天刷 Visa 卡，可以再打九五折。

羅　珊　蒂：那就刷卡。

店　　員：請等我一下。（拿著簽單跟發票回來）麻煩妳在這裡簽名。謝謝。歡迎下次再來。

（羅珊蒂隔天回百貨公司要求退換）

羅　珊　蒂：我昨天買的這件外套，裡面破了一個洞。我要換一件新的。

店　　員：請問妳帶發票來了嗎？

羅　珊　蒂：我弄丟了，找不到。

店　　員：那不好意思。按照我們公司的規定，沒有發票不能退換。

羅　珊　蒂：我昨天是刷卡買的，你們應該查得到資料。再說，衣服有問題也不是我的錯。

店　　員：對不起，對不起。請等一下，我去問問店長。

課文簡體字版 Text in Simplified Characters

（在百货公司里）

罗 珊 蒂： 谢谢妳陪我来买外套。没想到今天人这么多。

何 雅 婷： 现在百货公司周年庆。一般来说，周年庆的时候大部分的商品都会有不错的折扣。很多人趁这时候来买需要的东西，可以省不少钱。这个牌子品质不错，选择也多，我们进去看看吧。

（何雅婷指着一件衣服要罗珊蒂看）

何 雅 婷： 妳看，这件黄色的样子不错，摸起来也很舒服。妳觉得怎么样？

罗 珊 蒂： 我比较喜欢那件咖啡色的。

何 雅 婷： 妳还是两件都拿去试穿吧。有时候得穿上才知道好看不好看。

店　　员： 小姐，这件外套妳穿起来真漂亮。大小、长短都很合适，颜色也好看，而且是羊毛的，又轻又暖和。

何 雅 婷： 这件打完折多少钱？

店　　员： 原价 3,900。现在九折，打完折 3,510，算妳 3,500。

何 雅 婷： 广告上不是写八折吗？

店　　员： 不好意思，是八折起。那件八折，可是这件打九折。

何 雅 婷： 羊毛外套 3,500，虽然不便宜，可是品质不错，样子也好，值得买。

罗 珊 蒂： 好吧。我就买这件。

店　　员： 刷卡还是付现金？今天刷 Visa 卡，可以再打九五折。

罗 珊 蒂： 那就刷卡。

店　　员： 请等我一下。（拿着签单跟发票回来）麻烦妳在这里签名。谢谢。欢迎下次再来。

（罗珊蒂隔天回百货公司要求退换）

罗 珊 蒂： 我昨天买的这件外套，里面破了一个洞。我要换一件新的。

店　　员： 请问妳带发票来了吗？

罗 珊 蒂： 我弄丢了，找不到。

店　　员： 那不好意思。按照我们公司的规定，没有发票不能退换。

罗 珊 蒂： 我昨天是刷卡买的，你们应该查得到资料。再说，衣服有问题也不是我的错。

店　　员： 对不起，对不起。请等一下，我去问问店长。

課文英譯 Text in English

(In a department store)

Luo Shandi : Thank you for accompanying me here to buy a coat. I had no idea there would be this many people today.

He Yating : The department store is having its anniversary. Generally speaking, during anniversaries, most products have pretty good discounts. Many people take advantage of this time to come buy things they need. You can save quite a bit of money. This is a good brand and it offers a lot of choices. Let's go inside and look around.

(Pointing at something for Luo Shandi to look at)

He Yating : Look, this yellow one looks nice and feels nice. What do you think?

Luo Shandi : I prefer the brown one.

He Yating : Go ahead and take both and try them on. Sometimes, you have to put something on before you can know if it looks good or not.

Salesperson : Miss, this coat looks really pretty on you. The size and length suit you and the color is attractive. What's more, it's wool, so it's light and warm.

He Yating : How much is this after discount?

Salesperson : The original price is NT$3,900. It's currently 10% off. After the discount, it is NT$3,510. I'll let you have it for NT$3,500.

He Yating : Doesn't the ad say 20% off?

Salesperson : I'm sorry. It says up to 20% off. That one is 20% off, but this one is 10% off.

He Yating : Although NT$3,500 for a wool coat is not cheap, the quality isn't bad and it looks nice. It's worth buying.

Luo Shandi : Oh, alright. I'll buy this one.

Salesperson : Credit card or cash? Today, if you use a Visa card, you can get a further 5% off.

Luo Shandi : Then, I'll use my credit card.

Salesperson : Please wait a moment. (*Comes back holding credit card sales slip and customer copy.*) Please sign here. Thank you. Please come again.

(The next day, Luo Shandi returns to the department store and asks for an exchange.)

Luo Shandi : This coat that I bought yesterday has a hole inside. I would like to exchange it for a new one.

Salesperson : Did you bring the receipt?

Luo Shandi : I lost it. I can't find it.

Salesperson : Then, I'm sorry. According to our company's policy, no exchanges without receipts.

Luo Shandi : Yesterday, I used my credit card to buy it. You should be able to look up the information. What's more, it's not my fault that the garment has a problem.

Salesperson : I'm sorry. Please wait a moment. I'll go ask the shop manager.

生詞一 Vocabulary I   02-02

Vocabulary

1	起 起起起	qǐ	ㄑㄧˇ	(Vp)	starting from...
2	外套 外套外 wàitào 套外套		ㄨㄞˋ ㄊㄠˋ	(N)	coat, jacket
3	一般 一般般 yìbān 一般		ㄧˋ ㄅㄢ	(Adv)	generally; in general
4	商品 商品商 shāngpǐn 品		ㄕㄤ ㄆㄧㄣˇ	(N)	goods, commodities
5	折扣 折扣折 zhékòu 扣		ㄓㄜˊ ㄎㄡˋ	(N)	discount
6	省省省省	shěng	ㄕㄥˇ	(V)	to save, to put away
7	牌子 牌牌子 páizi 牌子		ㄆㄞˊ ㄗ	(N)	brand
8	品質 品質品 pǐnzhí 質品質		ㄆㄧㄣˇ ㄓˊ	(N)	quality
9	選擇 選擇選 xuǎnzé 擇		ㄒㄩㄢˇ ㄗㄜˊ	(N)	choices
10	樣子 樣樣子 yàngzi		ㄧㄤˋ ㄗ	(N)	appearance, looks
11	摸 摸摸	mō	ㄇㄛ	(V)	to feel, to touch
12	店員 店員店 diànyuán 員		ㄉㄧㄢˋ ㄩㄢˊ	(N)	salesperson, store employee, clerk
13	短	duǎn	ㄉㄨㄢˇ	(Vs)	short
14	羊毛	yángmáo	ㄧㄤˊ ㄇㄠˊ	(N)	lamb's wool
15	暖和	nuǎnhuo	ㄋㄨㄢˇ ㄏㄨㄛ	(Vs)	warm
16	打折	dǎzhé	ㄉㄚˇ ㄓㄜˊ	(V-sep)	to offer a discount
17	原價	yuánjià	ㄩㄢˊ ㄐㄧㄚˋ	(N)	original price

18	刷卡	shuākǎ	ㄕㄨㄚ ㄎㄚˇ	(V-sep)	to swipe, i.e., use a credit card
19	現金	xiànjīn	ㄒㄧㄢˋ ㄐㄧㄣ	(N)	cash
20	麻煩	máfán	ㄇㄚˊ ㄈㄢˊ	(V)	please (lit. allow me to trouble you)
21	簽名	qiānmíng	ㄑㄧㄢ ㄇㄧㄥˊ	(V-sep)	to sign
22	破洞	pòdòng	ㄆㄛˋ ㄉㄨㄥˋ	(Vp-sep)	to have a hole
23	發票	fāpiào	ㄈㄚ ㄆㄧㄠˋ	(N)	receipt
24	弄	nòng	ㄋㄨㄥˋ	(V)	(pro-verb) to cause, to do
25	退	tuì	ㄊㄨㄟˋ	(V)	to return (purchases)
26	換	huàn	ㄏㄨㄢˋ	(V)	to exchange
27	店長	diànzhǎng	ㄉㄧㄢˋ ㄓㄤˇ	(N)	store manager

Phrases

28	週年慶	zhōunián qìng	ㄓㄡ ㄋㄧㄢˊ ㄑㄧㄥˋ	anniversary
29	一般來說	yìbān láishuō	ㄧˋ ㄅㄢ ㄌㄞˊ ㄕㄨㄛ	generally speaking
30	試穿	shì chuān	ㄕˋ ㄔㄨㄢ	to try on (garments)
31	打完折	dǎ wán zhé	ㄉㄚˇ ㄨㄢˊ ㄓㄜˊ	after discount
32	弄丟	nòng diū	ㄋㄨㄥˋ ㄉㄧㄡ	to lose

短文 Reading 🎧 02-03

購物糾紛

安德思上個月在電信公司的門市辦了一支新手機。他剛到台灣的時候，用的是預付卡，所以一拿到居留證就馬上去換成月租型的。店員告訴他，一個月只要一千多塊就能吃到飽。安德思高興得不得了，

就放心地給親戚朋友打電話。沒想到前幾天收到帳單，一看要三千多塊，嚇了他一大跳。

他馬上找何雅婷陪他去問清楚。店員告訴他，按照合約，吃到飽只是網路，並不包括打電話。何雅婷聽了店員的解釋，非常生氣。外國人怎麼看得懂這麼複雜的中文合約？店員應該把重要的事情跟顧客說清楚，尤其是對外國人的時候。這不是騙人嗎？何雅婷把店員罵了一頓，可是一點辦法也沒有。

回家的路上，何雅婷告訴安德思，她在報上看到過不少買手機的糾紛。有人剛買的新手機常常自動關機，修理了幾次都修不好，可是電信公司不願意換新的給他。還有人手機聽不清楚，電信公司也說是因為他們住在山邊，不同意退錢。何雅婷建議安德思給電信公司的客服中心打電話。要是還不行，就只好去繳費了。

課文簡體字版 Text in Simplified Characters

购物纠纷

安德思上个月在电信公司的门市办了一支新手机。他刚到台湾的时候，用的是预付卡，所以一拿到居留证就马上去换成月租型的。店员告诉他，一个月只要一千多块就能吃到饱。安德思高兴得不得了，就放心地给亲戚朋友打电话。没想到前几天收到帐单，一看要三千多块，吓了他一大跳。

他马上找何雅婷陪他去问清楚。店员告诉他，按照合约，吃到饱只是网路，并不包括打电话。何雅婷听了店员的解释，非常生气。外国人怎么看得懂这么复杂的中文合约？店员应该把重要的事情跟顾客说清楚，尤其是对外国人的时候。这不是骗人吗？何雅婷把店员骂了一顿，可是一点办法也没有。

回家的路上，何雅婷告诉安德思，她在报上看到过不少买手机的纠纷。有人刚买的新手机常常自动关机，修理了几次都修不好，可是电信公司不愿意换新的给他。还有人手机听不清楚，电信公司也说是因为他们住在山边，不同意退钱。何雅婷建议安德思给电信公司的客服中心打电话。要是还不行，就只好去缴费了。

課文英譯 Text in English

Shopping Dispute

Last month, An Desi went to a retail office of a phone company, to get a new cell phone. When he first arrived in Taiwan, he used a prepaid phone card, so as soon as he got his Alien Resident Certificate (ARC), he went to switch to a phone with a monthly plan. A salesperson told him that for only NT$1,000 plus, he could have unlimited data. An Desi was thrilled. When he called family and friends, his mind set at ease. However, he was shocked when he received a bill for more than NT$3,000 the other day.

He immediately went to see He Yating and ask her to go with him to get the matter clarified. The store employee told him that according to the contract, "unlimited data" only means for the internet and does not include phone calls. After hearing the salesperson's explanation, He Yating was very angry. How is a foreigner going to understand a complicated Chinese contract like that? A salesperson should explain clearly the important items for customers, especially foreigners. Isn't this deceit? He Yating scolded the salesperson, but it was no use.

On the way home, He Yating told An Desi that she had seen in the paper a number of cell phone purchase disputes. One person's new cell phone often shut off automatically. He had it fixed a few times, but it still didn't work. The phone company wasn't willing to exchange it for a new one. Another person couldn't hear clearly on his cell phone. The phone company said it was because he lived next to a mountain and wouldn't agree to refund the money. He Yating suggested that An Desi call the phone company's customer service center. If that still didn't work, he would have no choice but to pay the bill.

生詞二 Vocabulary II 02-04

Vocabulary

1	購物	gòuwù	ㄍㄡˋ ㄨˋ	(Vi)	to go shopping
2	糾紛	jiūfēn	ㄐㄧㄡ ㄈㄣ	(N)	dispute
3	電信	diànxìn	ㄉㄧㄢˋ ㄒㄧㄣˋ	(N)	telecommunications
4	門市	ménshì	ㄇㄣˊ ㄕˋ	(N)	retail outlet
5	居留證	jūliúzhèng	ㄐㄩ ㄌㄧㄡˊ ㄓㄥˋ	(N)	Alien Resident Certificate (ARC in Taiwan)
6	月租型	yuèzūxíng	ㄩㄝˋ ㄗㄨ ㄒㄧㄥˊ	(N)	a monthly plan

7	帳單	zhàngdān	ㄓㄤˋ ㄉㄢ	(N)	bill
8	並	bìng	ㄅㄧㄥˋ	(Adv)	contrary to assumption (followed by a negative statement)
9	包括	bāokuò	ㄅㄠ ㄎㄨㄛˋ	(V)	to include
10	解釋	jiěshì	ㄐㄧㄝˇ ㄕˋ	(N)	explanation
11	顧客	gùkè	ㄍㄨˋ ㄎㄜˋ	(N)	customer
12	尤其	yóuqí	ㄧㄡˊ ㄑㄧˊ	(Adv)	especially, in particular
13	騙	piàn	ㄆㄧㄢˋ	(V)	to cheat, to swindle
14	頓	dùn	ㄉㄨㄣˋ	(M)	verbal measure word for a duration of action
15	辦法	bànfǎ	ㄅㄢˋ ㄈㄚˇ	(N)	solution
16	自動	zìdòng	ㄗˋ ㄉㄨㄥˋ	(Adv)	by itself, on its own, automatically
17	關機	guānjī	ㄍㄨㄢ ㄐㄧ	(Vp-sep)	to turn off, to shut down
18	修理	xiūlǐ	ㄒㄧㄡ ㄌㄧˇ	(V)	to repair
19	繳費	jiǎofèi	ㄐㄧㄠˇ ㄈㄟˋ	(V-sep)	to pay a fee

Phrases

20	預付卡	yùfù kǎ	ㄩˋ ㄈㄨˋ ㄎㄚˇ		prepaid SIM card
21	換成	huàn chéng	ㄏㄨㄢˋ ㄔㄥˊ		to change to
22	吃到飽	chī dào bǎo	ㄔ ㄉㄠˋ ㄅㄠˇ		unlimited data (lit. all you can eat)
23	嚇一跳	xià yí tiào	ㄒㄧㄚˋ ㄧˊ ㄊㄧㄠˋ		shocked, startled, taken aback
24	客服中心	kèfú zhōngxīn	ㄎㄜˋ ㄈㄨˊ ㄓㄨㄥ ㄒㄧㄣ		customer service center

文法 Grammar

I. 一般來說 *generally speaking* 🎧 02-05   英譯 p.40

Function: This expression introduces a general situation. It is typically placed at the beginning of the sentence.

➊ 一般來說，個性活潑、外語能力好的學生很適合念國際關係系。

➋ 在台灣，一般來說，退換商品的時候都得帶發票。

➌ 一般來說，有牌子的商品比較貴，但是品質也比較好。

➍ 一般來說，菜的味道不要太鹹比較健康。

➎ 跟南部比起來，一般來說，台北市區大樓比較多，馬路也比較寬。

Usage: 一般來說 is interchangeable with 一般說來.

練習 Exercise

Use 一般來說 to describe a generality when answering the questions below.

➊ A：泰國菜跟法國菜的味道一樣嗎？
B：不一樣。一般來說，泰國菜用光，法國菜用面包　　　。

➋ A：夏天去墾丁旅行一定得先訂房間嗎？
B：一般來說不管去墾丁或是台北都先訂房間。

➌ A：我最近在找房子，準備搬家。沒想到捷運站附近的房子都這麼貴，我真的租不起。
B：一般來說城市裡的房bijiao貴　　　。

➍ A：週年慶的時候，商店都打幾折？
B：不一定。不過一般來說打折　　　。

➎ A：為什麼父母都希望孩子念熱門科系呢？孩子不一定有興趣啊。
B：一般來說jue de孩子的興趣是最zhong yao　　。

II. General Verb 弄 🎧 02-06

 英譯 p.40

Function: 弄 is a general verb that can be used as a substitute for verbs of more substantial meaning. Just like the English general verb do as in "doing the dishes", 弄 is used when the precise meaning of the verb is not clear or not that important in the context. 弄 can be followed by a noun indicating the object (e.g., 弄飯 "cooking a dinner"), but can also be followed by a state verb or a process verb e.g., 弄丟 "to lose something", 弄錯 "to get something wrong".

1. 弄 + Noun

(1) 你坐一下，我去弄飯。等一下就可以吃了。

(2) 你別一直弄我的衣服。

2. 弄 + Resultative complements (Vs or Vp)

(1) 是誰把我的玻璃瓶弄破的？

(2) 雨好大，把我的衣服弄濕了。

(3) 這一課的語法好難，我看了半天還是弄不清楚。

Usage:

1. 弄 is typically used when the result of a process is informationally more important than the process itself, e.g., 弄乾淨、弄好.

2. When 弄 is followed by a state or a process verb, no further degree adverbs, such as 很, are used to modify the verb, so *弄很乾淨 is not grammatical, unless 得 is used after 弄. E.g., 弄得乾乾淨淨的、弄得很濕、弄得好極了.

練習 Exercise

Use the following 弄 expressions to complete the following sentences.

（弄錯、弄好、弄乾淨、弄糊塗）

❶ 她跟她妹妹很像，所以朋友常常 __糊塗 shéi shì shéi__ 。

❷ 桌子上好多垃圾。你快 __nòng gānjìng ba__ 。不管你用什麼方法。

❸ 你要的資料我差不多 __弄好__ 了。你十分鐘以後就可以過來拿了。

❹ 對不起，是我 __弄 cuo__ 了。偷走我手機的人不是你。

❺ 他的話把我 _____ 了。我聽了半天，還是不懂他的意思。

III. 再說 *besides, moreover* 02-07　 英譯 p.40

Function: The adverb 再說 introduces a new sentence that provides further clarification or elaboration about what was said in the preceding sentences.

① 還是刷卡吧。我沒帶那麼多現金。再說，刷卡還可以再打九五折。

② 電信公司的中文合約那麼長。再說，安德思是外國人。怎麼可能看得懂？

③ 我女朋友一定會生我的氣的。這是我掉的第三支手機了。再說，手機是她送給我的生日禮物。

④ 我準備的材料夠包一百多個餃子。再說，我還做了好幾道菜。大家一定都能吃飽。

⑤ 你應該趁學校放假到南部海邊看看。再說，你還沒玩過水上摩托車。值得去試一試。

Usage:

1. Both 而且 and 再說 are used to connect the current sentence with preceding sentences, both translatable as "moreover". 而且 suggests that what is said in the current sentence and the preceding sentence are on equal footing, while 再說 highlights that what is said in the current sentence is a further addition or elaboration on top of what was said in the preceding sentences. For example, the 而且 in 他的房間要有家具，而且光線要好。'He wants a room with furniture and good lighting.' cannot be replaced by 再說.

2. 而且 can connect two clauses or two sentences. 再說 can connect only sentences. For example, the 而且 in 他一定能找到便宜而且合適的房子。'He's bound to be able to find an inexpensive and suitable house.' cannot be replaced by 再說.

練習 Exercice

Please provide further clarification by completing the following 再說 sentences.

❶ 她習慣大城市熱鬧的氣氛。再說，＿＿＿＿＿＿＿＿＿＿＿＿，
所以一點也不想搬到鄉下住。

❷ 今天的餃子是我最喜歡的豬肉餡兒。再說，＿＿＿＿＿＿，
我就把他煮的水餃都吃光了。

❸ 今天晚上我真的不能跟你們出去玩。我得準備明天的口頭報
告，再說，＿＿＿＿＿＿＿＿＿＿＿＿＿＿。

❹ 我覺得她轉到國際關係系是一個很好的決定。她對會計一點
興趣都沒有。再說，＿＿＿＿＿＿＿＿＿＿＿＿。

❺ 我認為買東西應該要買有牌子的。有牌子的東西，一般來
說，品質比較好。再說，＿＿＿＿＿＿＿＿＿＿＿＿。

IV. V + 成 *to become, to turn into* 02-08   英譯 p.40

Function: The post-verbal 成 introduces a noun that denotes the new entity (or state) that derives from the action denoted by the verb.

❶ 你看！你把餃子包成什麼樣子了？

❷ 我看不懂西班牙文。你能不能幫我把這段話翻譯成中文？

❸ 你在我房間裡做了什麼事？怎麼把我的房間弄成這樣？

❹ 她用蛋跟其他材料做成一個生日蛋糕，送給媽媽。

❺ 這是用 Word 寫的。我幫你存成 PDF，可以嗎？

Usage:

1. V + 成 is typically followed by a noun. If the new state is denoted by a state verb, then 成 is not inserted between the action verb and the state verb. So *他把我的杯子弄成破了 is no good.

2. Negation 不 or 沒 is placed before the action verb. For example, 她的手機沒換成月租型。 'She didn't change her cell phone plan to a monthly plan.'

練習 Exercise

Use the V + 成 expressions in the list to complete the following sentences.

> 翻譯成、拍成、弄成、寫成、包成、做成、換成

❶ 要是我們把這本書＿＿＿拍成＿＿＿電影，你會不會想看？

❷ 我聽不懂他的話。請你幫我＿＿＿翻譯成＿＿＿中文，好嗎？

❸ 我們用這幾個蛋，再加一些糖，＿＿＿＿＿＿＿＿＿＿吧。

❹ 你已經拿到居留證了。為什麼不把手機＿＿＿＿＿＿＿＿＿？

❺ 你看！他把我的腳踏車＿＿＿＿＿＿＿＿。我怎麼騎呢？

V. Contrary to Expectation with 並 02-09   英譯 p.40

Function: The adverb 並 is typically followed by negation, forming 並不 or 並沒（有）. Its use suggests that a statement runs contrary to expectations or common assumptions. Used in dialogues, these expressions indicate the speaker's strong opposition to what was said previously.

❶ 你們為什麼都來問我？我並不知道怎麼包餃子啊。

❷ 這些菜的作法雖然簡單，但是味道並不差。

❸ 這件事說起來容易，做起來並不容易。

❹ 網路雖然把世界變小了，但是人跟人的關係並沒有變得比較近。

❺ 垃圾分類並沒有你想的那麼麻煩。

Usage:

1. 並 is an adverb. It is placed after the subject and before the verb.

2. When one wants to indicate 'it is not the case (that)...', the expression is 並 + 不是. For example, 並不是所有的牌子都打七折。 'It's not the case that all brands are 30% off.'

3. The speaker uses 並 to indicate that what he is saying is contrary to what the addressee assumes or expects. By contrast, without 並, the speaker's statement is a straightforward one.

   A：你們班上不是還有位子嗎？妳怎麼沒叫我去旁聽？

   B：a. 我並不知道還有位子。 (relatively tactful way of saying it)

   　　b. 我不知道還有位子。 (more direct)

means no? or...?

37

練習 Exercise

Please complete the dialogues by using 並 to refer to something contrary to expectation.

1 A：這份工作很適合你。面談很順利吧？

B：我原來也以為會很順利，沒想到 並不容易的工作 。

2 A：（在電話上）你不是答應幫我搬家嗎？怎麼還不快點過來？

B：＿＿＿＿＿＿＿＿＿＿＿＿＿＿＿ 。

3 A：你放了什麼東西？這個菜怎麼這麼甜？

B：做菜的 shíhòu 我並不用 táng（糖） 。

4 A：你怎麼把我的房間弄成這樣？你在房間裡做什麼了？

B：不是我弄的。我這個星期並不進去你的房間 。

5 A：有了網路，做什麼都很方便。有了網路，什麼都做得到。

B：我不這麼認為，並 méiyǒu 網路什麼都可以弄 。

VI. 尤其是 *especially* 🎧 02-10

 英譯 p.41

Function: The adverb 尤其是 is used to show that what you are saying applies more to one thing or situation than to others. 尤其是 usually occurs in the latter part of a sentence.

1 這學期的功課給他很大的壓力，尤其是口頭報告。

2 過春節，小孩都很開心，尤其是拿紅包的時候。

3 中文很難學，尤其是聲調和發音，得花很多時間練習。

4 他對網路上好幾個徵求教師的廣告都很有興趣，尤其是去美國大學教中文的廣告。

5 最近他的中文進步了很多，尤其是發音。

練習 Exercise

Complete the following 尤其是 sentences.

❶ 我什麼餡兒的餃子都喜歡吃，尤其是<u>素餡兒</u>　　　。
❷ 他非常喜歡吃中國菜，尤其是<u>四川菜</u>　　　。
❸ 我的國家跟台灣很不一樣，尤其是<u>房子</u>　　　。
❹ 墾丁有很多非常好玩的水上活動，尤其是<u>滑水</u>　　。
❺ 這幾件外套穿起來都又輕又暖和，尤其是<u>暖和</u>　　。

VII. Concession with 只好 *could only, have no choice but to* 02-11 　 英譯 p.41

Function: The adverb 只好 introduces the best possible option under the given circumstances.

❶ 電信公司的門市不能刷卡，顧客只好付現金。
❷ 他好不容易考上熱門科系，可惜念了一個學期發現興趣不合，只好轉系。
❸ 水餃都煮破了，我只好留下來自己吃。
❹ 上課以前我才發現書被我弄丟了。我只好趕快去跟朋友借。
❺ 他快遲到了，只好搭計程車去上班。

練習 Exercise

Complete each 只好 sentence by describing a concession.

❶ 捷運站附近的房子太貴了，我住不起，只好<u>住在鄉下</u>　。
❷ 他不小心把鞋子弄濕了，只好<u>弄乾</u>　　　。
❸ 我的錢包被偷走了，我只好<u>從 huātien 再 bèi tōu zǒu</u>　　。
❹ 新家太小，我的書桌放不下，只好<u>買新家</u>　　。
❺ 他感冒很嚴重，只好　　　　　　　　　　　。

語法例句英譯
Grammar Examples in English

I. 一般來說 *generally speaking*
Function:

1. Generally speaking, students with vibrant personalities and good foreign language skills are suited to studying international relations.
2. In Taiwan, generally speaking, when you exchange products, you need to bring the receipt with you.
3. Generally speaking, brand name products are more expensive, but they are also higher quality.
4. Generally speaking, dishes that are less salty are healthier.
5. Generally speaking, when you compare downtown Taipei with the south, there are more buildings and the roads are wider.

II. General Verb 弄
Function:

1. (1) Have a seat. I'll go make supper. We'll be eating soon.
   (2) Stop pulling on my clothes.
2. (1) Who was it that broke my glass bottle?
   (2) The rain is really heavy and soaked my clothes.
   (3) The grammar in this chapter is really hard. I've been studying it for a long time and I still can't figure it out.

III. 再說 *besides, moreover*
Function:

1. I'm just going to use my credit card. I didn't bring that much cash. What's more, I can get another 5% off by swiping my credit card.
2. The phone company's Chinese contract is so long. In addition, An Desi is a foreigner. How is he possibly going to understand?

3. My girlfriend is bound to be angry with me. This is the third cell phone I've lost. Besides, this was the cell phone she gave me for my birthday.
4. I prepared enough ingredients to make over 100 dumplings. In addition, I made several other dishes. Everybody is bound to eat their fill.
5. You should take advantage of the school break to go to the seaside down south and check it out. What's more, you've never ridden a jet ski. It's worth a try.

IV. V + 成 *to become, to turn into*
Function:

1. Look at you! What kind of dumplings are you making?
2. I don't understand Spanish. Can you translate this section into Chinese for me?
3. What did you do in my room? How did it get so messed up?
4. She used eggs and some other ingredients and made them into a birthday cake for her mom.
5. This was written in Word. I saved it for you in a PDF file. Is that OK?

V. Contrary to Expectation with 並
Function:

1. Why did you all come to ask me? I have no idea how to wrap dumplings.
2. Although these dishes are easy to make, they taste good.
3. This is easy to talk about, but it's not easy to do. (This is easier said than done.)
4. The internet has made the world smaller, but it hasn't brought people closer together.
5. Sorting garbage isn't as much a hassle as you think it is.

Usage:

3.   A: Aren't there still empty seats in your class? Why didn't you tell me to go audit?

    B: a. I had no idea there were any empty seats.

       b. I had no idea there were any empty seats.

VI. 尤其是 *especially*

Function:

1 The homework this semester is really stressing him out, especially the oral reports.

2 Kids really have a great time during the Spring Festival, especially when they get red envelopes.

3 Chinese is really hard to learn. In particular, you have to spend a lot of time practicing tones and pronunciation.

4 He is interested in a lot of ads for teachers on the internet, especially the ones for Chinese teachers in US universities.

5 His Chinese has improved a great deal lately, especially his pronunciation.

VII. Concession with 只好 *could only, have no choice but to*

Function:

1 The telephone company's retail outlet doesn't let you pay with credit cards. Customers can only pay in cash.

2 He managed to test into a really popular department. Unfortunately, after a semester, he discovered that it's not where his interests lie. He had no choice but to change majors.

3 All of the dumplings split open during cooking. I had no choice but to keep them for myself to eat.

4 I didn't notice that I had lost my book until just before class. I had no choice but to quickly borrow one from a friend.

5 He was going to be late, so he had no choice but to take a taxi to work.

課室活動 Classroom Activities

I. I Don't Know Which One to Choose

Goal: Learning to give suggestions and explain them using objective reasons.

Task: He Yating goes with Luo Shandi to a department store to buy a winter coat. Luo Shandi tries on two and likes both. She doesn't know which to choose. She doesn't make a decision until after she discusses it with He Yating. Pair up and role play, using a similar theme and dialogue.

Try to use the following sentence patterns and vocabulary words:

大小／長短	一般來說	再說	尤其是	折扣
並	樣子	品質	省	刷卡

II. Returning Merchandise to a Department Store

Goal: Learning to handle consumer disputes.

Task: Luo Shandi used a credit card to buy a coat. The next day, she went back to the department store to exchange it. The store manager refused, because.... Luo Shandi and the store manager later agreed to handle the situation by.... Pair up and role play the dialogue between Luo Shandi and the store manager.

Try to use the following sentence patterns and vocabulary words:

按照規定	再說	尤其是	原價	折扣
試穿	弄 Vs	V 成	包括	騙人

III. Customer Complaints

Goal: Learning to handle consumer disputes in Chinese.

Task: After talking with store personnel, An Desi is still unhappy. Although he didn't ask and he is partly responsible, the fact of the matter is.... He decides to write a letter to the customer service center manager. Have students get into groups of three and finish writing An Desi's letter, to be presented in class.

Try to use the following sentence patterns and vocabulary words:

辦法	按照合約	帳單	門市	顧客
一般來說	解釋	只好	再說	尤其是

文化 _Bits of Chinese Culture_

Six of One, a Half Dozen of the Other 半斤八兩（bànjīn bāliǎng）

Have you ever bought 一斤（yìjīn）of fruit at a traditional market, but when you held your purchase in your hand realized that it wasn't 1,000 grams in weight? Did you think that the fruit vendor made a mistake?

Well, he probably didn't. The Taiwan government officially adopted the metric system way back in 1985 and most businesses, including supermarkets, now use it, but traditional markets, jewelry shops, and Chinese medicine shops continue to commonly use the traditional system. Originating in China, the traditional weight system has been in use in Taiwan since 1906 when the island was a colony of Japan. The term 一斤（catty）is actually just another name for 台斤（Táijīn, Taiwanese catty）. One Taiwanese catty is equivalent to 600 grams in contrast to the 1,000 grams in a kilogram.

If you go to Mainland China, however, you'll discover that the 一斤 used in traditional markets there is equivalent to 500 grams. This is because in 1928, the Nationalist government established the 市斤（shìjīn, market catty）system for markets as a transitional measure to the metric system. 2 market catties is equivalent to 1 kilogram, so 1 market catty is equivalent to 500 grams. The people of China continue to use the market catty today.

Interestingly, although the Taiwanese catty and the market catty represent different weights, both continue to use China's traditional calculation method based on the number 16, so that 16 "liang" is equivalent to 一斤. Incidently, the English phrase "six of one, half dozen of the other" can often be translated using a phrase that employs terms from China's traditional weight system 半斤八兩（bànjīn bāliǎng, half a jin or eight liang）.

▲ The term 一斤 actually means 一台斤 (Taiwanese catty).

▲ An electronic scale used at traditional markets.

▲ A scale used at traditional markets.

Self-Assessment Checklist

I can talk about shopping.

20%   40%   60%   80%   100%

I can understand simple regulations and contracts.

20%   40%   60%   80%   100%

I can refute arguments.

20%   40%   60%   80%   100%

I can offer clear reasons for why I like or dislike certain things.

20%   40%   60%   80%   100%

LESSON 3

第三課

外套帶了沒有？

Did You Bring Your Coat?

....

學習目標 Learning Objectives

Topic: 氣候與節日 Climate and Holidays

- Learning to describe changes in climate and weather.
- Learning to talk about the seasons and activities particular to each.
- Learning to talk about traditional Chinese New Year, Dragon Boat Festival, and Mid-Autumn Moon Festival customs.
- Learning to read about the origins of important festivals.

外套帶了沒有？

Did You Bring Your Coat?

對話 Dialogue 03-01

（在火鍋店門口）

陳敏萱：妳怎麼現在才來？我們等妳等半天了。

羅珊蒂：對不起，我來晚了。我走到半路下起雨來了，只好又回去拿傘。台灣的天氣真奇怪，說變就變。

陳敏萱：就是啊。昨天還出大太陽，今天就又颱風又下雨。

高橋健太：台灣是個海島，冬天的時候，受到北方來的冷空氣的影響，天氣很不穩定。

羅珊蒂：幸虧我買了外套，要不然就只好躲在家裡了。

陳敏萱：沒那麼嚴重吧，今天還有 18 度。這樣的溫度在荷蘭只能算是夏天。荷蘭的冬天還常常到零下呢。

高橋健太：今天溫度是不低，不過因為下雨，感覺比實_{shí}際溫度低得多，難怪羅珊蒂受不了。

（他們走進火鍋店坐下）

羅　珊　蒂：我餓死了，我們趕快點菜吧。天氣這麼冷，吃牛肉最好。你們呢？想吃點什麼？

陳　敏　萱：我昨天剛吃過烤肉，今天就點素菜鍋吧。這個季節的大白菜最甜了。

高橋健太：聽說這家火鍋店的海鮮很新鮮。我要海鮮。

羅　珊　蒂：沒想到台灣的冬天這麼冷，看起來我得讓我男朋友春天的時候再來。

高橋健太：春天真的很浪漫_{làngmàn}，到處都看得到櫻_{yīng}花，可是在台灣有句話說：「春天後母臉」。春天天氣變化比冬天更大，早晚的氣溫也差很多。

陳　敏　萱：高橋說的沒錯。我朋友告訴我，去年春天幾乎每天都下雨，衣服總是乾不了。

高橋健太：是啊，衣服、鞋子都發霉_{fā méi}了，所以我去年買了除濕機。

羅　珊　蒂：我們雖然也有雨季，可是下過雨以後晚上就涼快了。不像台北這麼潮濕。我六月來的時候，又悶又熱，又沒有冷氣，真受不了。

陳　敏　萱：我是八月來的。我一來就去海邊曬_{shài}太陽，朋友都羨慕死了。本來打算六月底回國，但是因為台灣的夏天可以玩很多水上活動，而且吃得到很多熱帶_{rè dài}水果，所以我決定晚一點再回去。

高橋健太：快吃吧。肉煮久了就不好吃了。

羅　珊　蒂：真的很好吃。我男朋友來的時候，我們一定要再來這裡聚一聚。

陳敏萱、高橋健太：那有什麼問題。

課文簡體字版 Text in Simplified Characters

（在火锅店门口）

陈 敏 萱 ：妳怎么现在才来？我们等妳等半天了。

罗 珊 蒂 ：对不起，我来晚了。我走到半路下起雨来了，只好又回去拿伞。台湾的天气真奇怪，说变就变。

陈 敏 萱 ：就是啊。昨天还出大太阳，今天就又刮风又下雨。

高桥健太 ：台湾是个海岛，冬天的时候，受到北方来的冷空气的影响，天气很不稳定。

罗 珊 蒂 ：幸亏我买了外套，要不然就只好躲在家里了。

陈 敏 萱 ：没那么严重吧，今天还有 18 度。这样的温度在荷兰只能算是夏天。荷兰的冬天还常常到零下呢。

高桥健太 ：今天温度是不低，不过因为下雨，感觉比实际温度低得多，难怪罗珊蒂受不了。

（他们走进火锅店坐下）

罗 珊 蒂 ：我饿死了，我们赶快点菜吧。天气这么冷，吃牛肉最好。你们呢？想吃点什么？

陈 敏 萱 ：我昨天刚吃过烤肉，今天就点素菜锅吧。这个季节的大白菜最甜了。

高桥健太 ：听说这家火锅店的海鲜很新鲜。我要海鲜。

罗 珊 蒂 ：没想到台湾的冬天这么冷，看起来我得让我男朋友春天的时候再来。

高桥健太 ：春天真的很浪漫，到处都看得到樱花，可是在台湾有句话说：「春天后母脸」。春天天气变化比冬天更大，早晚的气温也差很多。

陈 敏 萱 ：高桥说的没错。我朋友告诉我，去年春天几乎每天都下雨，衣服总是干不了。

高桥健太 ：是啊，衣服、鞋子都发霉了，所以我去年买了除湿机。

罗 珊 蒂 ：我们虽然也有雨季，可是下过雨以后晚上就凉快了。不像台北这么潮湿。我六月来的时候，又闷又热，又没有冷气，真受不了。

陈 敏 萱 ：我是八月来的。我一来就去海边晒太阳，朋友都羡慕死了。本来打算六月底回国，但是因为台湾的夏天可以玩很多水上活动，而且吃得到很多热带水果，所以我决定晚一点再回去。

高桥健太 ：快吃吧。肉煮久了就不好吃了。

罗 珊 蒂 ：真的很好吃。我男朋友来的时候，我们一定要再来这里聚一聚。

陈敏萱、高桥健太：那有什么问题。

課文英譯 Text in English

(At the entrance to a hotpot restaurant)

Chen Minxuan : What took you so long to get here? We've been waiting for you for a long time.

Luo Shandi : Sorry, I've come late. I walked half way here and it started raining, so I had to go back again and get my umbrella. Taiwan's weather is strange. It can change just like that.

Chen Minxuan : Quite right. Yesterday, the sun was out; today, it's windy and rainy.

Gaoqiao Jiantai : Taiwan is a sea island. In the winter, it is influenced by cold air from the north. The weather is very unstable.

Luo Shandi : Fortunately, I bought a coat; otherwise, I would have no choice but to hide in my house.

Chen Minxuan : It's not that serious. It even got up to 18 degrees today. This kind of temperature in the Netherlands would only be regarded as summer. In the winter, it often goes below zero in the Netherlands.

Gaoqiao Jiantai : The temperature today actually isn't that low, but because it's raining, it feels much colder than it really is. It's no wonder Luo Shandi can't stand it.

(They enter the hotpot restaurant and sit down.)

Luo Shandi : I'm starving to death. Let's order right away. With the weather this cold, eating beef would be best. And you guys? What would you like to eat?

Chen Minxuan : I just had barbecue yesterday. Today, I'll go ahead and order a vegetarian pot. Chinese cabbage is sweetest this time of year.

Gaoqiao Jiantai : People say that this hotpot restaurant's seafood is fresh. I want seafood.

Luo Shandi : I had no idea that Taiwan's winter was this cold. It looks like I have to have my boyfriend come in spring.

Gaoqiao Jiantai : Spring is really romantic. You can see cherry blossoms everywhere. But the Taiwanese have a saying, "Spring is like a stepmother's face". The weather in spring changes even more drastically. And there are big differences between temperatures in the mornings and evenings.

Chen Minxuan : Gaoqiao is not wrong in what he says. My friend told me that last spring, it rained almost every day. Clothes could never get dry.

Gaoqiao Jiantai : That's right. Clothes and shoes all mildewed, so I bought a dehumidifier last year.

Luo Shandi	: We also have a rainy season, but after it rains, the evenings are cool. It's not as humid as Taipei. When I arrived in June, it was stuffy and hot and I didn't have an air conditioner. I really couldn't stand it.
Chen Minxuan	: I arrived in August. Right after I arrived, I went to the seaside to bask in the sun. My friends were beside themselves with envy. I originally planned to go home at the end of June, but because there are a lot of water activities to do in Taiwan in the summer and there is a lot of tropical fruit, I decided to go back a little later.
Gaoqiao Jiantai	: Eat up. Meat doesn't taste good when it's cooked too long.
Luo Shandi	: This is really good. When my boyfriend comes, we have got to have another get-together here.
Chen Minxuan & Gaoqiao Jiantai	: I have no problem with that.

生詞一 Vocabulary I　　🎧 03-02

People in the Dialogue

| 1 | 陳敏萱 | Chén Mǐnxuān | ㄔㄣˊ ㄇㄧㄣˇ ㄒㄩㄢ | | a woman from the Netherlands |
| 2 | 高橋健太 | Gāoqiáo Jiàntài | ㄍㄠ ㄑㄧㄠˊ ㄐㄧㄢˋ ㄊㄞˋ | | a man from Japan |

Vocabulary

3	空氣	kōngqì	ㄎㄨㄥ ㄑㄧˋ	(N)	air
4	影響	yǐngxiǎng	ㄧㄥˇ ㄒㄧㄤˇ	(N)	influence
5	穩定	wěndìng	ㄨㄣˇ ㄉㄧㄥˋ	(Vs)	stable
6	幸虧	xìngkuī	ㄒㄧㄥˋ ㄎㄨㄟ	(Adv)	fortunately
7	躲 躲	duǒ	ㄉㄨㄛˇ	(Vi)	to hide, to go into hiding
8	度	dù	ㄉㄨˋ	(M)	degree
9	溫度	wēndù	ㄨㄣ ㄉㄨˋ	(N)	temperature
10	零下	língxià	ㄌㄧㄥˊ ㄒㄧㄚˋ	(Vs-attr)	below zero
11	感覺 感	gǎnjué	ㄍㄢˇ ㄐㄩㄝˊ	(Vst)	to feel
12	實際	shíjì	ㄕˊ ㄐㄧˋ	(Vs)	actual

13	難怪怪	nánguài	ㄋㄢˊ ㄍㄨㄞˋ	(Adv)	it's no wonder, no wonder
14	季節季節季節	jìjié	ㄐㄧˋ ㄐㄧㄝˊ	(N)	season
15	火鍋火鍋	huǒguō	ㄏㄨㄛˇ ㄍㄨㄛ	(N)	hotpot
16	海鮮鮮鮮	hǎixiān	ㄏㄞˇ ㄒㄧㄢ	(N)	seafood
17	新鮮	xīnxiān	ㄒㄧㄣ ㄒㄧㄢ	(Vs)	fresh
18	櫻花	yīnghuā	ㄧㄥ ㄏㄨㄚ	(N)	cherry blossom
19	變化變變	biànhuà	ㄅㄧㄢˋ ㄏㄨㄚˋ	(N)	change
20	氣溫	qìwēn	ㄑㄧˋ ㄨㄣ	(N)	temperature (weather)
21	差	chā	ㄔㄚ	(Vst)	to differ
22	幾乎	jīhū	ㄐㄧ ㄏㄨ	(Adv)	almost
23	乾	gān	ㄍㄢ	(Vs)	dry
24	發霉	fāméi	ㄈㄚ ㄇㄟˊ	(Vp-sep)	to mildew
25	除濕機	chúshījī	ㄔㄨˊ ㄕ ㄐㄧ	(N)	dehumidifier
26	雨季	yǔjì	ㄩˇ ㄐㄧˋ	(N)	rainy season
27	涼快	liángkuài	ㄌㄧㄤˊ ㄎㄨㄞˋ	(Vs)	cool
28	潮濕	cháoshī	ㄔㄠˊ ㄕ	(Vs)	humid
29	悶	mēn	ㄇㄣ	(Vs)	stuffy
30	冷氣	lěngqì	ㄌㄥˇ ㄑㄧˋ	(N)	air conditioning

Names

| 31 | 荷蘭 | Hélán | ㄏㄜˊ ㄌㄢˊ | | the Netherlands (lit. Holland) |

Phrases

32	出大太陽	chū dà tàiyáng	ㄔㄨ ㄉㄚˋ ㄊㄞˋ ㄧㄤˊ		to be blazing hot
33	颱風	guā fēng	ㄍㄨㄚ ㄈㄥ		to be windy (lit. blow wind)
34	受到	shòu dào	ㄕㄡˋ ㄉㄠˋ		to receive, to be, to get
35	受不了	shòu bù liǎo	ㄕㄡˋ ㄅㄨˋ ㄌㄧㄠˇ		can't stand it
36	餓死了	è sǐle	ㄜˋ ㄙˇ ˙ㄌㄜ		to starve to death (an exaggeration)
37	後母臉	hòumǔ liǎn	ㄏㄡˋ ㄇㄨˇ ㄌㄧㄢˇ		stepmother's face, i.e., stern and cruel look

短文 Reading 🎧 03-03

華人的重要節日

在台灣，除了原住民以外，大部分的人的祖先都是從中國移民來的，所以我們的傳統節日都跟中國一樣。一年當中，最重要的三個節日——春節、端午節跟中秋節——都是根據農曆來的。

古時候，中國是一個農業國家，農人的生活和節日都跟季節的變化有關係。比方說，新年又叫春節，就是春天的開始。這時候，天氣還很冷，農人利用這段難得的休息時間，跟家人好好地聚聚。除夕這一天，在家除了祭祖，還要拜神。大年初一，全家人到廟裡拜拜，希望新的一年，神能讓他們一家人平安、健康。

到了農曆五月，天氣越來越熱，蚊蟲慢慢多起來，人也容易生病。五月五號端午節這一天，古代的人戴香包、喝雄黃酒，還在門上掛一些植物。這些都是為了把瘟疫趕走。在現代，有人還按照傳統的做法過節，他們覺得這麼做多少有一點作用，有的人認為這是一種迷信。

秋天是收成的季節，很多民族都有慶祝活動。農曆八月十五日的中秋節就是這樣來的。這一天，月亮又大又圓。雖然現在台灣已經不是農業社會了，但是離開家鄉的人，再遠也要回家團聚。晚餐以後，一家人吃著月餅、柚子，一邊給孩子說月亮的故事，過一個溫馨的節日。

課文簡體字版 Text in Simplified Characters

华人的重要节日

在台湾，除了原住民以外，大部分的人的祖先都是从中国移民来的，所以我们的传统节日都跟中国一样。一年当中，最重要的三个节日——春节、端午节跟中秋节——都是根据农历来的。

古时候，中国是一个农业国家，农人的生活和节日都跟季节的变化有关系。比方说，新年又叫春节，就是春天的开始。这时候，天气还很冷，农人利用这段难得的休息时间，跟家人好好地聚聚。除夕这一天，在家除了祭祖，还要拜神。大年初一，全家人到庙里拜拜，希望新的一年，神能让他们一家人平安、健康。

到了农历五月，天气越来越热，蚊虫慢慢多起来，人也容易生病。五月五号端午节这一天，古代的人戴香包、喝雄黄酒，还在门上挂一些植物。这些都是为了把瘟疫赶走。在现代，有人还按照传统的做法过节，他们觉得这么做多少有一点作用，有的人认为这是一种迷信。

秋天是收成的季节，很多民族都有庆祝活动。农历八月十五日的中秋节就是这样来的。这一天，月亮又大又圆。虽然现在台湾已经不是农业社会了，但是离开家乡的人，再远也要回家团聚。晚餐以后，一家人吃着月饼、柚子，一边给孩子说月亮的故事，过一个温馨的节日。

课文英译 Text in English

Important Chinese Holidays

In Taiwan, with the exception of the aborigines, the ancestors of most people emigrated from China, so our traditional holidays are the same as China's. The three most important holidays of the year, the Spring Festival, the Dragon Boat Festival, and the Mid-Autumn Moon Festival, are all based on the lunar calendar.

In ancient times, China was an agricultural country. The day-to-day lives and festivities of farmers revolved around changes in the seasons. For example, the Chinese New Year, also known as the Spring Festival, is the beginning of spring. At this time, the weather is still cold and farmers use this hard-to-come-by time of rest to focus on getting together with family. At home on Chinese New Year's Eve, in addition to venerating ancestors, they honor gods. On the first day of the Chinese New Year, the entire family goes to temple to worship, in hopes that in the new year, the gods will grant them peace and health.

By the fifth month of the lunar calendar, it starts getting hotter and hotter. Mosquitoes and other insects gradually increase in number and people get sick easily. On the fifth day of the fifth month of the lunar calendar, the day of the Dragon Boat Festival, people in ancient times wore fragrant sachets, drank realgar liquor, and hung certain plants on their doors. These were all for driving away pestilence. In modern times, some people still spend holidays in the traditional manner. They feel that doing so is somewhat effective. Others think that it's a kind of superstition.

Autumn is the season of harvest. Many ethnic groups have celebratory activities. This is the origin of the Mid-Autumn Moon Festival which is on the fifteenth day of the eighth month of the lunar calendar. On this day the moon is big and round, and even though Taiwan is no longer an agrarian society, those who have left home, no matter how far, always long to be with family. After dinner, families enjoy the holiday by eating moon cakes and pomelos as they tell children stories of the moon.

生詞二 Vocabulary II 🎧 03-04

Vocabulary

1	祖先	zǔxiān	ㄗㄨˇ ㄒㄧㄢ	(N)	ancestor
2	移民移民	yímín	ㄧˊ ㄇㄧㄣˊ	(Vi)	to immigrate, to emigrate
3	當中	dāngzhōng	ㄉㄤ ㄓㄨㄥ	(N)	of, amongst
4	根據	gēnjù	ㄍㄣ ㄐㄩˋ	(Prep)	based on, in accordance with, according to
5	農曆	nónglì	ㄋㄨㄥˊ ㄌㄧˋ	(N)	the lunar calendar (lit. the agricultural calendar)
6	農業	nóngyè	ㄋㄨㄥˊ ㄧㄝˋ	(N)	agriculture
7	農人	nóngrén	ㄋㄨㄥˊ ㄖㄣˊ	(N)	farmer
8	難得	nándé	ㄋㄢˊ ㄉㄜˊ	(Vs)	hard-to-come-by, rare
9	祭祖	jìzǔ	ㄐㄧˋ ㄗㄨˇ	(Vi)	to venerate ancestors
10	拜	bài	ㄅㄞˋ	(V)	to honor, to pay homage to

11	神	shén	ㄕㄣˊ	(N)	gods, divinities
12	拜拜	bàibài	ㄅㄞˋ ㄅㄞˋ	(Vi)	to present offerings to gods or ancestors
13	蚊蟲	wénchóng	ㄨㄣˊ ㄔㄨㄥˊ	(N)	mosquitoes and other insects
14	戴	dài	ㄉㄞˋ	(V)	to wear (items other than those that cover the torso, legs, or feet, mostly ornamental items.)
15	香包	xiāngbāo	ㄒㄧㄤ ㄅㄠ	(N)	fragrant sachet
16	掛	guà	ㄍㄨㄚˋ	(V)	to hang
17	瘟疫	wēnyì	ㄨㄣ ㄧˋ	(N)	pestilence, plague
18	做法做	zuòfǎ	ㄗㄨㄛˋ ㄈㄚˇ	(N)	method, way of doing something
19	多少	duōshǎo	ㄉㄨㄛ ㄕㄠˇ	(Adv)	somewhat
20	作用	zuòyòng	ㄗㄨㄛˋ ㄩㄥˋ	(N)	effect
21	迷信	míxìn	ㄇㄧˊ ㄒㄧㄣˋ	(N)	superstition
22	收成收成收成	shōuchéng	ㄕㄡ ㄔㄥˊ	(N)	harvest
23	民族	mínzú	ㄇㄧㄣˊ ㄗㄨˊ	(N)	ethnic group
24	月亮	yuèliàng	ㄩㄝˋ ㄌㄧㄤˋ	(N)	moon
25	圓圓	yuán	ㄩㄢˊ	(Vs)	round
26	社會社會	shèhuì	ㄕㄜˋ ㄏㄨㄟˋ	(N)	society
27	團聚	tuánjù	ㄊㄨㄢˊ ㄐㄩˋ	(Vi)	to get-together, to reunite; reunion of family members (in this lesson)
28	月餅	yuèbǐng	ㄩㄝˋ ㄅㄧㄥˇ	(N)	moon cake (shaped like the moon)
29	柚子	yòuzi	ㄧㄡˋ ㄗ˙	(N)	pomelo
30	故事	gùshì	ㄍㄨˋ ㄕˋ	(N)	story
31	溫馨	wēnxīn	ㄨㄣ ㄒㄧㄣ	(Vs)	warm, heart-warming

Names

| 32 | 端午節 | Duānwǔ jié | ㄉㄨㄢ ㄨˇ ㄐㄧㄝˊ | | the Dragon Boat Festival (the 5th day of the 5th month) |

| 33 | 中秋節 | Zhōngqiū jié | ㄓㄨㄥ ㄑㄧㄡ ㄐㄧㄝ | the Mid-Autumn Moon Festival (the 15th day of the 8th month) |
| 34 | 雄黃酒 | xiónghuáng jiǔ | ㄒㄩㄥ ㄏㄨㄤ ㄐㄧㄡ | realgar liquor, a wine seasoned with realgar, a type of arsenic, and is traditionally considered to be an antidote to other poisons |

Phrases

35	古時候	gǔ shíhòu	ㄍㄨ ㄕ ㄏㄡ	historically; in ancient times
36	趕走	gǎnzǒu	ㄍㄢ ㄗㄡ	to drive away
37	過節	guò jié	ㄍㄨㄛ ㄐㄧㄝ	to spend the holiday in some manner

文法 Grammar

I. 受到（…的）影響 *to be influenced by, affected by* 03-05 　　 英譯 p.68

Function: In a sentence with this pattern, the subject is influenced by what comes after 受到.

❶ 小明受到父母的影響，也很喜歡音樂。

❷ 台灣人受到西方文化的影響，喜歡喝咖啡的人越來越多了。

❸ 他的公司受到經濟不好的影響，快要做不下去了。

❹ 小孩子容易受到廣告的影響，總是要買一些對健康不好的東西。

❺ 颱風快要來了。天氣受到影響，變得很不穩定。

❻ 今年的氣溫特別高，雨又下得特別少。柚子的收成受到影響，比去年少了很多。

❼ 地球的汙染越來越嚴重，有的人的健康已經受到影響了。

Usage: 受到 is a bit formal, but is still used a great deal. It combines with many other nouns in addition to 影響, e.g., education, encouragement and guidance. They will be introduced in later lessons.

練習 Exercise

Please complete the dialogue below, making use of the 受到 pattern.

❶ A：聽說小美要到東部教原住民英文，你知道為什麼嗎？

B：電視新聞說東部的英文老師不夠，＿＿＿＿＿＿＿＿＿＿，就到東部去教英文了。

❷ A：珊珊有了孩子以後就一直打算搬到鄉下去，你知道為什麼嗎？（環境）

B：她認為孩子很容易＿＿＿＿＿＿＿＿＿＿＿＿＿＿＿。

❸ A：在台灣，很多人過年過節的時候為什麼一定要拜拜？（傳統）

B：＿＿＿＿＿＿＿＿＿＿＿＿＿＿＿＿＿＿。

❹ A：台灣的春天為什麼這麼潮濕？（南方來的熱空氣）

B：＿＿＿＿＿＿＿＿＿＿＿＿＿＿＿＿＿＿。

❺ A：台灣到了六月為什麼蚊蟲就多起來了？（氣溫高）

B：蚊蟲喜歡熱的天氣，＿＿＿＿＿＿＿＿＿＿＿＿＿。

❻ A：端午節大家都戴香包，還在門上掛植物，我認為是迷信。

B：我多少＿＿＿＿＿＿＿＿＿＿。有的時候會戴香包，或是在門上掛植物。

❼ A：我的朋友都喜歡吃辣的東西。

B：你越來越喜歡吃辣的，是＿＿＿＿＿＿＿＿＿＿吧。

II. 幸虧… *fortunately…* 🎧 03-06

Function: The adverb 幸虧 introduces an event that nullifies the negative content of the previous clause. 要不然 or 才 often follows.

① 這幾天天天下雨。幸虧我買了除濕機,要不然衣服都發霉了。

② 我弄丟了報告。幸虧朋友撿到了,才不用再寫一次。

③ 他爸爸常說幸虧這幾年生意還可以,才有錢付他的學費。

④ 幸虧我一到車站,公車就來了,才沒有遲到。

⑤ 幸虧他有實際的經驗,才能這麼快地找到工作。

練習 Exercise

Please complete the following dialogues by describing a fortunate situation with 幸虧….

① A:上個週末你去爬山。山上冷不冷?(我帶了外套)

　　B:冷極了。＿＿＿＿＿＿＿＿＿＿＿＿＿＿＿＿＿。

② A:最近經濟不好。你的工作有沒有影響?(老闆對我們很好)

　　B:＿＿＿＿＿＿＿＿＿＿＿＿＿＿＿＿＿＿＿＿。

③ A:中秋節車票很難買,你還要回家團聚嗎?(我買到高鐵票)

　　B:＿＿＿＿＿＿＿＿＿＿＿＿＿＿＿＿＿＿＿＿。

④ A:昨天你去電信公司門市買手機,店員的說明,你都懂嗎?
　　　(台灣朋友陪我去)

　　B:＿＿＿＿＿＿＿＿＿＿＿＿＿＿＿＿＿＿＿＿。

⑤ A:上星期六又颱風又下雨的,你還是去看電腦展了嗎?(朋
　　　友開車載我去)

　　B:還是去了。＿＿＿＿＿＿＿＿＿＿＿＿＿＿＿＿＿。

III. 算是… *can be considered...* 🎧 03-07

英譯 p.68

Function: 算是 is a verb that introduces an estimate after comparing the subject with other (comparable) things.

❶ 教書算是穩定的工作。

❷ 這裡的櫻花算是多的，所以來玩的人不少。

❸ 最近氣溫都很低，而且每天下雨。今天雨停了，天氣算是不錯的。

❹ 台北的建築每一棟都差不多，101 大樓算是有特色的。

❺ 國際關係系算是熱門的科系嗎？

Usage: The negative form of 算是 is 不算. So, it is fine to say 休學手續不算麻煩, 'the application process for taking leave of absence isn't really a hassle' but *休學手續算是不麻煩 is not acceptable.

❶ 跟鄉下比起來，這裡的蚊蟲不算多。

❷ 他只有一點發燒，感冒不算嚴重。

❸ 這家店的餃子不算好吃。我帶你去別家吃。

練習 Exercise

Complete the following dialogues using 算是 or 不算.

❶ A：在你的國家，春天的氣溫變化大嗎？

　　B：跟台灣比起來＿＿＿＿＿＿＿＿＿＿＿＿＿。

❷ A：你的鞋子曬了一天的太陽，乾了沒有？

　　B：還有一點濕，＿＿＿＿＿＿＿＿＿＿＿＿＿。

❸ A：今天雖然下雨了，可是還很悶。

　　B：今天有一點風，＿＿＿＿＿＿＿＿＿＿＿＿＿。

❹ A：住在台北生活費高嗎？

　　B：＿＿＿＿＿＿＿＿＿＿＿＿＿＿＿＿＿。

❺ A：這件衣服的樣子新嗎？

　　B：＿＿＿＿＿＿＿＿＿＿＿＿＿＿＿＿＿。

IV. 是… *it is indeed true that...* 03-08

Function: 是 in this instance is not a full verb. Rather, it's an agreement marker. What follows 是 is old information. The speaker uses this pattern to indicate that his view is the same as that of the previous speaker.

① A：買鞋子是不是先試穿，才知道合適不合適？

　　 B：是應該先試穿，而且還要穿著走一走。

② A：這位老師把語法解釋得很清楚，大家都很快地了解了。

　　 B：她解釋得是很清楚，而且她說話很有趣。

③ A：你有居留證，可以打工了吧？

　　 B：我是有居留證了，可是還不能打工，得再等八個月。

④ A：你說話的聲音不對。你感冒了嗎？

　　 B：我是感冒了，今天喉嚨好痛。

⑤ A：這個牌子的衣服品質很好。

　　 B：他們的品質是很好，可是打八折以後還很貴。

Usage: As an agreement marker, 是 is stressed slightly, e.g., 百貨公司的東西是比其他的商店貴，可是都是有名的牌子，品質跟樣子都比較好。'Things sold in department stores ARE more expensive than things in other stores, but it's all famous brand names, so the quality and styles are better.'

練習 Exercise

Complete the following dialouges with the information marker 是.

① A：小美最近的壓力很大。

　　 B：＿＿＿＿＿＿＿＿＿＿＿＿，因為＿＿＿＿＿＿＿＿＿＿＿＿。

② A：買衣服一定要摸一摸。

　　 B：＿＿＿＿＿＿＿＿＿＿＿＿，要不然＿＿＿＿＿＿＿＿＿＿。

③ A：這件外套很暖和。

　　 B：＿＿＿＿＿＿＿＿＿＿＿＿，不過＿＿＿＿＿＿＿＿＿＿＿。

---

❹ A：你不需要幫助嗎？為什麼不告訴我們？

　　B：_____，可是_____。

❺ A：學期結束了，你可以輕鬆一點了吧？

　　B：_____，可是_____。

V. 難怪 *no wonder* 03-09　　　　　　　 英譯 p.69

Function: 難怪, an adverb, introduces a 2nd clause in a 2-clause sentence. The second clause is concerned with the speaker's previous puzzlement, which has been clarified by a new observation presented in the first clause. The semantic structure is like this: 'new fact' clears away 'old puzzlement'.

❶ 他家過年過節都要拜祖先，難怪那麼早回家幫忙。

❷ 他下個星期有口頭報告，難怪這幾天都熬夜念書。

❸ 美美要申請獎學金，難怪她請教授寫推薦信。

❹ 他剛才跟店員發生了一點糾紛，難怪說話的聲音那麼大。

❺ 美美的爸爸最近沒工作了，難怪她哥哥放棄去法國留學。

練習 Exercise

Match the two columns so as to fulfill the meaning of 難怪.

（ D ）❶ 你不是這個學校的學生，

（ E ）❷ 你弄丟了發票，

（ A ）❸ 老師說很多台灣人的祖先是從中國移民來的，

（ C ）❹ 最近氣溫變化很大，

（ B ）❺ 美美是獨生女，

a. 難怪重要的節日都跟中國一樣。

b. 難怪她媽媽捨不得讓她去西班牙念書。

c. 難怪小美又感冒了，喉嚨發炎，痛得說不出話來。

d. 難怪不知道上課要簽名。

e. 難怪店員不讓你退換。

VI. A Post-verbal Intensifier 死了 *terribly* 03-10

Function: The post-verbal –死了 indicates extreme degree and is usually used for complaining.

1 他念的是自己沒興趣的科系，痛苦死了。
2 申請居留證的手續麻煩死了，他不想辦居留證了。
3 這條路好長，走起來累死了。
4 檸檬酸死了。我的烤魚上面不要加檸檬。
5 你別再打電腦了，吵死了。

Usage:

1. The post-verbal –死了 is similar to –極了 , –得不得了 , and –得很. They all express intensity, but –死了 carries the highest intensity, though negatively.

2. When –死了 is used, most of the time, it is about something negative with a handful of exceptions, e.g., 高興死了、羨慕死了、樂死了.

練習 Exercise

Please complete the following sentences with a –死了 expression from the following list. 難死了、忙死了、累死了、擠死了、冷死了、熱死了、難看死了、難聽死了、貴死了、鹹死了、酸死了、甜死了、餓死了、痛死了、急死了、擔心死了、吵死了、高興死了、樂死了、羨慕死了….

1 我最近＿＿＿＿＿＿＿＿＿＿＿＿＿，沒有時間跟朋友見面。
2 聽說那個牌子的鞋一雙要 5000 塊，＿＿＿＿＿＿＿＿＿。
3 電腦展人那麼多，＿＿＿＿＿＿，我不去。我們去看電影吧。
4 我哥哥昨天做菜，放了兩次鹽。那個菜＿＿＿＿，沒人要吃。
5 他申請到獎學金，＿＿＿＿＿＿＿＿＿＿＿＿＿。

VII. 幾乎 *almost* 03-11

Function: The adverb 幾乎 indicates near totality. Its meaning is similar to 'almost' in English.

❶ 這幾天幾乎每天都下雨。

❷ 他為了省錢，幾乎每天都在學生餐廳吃飯。

❸ 這裡的人，她幾乎都認識。

❹ 他的婚禮幾乎花光了他所有的錢。

❺ 他很節省。衣服幾乎都是朋友穿不下送他的。

Usage:

1. When 差不多 means 'almost', 幾乎 and 差不多 are interchangeable. Expressions indicating totality of some sort, e.g.,
他差不多每天都運動。他幾乎每天都運動。 'He exercises almost every day.'

2. 差不多 can mean 'approximately' when it is followed by a number. However, 幾乎 does not mean 'approximately'. So, 我吃了差不多二十個水餃 means 'I ate approximately/about 20 dumplings'. The person may have eaten more than or fewer than 20 dumplings. By contrast, 我吃了幾乎二十個水餃 means 'I ate almost 20 dumplings'. In this case, the person definitely ate fewer than 20 dumplings.

練習 Exercise

Answer the following questions by using the adverb 幾乎, which means 'almost always'.

❶ A：週年慶的時候，百貨公司的商品都打折嗎？

  B：＿＿＿＿＿＿＿＿＿＿＿＿＿＿＿＿＿＿。

❷ A：泰國菜有沒有不辣的？

  B：＿＿＿＿＿＿＿＿＿＿＿＿＿＿＿＿＿＿。

❸ A：台灣有不少有名的風景區，你都去過嗎？

  B：＿＿＿＿＿＿＿＿＿＿＿＿＿＿＿＿＿＿。

❹ A：你看不看籃球比賽？

  B：我對籃球比賽非常有興趣，＿＿＿＿＿＿＿＿＿＿。

❺ A：去便利商店買東西，有人刷卡嗎？

  B：＿＿＿＿＿＿＿＿＿＿＿＿＿＿＿＿＿＿。

VIII. 多少 *somewhat* 03-12

Function: The adverb 多少 refers to the possibility of a vague and minimal amount, similar to English 'at least, somewhat, a little'.

❶ 你雖然不餓，可是美美準備了這麼多菜，你多少吃一點。

❷ 你在西班牙住了半年，多少會說幾句西班牙文吧。

❸ 你買的電腦這麼便宜，多少會有一點問題吧。

❹ 那個店員是我朋友。我帶你去買東西，多少可以打一點折。

❺ 我不常做飯，可是調味料多少準備了一點。

Usage: Although the quantity or degree indicated by 多少 isn't great, 多少 stresses that there exists at least a certain amount of that quantity or degree.

練習 Exercise

Complete the following dialogues, using 多少 to indicate the inevitility of some occurrence.

❶ A：你對食物的營養有研究嗎？

B：沒什麼研究，不過_____。

❷ A：你在餐廳工作了兩年，學會做不少菜了吧？

B：會的不多，_____。

❸ A：我最近常感冒。

B：那是因為你不愛曬太陽，人每天應該_____。

❹ 孩子：我要出去玩了。

媽媽：明天考試，_____。

❺ A：大學成績不好，對將來有沒有影響？

B：_____。

IX. 再⋯也⋯ *no matter how..., still...* 🎧 03-13　　　　　　🔍 英譯 p.69

Function: This pattern indicates that a situation still holds true (after 也) regardless of the circumstances (after 再).

❶ 學中文壓力再大，我也要繼續學。
❷ 你再生氣也不能罵人。
❸ 豬腳麵線再好吃也不能天天吃。
❹ 工作再穩定也可能發生變化。
❺ 考試再簡單，也有人考不好。

Usage: This pattern is similar to 不管 A，⋯都 B in usage. However, the 不管 pattern comes with 都 and suggests that the B situation always happens regardless of what circumstance A is. On the other hand, the 再 pattern comes with 也 and usually the A in this pattern refers to the most extreme circumstance. For example,

自己做的菜不管多麼難吃，都得吃光。 vs.

自己做的菜，再難吃也得吃光。

Note: The two sentences are similar, but the 再⋯ 也⋯ is more intense.

練習 **Exercise**

Complete the following dialogues, using 再⋯也⋯ to indicate an insistence.

❶ A：臭豆腐很好吃，你要不要嚐一嚐？
　 B：＿＿＿＿＿＿＿＿＿＿＿＿＿＿＿＿＿＿＿。

❷ A：捷運很擠，你要上車嗎？
　 B：快遲到了，＿＿＿＿＿＿＿＿＿＿＿＿＿＿。

❸ A：水上摩托車很安全，要不要騎？
　 B：我不會游泳，＿＿＿＿＿＿＿＿＿＿＿＿＿。

❹ A：他很節省，每天只吃一餐。
　 B：＿＿＿＿＿＿＿＿＿＿＿＿＿＿＿也要注意營養！

❺ A：最近百貨公司的商品都打折，東西都便宜很多。
　 B：我的錢快用光了，＿＿＿＿＿＿＿＿＿＿＿＿。

語法例句英譯
Grammar Examples in English ●

I. 受到（…的）影響 *to be influenced by, affected by*

Function:

1. Xiaoming was influenced by his parents, and he too likes music.
2. Taiwanese have been influenced by western culture and more and more of them like to drink coffee.
3. His company has been impacted by the bad economy and soon won't be able to continue operating.
4. Kids are easily affected by advertisements and always want to buy things that are bad for their health.
5. A typhoon is approaching. The weather is being influenced by it and has become very unstable.
6. The temperatures have been especially high this year and there has been little rain. The pomelo harvest has been affected. There are a lot fewer than last year.
7. Pollution is worsening globally. Some people's health is already being impacted.

II. 幸虧… *fortunately…*

Function:

1. It has been raining every day over the last few days. Luckily, I bought a dehumidifier; otherwise, my clothes would all mildew.
2. I lost my report. Fortunately, a friend picked it up (found it), so I don't have to rewrite it.
3. His dad often says it's a good thing business has been OK in recent years. That's why he has the money to pay his tuition.
4. Luckily, the bus arrived just as I got to the bus stop, so I wasn't late.
5. Fortunately he has real-life experience; that is why he found a job so quickly.

III. 算是… *can be considered...*

1. Teaching is considered a stable job.
2. You could say that there are a lot of cherry blossoms here, so many people have come to visit.
3. It has been cold and rainy lately, but today the rain stopped so the weather is nice again.
4. The buildings in Taipei all look about the same. Taipei 101 is probably more distinctive.
5. Would the department of international relations be considered a popular department?

Usage:

1. Compared to the countryside, there are not that many bugs here.
2. He only has a low fever. I wouldn't say it is serious.
3. I wouldn't say that the dumplings in this shop are good. I'll take you to another shop to eat.

IV. 是… *it is indeed true that...*

Function:

1. A: Shall I try the shoes on before I buy them to know if they fit or not?
   B: You should indeed try them on first and even walk around in them.
2. A: This teacher explains grammar very clearly. Everybody catches on quite quickly.
   B: She does explain very clearly and she's an interesting speaker too.
3. A: You have an ARC, so you can work, right?
   B: I do have an ARC, but I can't work. I have to wait another eight months.
4. A: Your voice sounds a bit off. Do you have a cold?
   B: Yes, I do have a cold. My throat is really sore today.

⑤ A: The quality of this brand of clothing is good.

B: The quality is indeed good, but even with 20% off, it's still expensive.

V. 難怪 *no wonder*

Function:

① His family venerates ancestors during Chinese New Year and other holidays. No wonder, he goes home so early to help out.

② He has an oral report next week. No wonder, he's been burning the midnight oil lately.

③ Meimei wants to apply for a scholarship. No wonder, she asked the professor to write a letter of recommendation.

④ He had a little dispute with the store employee just now. No wonder, his voice was so loud.

⑤ Meimei's dad has been out of work lately. No wonder, her brother gave up going to France to study.

VI. A Post-verbal Intensifier 死了 *terribly*

Function:

① He's studying a major he has no interest in. He couldn't be more miserable.

② Applying for an ARC is a royal pain. He doesn't want to apply anymore.

③ This road is really long. It's exhausting to walk it.

④ Lemon is way too tart. Don't put any on my grilled fish.

⑤ Get off the computer. The noise is bugging the heck out of me.

VII. 幾乎 *almost*

Function:

① It has rained almost every day lately.

② To save money, he has been eating in the student cafeteria almost every day.

③ She knows almost everybody here.

④ He spent almost all of his money on his wedding.

⑤ He's very frugal. Almost all of his clothes were given to him by friends after they could no longer wear them.

VIII. 多少 *somewhat*

Function:

① Even though you're not hungry, Meimei prepared a lot of dishes for you, so you should eat *something*.

② You lived in Spain for half a year; you must be able to speak *some* Spanish.

③ The computer you bought was so cheap. I reckon it's got to have *something* wrong with it.

④ That employee is my friend. If I take you to buy something, he's going to give you *some* kind of discount.

⑤ I don't cook often, but I do have *some* spices ready.

IX. 再…也… *no matter how…, still…*

Function:

① No matter how much stress I get from studying Chinese, I'm going to keep studying.

② No matter how mad you get, you can't ream other people out.

③ It doesn't matter how delicious pork knuckle rice threads are. You can't eat the dish every day.

④ No matter how stable a job is, changes can still happen.

⑤ Regardless of how easy a test is, there's always someone who does poorly.

Usage:

No matter how unpalatable the food you make is, you have to eat it all up.

I. Talking about Weather and Customs

Goal: Learning to talk about the weather and activities I take part in.
Task: Each student fill in the form below using checkmarks (✓) to indicate, then split off into pairs and discuss what types of activities are suited to different types of weather and why.

	旅行	在家	跟朋友去茶館	吃火鍋	運動	去海邊	洗衣服
出太陽							
下雨							
颱風							
潮濕							
悶熱							
天氣不穩定							
10度							
18度							
35度							
零下							

Example

A：出太陽的時候，我要洗衣服，因為台灣很潮濕。

B：我要去公園，因為應該利用難得的好天氣去運動。

II. Discussing the Origins of Important Holidays around the World

Goal: Learning to talk about the origins of important holidays.

Task: As a class, first discuss holidays in Taiwan, then pair up and ask questions about holidays in the other person's country and tell the other person whether or not you would follow that custom and why.

節日	春天	夏天	秋天	冬天
我國重要的節日 Major holiday(s) in my country				
節日的由來 History behind the holiday(s)				
重要的風俗習慣 Important customs				

III. The Ghost Holiday

Goal: Learning to explain the relationship between seasons or festivities and specific activities.

Task: Ask a student to lead the discussion. Discuss the ghost days of various countries. Discuss whether their home country has a holiday that involves ghosts. What do people do to celebrate that holiday? Is it a holiday for adults or for children? Do people in their home country believe in ghosts, and if they do, what kind of behaviors are attributed to them?

Try to use the following sentence patterns and vocabulary words:

幾乎	受到…影響	算是／不算
再 Vs 也	根據	

文化 *Bits of Chinese Culture*

Ghost Month Taboos

The seventh month on the lunar calendar is called Ghost Month, 鬼月（guǐ yuè）, a month when everybody is a bit more anxious and cautious out of fear that they could attract spirits who could bring with them calamity. As such, there are a variety of Ghost Month taboos.

▲ 《聯合報》程宜華／攝影

First of all, why is the seventh month of the lunar year referred to as Ghost Month? According to tradition, the gates of hell are opened for a month, starting on the first day of the 7th month and all of the unclaimed souls return from the netherworld to this world to accept offerings. People prepare a rich feast to serve as offerings for the spirits on the 15th day of the 7th lunar month, a day known as the Ghost Festival. Most people prepare the offerings partially out of compassion, partially out of fear that the hungry ghosts could cause mischief if they don't. They also ask a Taoist or Buddhist priest to help them back to the other side in hopes of bringing peace to their families.

▲ Feasts are prepared for spirits on the 15th day of the 7th lunar month.

There are also some taboos when paying honor to ghosts. For example, you can't venerate them at home. It must be done outside or in the street; otherwise, it's tantamount to inviting them into your house. You also can't offer pineapple（Taiwanese pronunciation: 旺來, wànglái）with bananas, plums, or pears, because the Taiwanese pronunciation together sounds like "Ask you to come"（招你來, zhāo nǐ lái）. In short, don't do anything to invite spirits into your home.

Ghost Month taboos that influence businesspeople include most people don't marry, buy vehicles, look at or buy new homes, or move into a new house. People also avoid going to hospitals, whistling, drying clothes on a clothesline at night, swimming in the ocean, and walking along walls. If you avoid these taboos, your Ghost Month will probably be peaceful and uneventful.

Westerners also have a holiday centered around ghosts--Halloween. It has evolved into a festival of sorts in which everybody parties and enjoys themselves. This is especially true of America where children and adults alike wear costumes of ghosts and monsters of every kinds. Kids even go door to door to "scare their neighbors" and saying trick or treat. People like to decorate their homes with jack-o-lanterns and skulls to create a scary atmosphere. This mindset is completely at odds with that of the Taiwanese during Ghost Month.

▲ Children trick-or-treating on Halloween.

Self-Assessment Checklist

I can describe changes in climate and weather.

20%   40%   60%   80%   100%

I can talk about the seasons and activities particular to each.

20%   40%   60%   80%   100%

I can talk about traditional Chinese New Year, Dragon Boat Festival, and Mid-autumn Moon Festival customs.

20%   40%   60%   80%   100%

I can read about the origins of important festivals.

20%   40%   60%   80%   100%

note

LESSON
4

第四課

我愛台灣的人情味

I Love Taiwanese Hospitality

學習目標 **Learning Objectives**

Topic: 社會環境 Social Environment

- Learning to discuss with your friends leisure activities that you enjoy.
- Learning to tell others about Taiwan's culture and provide travel information for different destinations.
- Learning to emphasize, give examples, and provide further information.
- Learning to talk about the unique characteristics and culture of small towns.

我愛台灣的人情味

I Love Taiwanese Hospitality

對話 Dialogue 🎧 04-01

（在活動中心）

陳敏萱：你們昨天去校外教學，玩得怎麼樣？

安德思：很不錯。我們去了很多地方。我最喜歡平溪老街，那裡的氣氛讓我想起了家鄉。

羅珊蒂：平溪，我元宵節的時候剛去過。我語言交換的朋友帶我去放天燈。他告訴我把願望寫在天燈上，就可以實現。

安德思：聽說那天放天燈的人特別多。

羅珊蒂：是啊，後來我找不到我朋友，手機又收不到訊號，還好碰到一位熱心的小姐，她不但帶我回車站，還請我吃了一碗元宵。

高橋健太：對、對、對，台灣人真有人情味。有一次，我去參觀台南孔廟，正在研究牆上的字，有一位老先生過來很有耐心地給我解釋。這件事情讓我非常感動。

安德思：我聽說台南有很多有特色的老店，夜市的小吃也很有名。你吃了擔仔麵嗎？

高橋健太：當然吃了。我朋友帶我去吃了好幾樣小吃。那些店都在巷子裡，沒有招牌，只有當地人才知道，可是東西都好吃得不得了。

陳敏萱：台北的巷子裡也有很多有特色的商店。像我們學校附近的巷子裡有一家茶館，你一進去老闆就拿好茶招待你，跟你談茶、談生活。老闆說，他開茶館，不是為了賺錢，而是為了讓大家認識茶文化，也交朋友。

高橋健太：台灣有特色的商店很多都不在大街上；你得走進巷子才找得到。

羅珊蒂：為什麼？

高橋健太：因為台北的房租太貴了，一些有理想的人只好把店開在巷子裡。

安德思：敏萱剛剛說的那家茶館，我很有興趣。改天我們一起去，怎麼樣？

羅珊蒂：去茶館，太無聊了吧。我還是比較喜歡去熱鬧的東區，尤其是台北101新年放煙火的時候，跟幾十萬人一起看煙火、跨年，以前我從來沒有過這樣的經驗。

高橋健太：我最喜歡逛夜市。那裡的東西種類又多，價錢又便宜。

陳敏萱：我也喜歡夜市的熱鬧，讓我有過節的感覺。在我家鄉，只有過年過節的時候才看得到這麼多人。

羅珊蒂：我到夜市一定先找吃的，像臭豆腐、水煎包這些都不錯，不過我最愛的還是炸雞排。一口雞排，一口冰紅茶，真是開心極了。

高橋健太：我們這個週末就一起去吧！

課文簡體字版 Text in Simplified Characters

（在活动中心）

陈敏萱：你们昨天去校外教学，玩得怎么样？

安德思：很不错。我们去了很多地方。我最喜欢平溪老街，那里的气氛让我想起了家乡。

罗珊蒂：平溪，我元宵节的时候刚去过。我语言交换的朋友带我去放天灯。他告诉我把愿望写在天灯上，就可以实现。

安德思：听说那天放天灯的人特别多。

罗珊蒂：是啊，后来我找不到我朋友，手机又收不到讯号，还好碰到一位热心的小姐，她不但带我回车站，还请我吃了一碗元宵。

高桥健太：对、对、对，台湾人真有人情味。有一次，我去参观台南孔庙，正在研究墙上的字，有一位老先生过来很有耐心地给我解释。这件事情让我非常感动。

安德思：我听说台南有很多有特色的老店，夜市的小吃也很有名。你吃了担仔面吗？

高桥健太：当然吃了。我朋友带我去吃了好几样小吃。那些店都在巷子里，没有招牌，只有当地人才知道，可是东西都好吃得不得了。

陈敏萱：台北的巷子里也有很多有特色的商店。像我们学校附近的巷子里有一家茶馆，你一进去老板就拿好茶招待你，跟你谈茶、谈生活。老板说，他开茶馆，不是为了赚钱，而是为了让大家认识茶文化，也交朋友。

高桥健太：台湾有特色的商店很多都不在大街上；你得走进巷子才找得到。

罗珊蒂：为什么？

高桥健太：因为台北的房租太贵了，一些有理想的人只好把店开在巷子里。

安德思：敏萱刚刚说的那家茶馆，我很有兴趣。改天我们一起去，怎么样？

罗珊蒂：去茶馆，太无聊了吧。我还是比较喜欢去热闹的东区，尤其是台北 101 新年放烟火的时候，跟几十万人一起看烟火、跨年，以前我从来没有过这样的经验。

高桥健太：我最喜欢逛夜市。那里的东西种类又多，价钱又便宜。

陈敏萱：我也喜欢夜市的热闹，让我有过节的感觉。在我家乡，只有过年过节的时候才看得到这么多人。

罗珊蒂：我到夜市一定先找吃的，像臭豆腐、水煎包这些都不错，不过我最爱的还是炸鸡排。一口鸡排，一口冰红茶，真是开心极了。

高桥健太：我们这个周末就一起去吧！

課文英譯 Text in English

(In an activity center)

Chen Minxuan : How was your field trip yesterday?

An Desi : Not bad at all. We went to a lot of places. I liked Pingxi's Old Street the best. The atmosphere there reminded me of my hometown.

Luo Shandi : Pingxi? I just went there during the Lantern Festival. My language exchange friend took me to set off sky lanterns. He told me that if you write wishes on a sky lantern, they will come true.

An Desi : I've heard that on that day, an extraordinarily large number of people set off sky lanterns.

Luo Shandi : That's right. Later, I couldn't find my friend and my cell phone wasn't getting a signal. Luckily, I ran into a warmhearted young lady. She not only took me back to the train station; she even treated me to a bowl of sweet sticky rice dumplings.

Gaoqiao Jiantai : Yeah, Taiwanese are really hospitable. One time, I visited the Tainan Confucian Temple and was studying the characters on a wall. An older gentleman came over and patiently explained them to me. This really touched me.

An Desi : I heard that Tainan has a lot of distinctive old shops. The snacks at the night market are also well known. Have you ever had danzai noodles?

Gaoqiao Jiantai : I sure have. My friends have taken me to try all kinds of light repasts. Those shops were all in the alleys and didn't have any shop signs. Only the locals know about them, but everything was simply delicious.

Chen Minxuan : The alleys of Taipei also have all kinds of distinctive shops. Like in the alley near our school, there's a teashop. As soon as you walk in, the owner treats you to a cup of good tea and chats about tea and life with you. The owner says he opened the teashop, not to make money but to have people learn about tea culture and to make friends.

Gaoqiao Jiantai : Many of Taiwan's distinctive shops aren't on main streets. You have to walk into the alleys to find them.

Luo Shandi : Why?

Gaoqiao Jiantai : Because rent in Taipei is too expensive, some people with dreams have no choice but to open shops in the alleys.

An Desi	: I'm interested in that teashop that Minxuan just mentioned. Let's go together sometime. What do you think?				
Luo Shandi	: Go to a teashop? Boring! I would still prefer going to the bustling East District, especially Taipei 101 when fireworks are being set off on New Year's. Watching fireworks and bringing in the New Year together with hundreds of thousands of other people. I'd never experienced anything like that.				
Gaoqiao Jiantai	: I like wandering around night markets most. There are all kinds of things at low prices there.				
Chen Minxuan	: I also like the hustle bustle of night markets. It gives me a feeling of observing a festival. In my hometown, only on New Year's and on holidays can you see that many people.				
Luo Shandi	: When I go to a night market, I have to first look for food, like stinky tofu and pan-fried pork buns. These are all pretty good, but my favorite is still deep-fried chicken fillet. A bite of chicken fillet, a sip of iced black tea and I'm in seventh heaven.				
Gaoqiao Jiantai	: Let's go this weekend.				

生詞一 Vocabulary I 🎧 04-02

Vocabulary

1	愛	ài	ㄞˋ	(Vst)	to love
2	人情味	rénqíngwèi	ㄖㄣˊ ㄑㄧㄥˊ ㄨㄟˋ	(N)	to be hospitable, kind, friendly
3	放	fàng	ㄈㄤˋ	(V)	to release
4	天燈	tiāndēng	ㄊㄧㄢ ㄉㄥ	(N)	sky lantern
5	願望	yuànwàng	ㄩㄢˋ ㄨㄤˋ	(N)	wish
6	訊號	xùnhào	ㄒㄩㄣˋ ㄏㄠˋ	(N)	signal (data connection)
7	元宵	yuánxiāo	ㄩㄢˊ ㄒㄧㄠ	(N)	sweet sticky rice dumplings
8	牆	qiáng	ㄑㄧㄤˊ	(N)	wall
9	耐心 耐心	nàixīn	ㄋㄞˋ ㄒㄧㄣ	(N)	patience

10	感動	gǎndòng	ㄍㄢˇ ㄉㄨㄥˋ	(Vs)	to be touched, moved
11	擔仔麵	dànzǎimiàn	ㄉㄢˋ ㄗㄞˇ ㄇㄧㄢˋ	(N)	danzai noodles (special dish from Tainan)
12	招牌	zhāopái	ㄓㄠ ㄆㄞˊ	(N)	store sign
13	當地當	dāngdì	ㄉㄤ ㄉㄧˋ	(Vs-attr)	local
14	賺賺賺	zhuàn	ㄓㄨㄢˋ	(V)	to earn
15	而	ér	ㄦˊ	(Adv)	on the other hand, rather
16	交	jiāo	ㄐㄧㄠ	(V)	to make (friends)
17	理想	lǐxiǎng	ㄌㄧˇ ㄒㄧㄤˇ	(N)	ideals, aspirations
18	剛剛	gānggāng	ㄍㄤ ㄍㄤ	(Adv)	just now
19	改天	gǎitiān	ㄍㄞˇ ㄊㄧㄢ	(Adv)	some other day
20	無聊	wúliáo	ㄨˊ ㄌㄧㄠˊ	(Vs)	boring, dull
21	東區	dōngqū	ㄉㄨㄥ ㄑㄩ	(N)	the East District (of Taipei)
22	煙火煙火	yānhuǒ	ㄧㄢ ㄏㄨㄛˇ	(N)	fireworks
23	跨年跨年	kuànián	ㄎㄨㄚˋ ㄋㄧㄢˊ	(Vi)	welcome in the (solar) New Year (lit. span the years)
24	種類種類	zhǒnglèi	ㄓㄨㄥˇ ㄌㄟˋ	(N)	type, category
25	價錢	jiàqián	ㄐㄧㄚˋ ㄑㄧㄢˊ	(N)	price
26	感覺	gǎnjué	ㄍㄢˇ ㄐㄩㄝˊ	(N)	feeling; a feeling of...
27	雞排	jīpái	ㄐㄧ ㄆㄞˊ	(N)	chicken fillet
28	口	kǒu	ㄎㄡˇ	(M)	mouthful
29	紅茶	hóngchá	ㄏㄨㄥˊ ㄔㄚˊ	(N)	black tea (lit. red tea)

Names

30	平溪	Píngxī	ㄆㄧㄥˊ ㄒㄧ		Pingxi, a town in northern Taiwan
31	元宵節	Yuánxiāo jié	ㄩㄢˊ ㄒㄧㄠ ㄐㄧㄝ		the Lantern Festival (15th day of the 1st month)
32	孔廟	Kǒngmiào	ㄎㄨㄥˇ ㄇㄧㄠˋ		Confucian Temple

Phrases

33	校外教學	xiàowài jiāoxué	ㄒㄧㄠ ㄨㄞ ㄐㄧㄠ ㄒㄩㄝ	field trip, class excursion
34	碰到	pèngdào	ㄆㄥ ㄉㄠ	to run into
35	水煎包	shuǐjiān bāo	ㄕㄨㄟ ㄐㄧㄢ ㄅㄠ	pan-fried pork bun

 短文 Reading 🎧 04-03

台灣南北走一趟

　　鈴木先生是高橋健太在日本的同事。他常聽高橋談到台灣的人情味和美食，所以上個星期他趁放假來台灣旅行。高橋帶他去參觀故宮博物院，上陽明山泡茶、泡溫泉，當然也沒錯過東區，逛了 24 小時營業的書店，看了 101 的夜景，也吃了很多台北的美食。健太還帶他在師大附近的巷子裡參觀了一些日本人留下來的木造房子。他覺得台北真是一個有特色的大城市。

　　高橋告訴他，台灣還有一個地方非去不可——台南。台南是台灣最古老的城市，有很多古蹟，而且那裡的人特別重視傳統。要是他對歷史有興趣或是想多了解一些台灣人傳統的風俗習慣，應該去台南走一趟。鈴木聽了，就決定第二天搭高鐵去。

　　高橋健太也說到，對台南人來說，早餐非常重要。在赤崁樓附近就有很多小店賣台南人常吃的道地美食，所以鈴木一下高鐵就去吃了鹹粥、牛肉湯。他沒想到台南人對吃這麼講究，每天花這麼多時間吃一頓早飯。

　　吃飽了，他在附近逛逛，發現台南人不但走路慢，說話速度也慢多了。窄窄的街道兩邊還留著很多日本人蓋的房子，跟台北真的很不一樣。雖然他在台北玩得很開心，可是在台南才讓他有輕鬆的感覺。他決定在台南多待幾天，好好地欣賞這個美麗的城市。

课文簡體字版 Text in Simplified Characters

台湾南北走一趟

铃木先生是高桥健太在日本的同事。他常听高桥谈到台湾的人情味和美食，所以上个星期他趁放假来台湾旅行。高桥带他去参观故宫博物院，上阳明山泡茶、泡温泉，当然也没错过东区，逛了 24 小时营业的书店，看了 101 的夜景，也吃了很多台北的美食。健太还带他在师大附近的巷子里参观了一些日本人留下来的木造房子。他觉得台北真是一个有特色的大城市。

高桥告诉他，台湾还有一个地方非去不可——台南。台南是台湾最古老的城市，有很多古迹，而且那里的人特别重视传统。要是他对历史有兴趣或是想多了解一些台湾人传统的风俗习惯，应该去台南走一趟。铃木听了，就决定第二天搭高铁去。

高桥健太也说到，对台南人来说，早餐非常重要。在赤崁楼附近就有很多小店卖台南人常吃的道地美食，所以铃木一下高铁就去吃了咸粥、牛肉汤。他没想到台南人对吃这么讲究，每天花这么多时间吃一顿早饭。

吃饱了，他在附近逛逛，发现台南人不但走路慢，说话速度也慢多了。窄窄的街道两边还留着很多日本人盖的房子，跟台北真的很不一样。虽然他在台北玩得很开心，可是在台南才让他有轻松的感觉。他决定在台南多待几天，好好地欣赏这个美丽的城市。

课文英譯 Text in English

Free Trip in Taiwan

Mr. Lingmu (Suzuki) is a colleague of Gaoqiao Jiantai in Japan. He often heard Gaoqiao speak of Taiwanese hospitality and good food, so last week, he took advantage of a holiday to come to Taiwan on a trip. Gaoqiao took him to visit the National Palace Museum, and also to Yangming Mountain to have some tea and soak in a hot spring. Of course, they didn't miss the East District, where they wandered around a 24-hour bookstore, saw the night view from Taipei 101, and ate a lot of Taipei's delicious foods. Jiantai also took him around alleys in the vicinity of Shida to visit some wooden houses left by the Japanese. He feels that Taipei really is a unique metropolis.

Gaoqiao told him that Taiwan has a must-see place—Tainan. Tainan is Taiwan's oldest city. It has many historical sites and the people there attach special emphasis to traditions. If he is interested in history or wants to better understand some traditional customs and ways of the Taiwanese, he should go to Tainan and walk around. Hearing this, Lingmu decided to take the HSR to Tainan the next day.

Gaoqiao Jiantai also mentioned that for the people of Tainan, breakfast is very important. Near Chihkan Tower (a.k.a. Fort Provintia), there are a lot of little shops that sell authentic foods frequently eaten by the people of Tainan, so right after alighting from the HSR, Lingmu went to have savory congee and beef soup. He didn't realize that the people of Tainan were so discriminating about eating. Every day, they spend so much time eating breakfast.

Having eaten his fill, he walked around nearby. He discovered that the people of Tainan not only walk slowly, the speed of their speech is much slower. On either side of the narrow streets, there are still many houses that were built by the Japanese. It's really different from Taipei. Although he had a good time in Taipei, it wasn't until he was in Tainan that he felt relaxed. He decided to stay a few more days in Tainan, so he could fully appreciate this beautiful city.

生詞二 Vocabulary II　　🎧 04-04

Vocabulary

1	同事	tóngshì	ㄊㄨㄥˊ ㄕˋ	(N)	colleague, coworker
2	美食	měishí	ㄇㄟˇ ㄕˊ	(N)	delicacies, delicious foods
3	上	shàng	ㄕㄤˋ	(V)	to go up to
4	泡	pào	ㄆㄠˋ	(V)	to steep (tea) / to soak oneself in, i.e., to bath in
5	錯過	cuòguò	ㄘㄨㄛˋ ㄍㄨㄛˋ	(Vpt)	to miss (an opportunity)
6	營業	yíngyè	ㄧㄥˊ ㄧㄝˋ	(Vi)	to open for business, in operation (businesses)
7	夜景	yèjǐng	ㄧㄝˋ ㄐㄧㄥˇ	(N)	night view
8	古老	gǔlǎo	ㄍㄨˇ ㄌㄠˇ	(Vs)	ancient, antiquated
9	古蹟	gǔjī	ㄍㄨˇ ㄐㄧ	(N)	historical site

10	重視	zhòngshì	ㄓㄨㄥˋ ㄕˋ	(Vst)	to place emphasis on, to lay stress on, to value
11	歷史 歷	lìshǐ	ㄌㄧˋ ㄕˇ	(N)	history
12	風俗	fēngsú	ㄈㄥ ㄙㄨˊ	(N)	customs
13	習慣 習慣	xíguàn	ㄒㄧˊ ㄍㄨㄢˋ	(N)	habit
14	道地	dàodì	ㄉㄠˋ ㄉㄧˋ	(Vs)	authentic
15	粥	zhōu	ㄓㄡ	(N)	congee, watery rice
16	講究 講究	jiǎngjiù 講究	ㄐㄧㄤˇ ㄐㄧㄡˋ	(Vst)	to be discriminating in, to be discerning, meticulous
17	頓	dùn	ㄉㄨㄣˋ	(M)	measure word for the duration of a meal
18	速度 速度 速	sùdù 度	ㄙㄨˋ ㄉㄨˋ	(N)	speed
19	窄	zhǎi	ㄓㄞˇ	(Vs)	narrow
20	街道	jiēdào	ㄐㄧㄝ ㄉㄠˋ	(N)	street
21	蓋 蓋	gài	ㄍㄞˋ	(V)	to build, to erect
22	待	dāi	ㄉㄞ	(Vi)	to stay, to remain
23	欣賞	xīnshǎng	ㄒㄧㄣ ㄕㄤˇ	(V)	to appreciate, to enjoy
24	美麗	měilì	ㄇㄟˇ ㄌㄧˋ	(Vs)	beautiful

Names

25	鈴木	Língmù	ㄌㄧㄥˊ ㄇㄨˋ		Japanese last name: Lingmu (Japanese: Suzuki)
26	赤崁樓	Chìkǎn Lóu	ㄔˋ ㄎㄢˇ ㄌㄡˊ		Chihkan Tower, a.k.a. Fort Provintia (stronghold built by the Dutch, in Tainan, in the 17th century)

Phrases

27	留下來	liú xià lái	ㄌㄧㄡˊ ㄒㄧㄚˋ ㄌㄞˊ	to leave behind
28	木造	mù zào	ㄇㄨˋ ㄗㄠˋ	wooden; made from wood
29	非去不可	fēiqù bùkě	ㄈㄟ ㄑㄩˋ ㄅㄨˋ ㄎㄜˇ	Visiting (it) is a must!!

文法 Grammar

I. 不但⋯，還⋯ *not only…, but also…*   🎧 04-05

 英譯 p.93

Function: This pattern provides two pieces of information about the subject of a sentence.

① 他昨天買的那件外套不但輕，還很暖和。

② 陳敏萱的中文不但聲調很準，說話還很流利。

③ 我新辦的手機，不但月租便宜，還可以上網吃到飽。

④ 外面不但下雨，還颳大風，你就別出去了。

⑤ 端午節這一天，古代的中國人不但戴香包，還喝雄黃酒。

Usage: Remember that conjunctions (不但) are placed either pre- or post-subject, while adverbs (還) occur before VP. If the conj 而且 appears after 不但, 還 can be omitted. E.g.,

① 他買的外套，不但樣子好看，而且價錢（還）很便宜。

② 他做的菜，不但顏色漂亮，而且味道（還）很香。

練習 Exercise

Please answer the following questions using 不但⋯還⋯.

① A：為什麼那麼多人愛吃小吃？

B：因為 <u>很多人沒那麼多錢，還沒有廚房。</u> 。
　　　　　　　　　　　yín chúao

② A：在那家商店買得到飲料嗎？

B：＿＿＿＿＿＿＿＿＿＿＿＿＿＿＿＿ 。

③ A：聽說你元宵節吃了好幾個元宵。

B：是啊。＿＿＿＿＿＿＿＿＿＿＿＿ 。

④ A：你後天要不要去參加愛麗的婚禮？

B：＿＿＿＿＿＿＿＿＿＿＿＿＿＿＿＿ 。

⑤ A：這個城市的馬路好寬啊！

B：＿＿＿＿＿＿＿＿＿＿＿＿＿＿＿＿ 。

II. *Speak* 說 vs. *Talk* 談 🎧 04-06

Function: In modern Mandarin Chinese, there are quite a few 'speak' verbs. Correct choice reflects mastery as well as politeness. In most cases, the type of object determines the verb, not the other way around. In rare instances, either choice is possible, with or without difference in meaning.

說話 to speak, to utter	vs.	談話 to chat, to have a conversation
他說明天天氣會很好 (said)	vs.	談天氣 (talk about, discuss)
說外語 (speak)	vs.	談外語教育（jiàoyù, education）(talk about, discuss)
說故事 (tell)	vs.	談理想 (talk about, discuss)
我們剛剛說了很多話 (said, talked about)	vs.	老師想找你談話 (speak with)
請你說一說這次旅行有趣的事 (tell, talk about)	vs.	請你談一談你對這件事的想法 (tell us, explain)
他們正在說哪裡好玩 (saying)	vs.	他們正在談台北的經濟、建築 (talking about, discussing)

Usage: 說 relates more to spontaneous events, while 談 more to arranged and scheduled events. 說 is almost always one-way and 談 two-way (back and forth between two or more people, so similar to talk with, discuss). In terms of frequency, 說 takes sentential objects more than 談.

練習 Exercise

Please fill in the blank with 說 or 談.

❶ 我的手機聽不清楚，電信公司的人 說 是因為我住在山邊。

❷ 他寫了兩本書，_____的都是他的專業，難怪你沒興趣。

❸ 台灣有句話_____：「春天後母臉」，意思是春天的天氣變化很大。

❹ 這件事我不知道怎麼辦，等一下能不能找你_____一_____？

❺ 你剛剛_____的那個牌子的除濕機很有名，品質不錯。

III. …不是…，而是… *not…; rather…* 🎧 04-07 🔍英譯 p.93

Function: This structure negates a claim and presents the correct answer. 而 is an adverb.

❶ 安德思喜歡的人不是王小姐，而是白小姐。
❷ 我不是不想去參加校外教學，而是因為最近忙死了。
❸ 這件衣服你不是用現金買的，而是刷卡買的，所以不能馬上退錢。
❹ 他來台灣不是為了旅行，而是為了學中文。
❺ 我換新工作，不是因為薪水比較高，而是新公司離我家比較近。

Usage: 是 is a highly versatile element, sometimes a verb and sometimes a grammatical marker, like 'be' in English. As a marker, it is rather like 'do' in English, as in 'He did do it.' 是 is a marker in examples ❷～❺ above, in which 是 cannot be translated as 'be'. 而 is also a high frequency grammatical element, always an adverb, which is slightly literary in style.

練習 Exercise

Complete the following dialogues, using 不是…而是… to present a correction.

❶ A：你們點的烤魚來了。
   B：對不起，＿＿＿＿＿＿＿＿＿＿＿＿＿。
❷ A：這個春捲不好吃嗎？你怎麼不吃？
   B：＿＿＿＿＿＿＿＿＿＿＿＿＿＿＿。
❸ A：這次去歐洲旅行，是你決定的吧？
   B：＿＿＿＿＿＿＿＿＿＿＿＿＿＿＿。
❹ A：這個瓶子好漂亮啊！是用玻璃做的嗎？
   B：你摸摸看，＿＿＿＿＿＿＿＿＿＿＿。
❺ A：林先生吃素，是因為宗教的關係嗎？
   B：＿＿＿＿＿＿＿＿＿＿＿＿＿＿＿。

IV. 從來 + **Negation** *never* 04-08

Function: The pattern 從來 + 沒 refers to events that never took place in the past (in which case, the main verb is followed by the aspect 過). And the pattern 從來不 refers to situations that do not generally happen.

❶ 他雖然是台灣人，可是從來沒吃過道地的台南美食。

❷ 我從來沒參加過跨年活動。難得今年有機會參加。

❸ 羅珊蒂從來沒逛過24小時營業的書店，所以我今天要帶她去。

❹ 我從來沒喝過雄黃酒，今天想喝喝看味道怎麼樣。

❺ 我從來沒在餐廳打過工，不知道在餐廳打工累不累。

❻ 妹妹年紀還小，媽媽從來不讓她一個人出門。

❼ 他說在山區騎摩托車不太安全，所以他從來不這樣做。

❽ 為了身體健康，他從來不吃炸的東西。

Usage: The use of 沒 and 不 in this pattern is summarised in the table below.

	Action Verb	State Verb	Process Verb
從來不	✓	✓	✗
從來沒（…過）	✓	✗	✓

練習 Exercise

Please answer the following questions using 從來沒 V 過 or 從來不 V.

❶ A：站在門口的那位先生，你認識嗎？

　 B：不認識。我＿＿＿＿＿＿＿＿＿＿＿＿＿＿＿＿。

❷ A：你知道端午節的時候，為什麼要戴香包嗎？

　 B：不知道。我＿＿＿＿＿＿＿＿＿＿＿＿＿＿＿＿。

❸ A：你的成績那麼好，考不考慮念研究所？

　 B：＿＿＿＿＿＿＿＿＿＿＿＿＿＿＿＿＿＿＿。

④ A：你常常用手機打國際電話嗎？

　　B：用手機打國際電話有點貴，所以我＿＿＿＿＿＿＿＿＿＿。

⑤ A：陳麗美喜歡在百貨公司買東西，你呢？

　　B：＿＿＿＿＿＿＿＿＿＿＿＿＿＿＿＿＿＿。

V. Various Meanings of the Verb 上　🎧 04-09　英譯 p.94

Function: The verb 上 has various meanings, the most typical of which indicates an upward movement. Atypical cases will have to be learned as such. No general rules apply.

❶ 春天的時候，很多人上陽明山泡溫泉、欣賞櫻花。

❷ 下課以後，我要上樓去找同學討論功課。

❸ 車子來了。快上車吧！

❹ 早點睡吧。明天 6 點要上飛機呢。

❺ 他習慣週末上超市買菜。

❻ 為了身體健康，晚上最好 11 點以前上床。

❼ 上班時間，捷運上人很多，擠死了。

❽ 他每星期六都上教堂。

❾ 台北 101 跨年放煙火活動，昨天上電視新聞了。

練習 Exercise

Please use 上 to complete the sentences below.

❶ 他第一次坐船，才＿＿＿＿＿＿＿＿＿＿沒多久，就吐了。

❷ 老師說＿＿＿＿＿＿＿＿＿＿的時候，不可以用手機查資料。

❸ 公車來了，快＿＿＿＿＿＿＿＿＿＿＿＿＿＿吧。

❹ 怎麼連這麼小的事情都可以＿＿＿＿＿＿＿＿＿＿＿＿。

❺ 他昨晚熬夜，今天＿＿＿＿＿＿＿＿＿＿的時候，精神很不好。

VI. 非…不可 *it is imperative that…* 04-10　　　 英譯 p.94

Function: With this pattern, the speaker indicates that something must be done. There are no alternatives.

❶ 哥哥已經兩年沒回國了，媽媽說今年除夕他非回來跟家人團聚不可。

❷ 想要找到好工作，非充實自己的專業能力不可。

❸ 台北這麼潮濕，我的鞋子都發霉了，非買除濕機不可。

❹ 最近發生很多不好的事情，我非去廟裡拜拜不可。

❺ 沒想到這份英文合約這麼複雜，公司非找人翻譯成中文不可。

Usage: Both 非 and 可 in this pattern are literary in style, i.e., both are from classical Chinese originally.

練習 Exercise

Please complete the sentences with 非…不可 to indicate the urgency of something.

❶ 為了拿到獎學金，＿＿＿＿＿＿＿＿＿＿＿＿＿＿＿＿＿。

❷ 台北東區有很多有特色的商店，＿＿＿＿＿＿＿＿＿＿＿。

❸ 你的手機月租費太貴了，＿＿＿＿＿＿＿＿＿＿＿＿＿＿。

❹ 想多了解台灣人傳統的風俗習慣，＿＿＿＿＿＿＿＿＿＿。

❺ 昨天買的外套，裡面破了一個洞，＿＿＿＿＿＿＿＿＿＿。

VII. 對…來說 *as far as…is concerned, for* 04-11　　 英譯 p.94

Function: This pattern presents a statement which applies to the object of 對. The statement may not be true to others.

❶ 對台南人來說，早餐非常重要。

❷ 對喜歡中國文化的人來說，故宮博物院是一個值得參觀的地方。

③ 一件羊毛外套 8000 塊錢，對我來說，太貴了。

④ 對日本人來說，寫漢字不難。

⑤ 對中國人來說，春節、端午節、中秋節是一家人團聚的日子。

練習 Exercise

Please answer the following questions using 對…來說.

① A：提款機上的中文說明你都看得懂嗎？

B：我是外國人。＿＿＿＿＿＿＿＿＿＿＿＿＿＿＿＿。

② A：你父母為什麼要留在鄉下，不搬到大城市來呢？

B：他們不喜歡大城市。＿＿＿＿＿＿＿＿＿＿＿＿。

③ A：最近世界經濟不太好，找工作會不會比較難？

B：我是學電腦的，＿＿＿＿＿＿＿＿＿＿＿＿。

④ A：你念的是企業管理系，為什麼還要學外語呢？

B：＿＿＿＿＿＿＿＿＿＿＿＿＿＿＿＿＿＿。

⑤ A：現在日本最重視的是什麼？

B：＿＿＿＿＿＿＿＿＿＿＿＿；發展經濟是最重要的。

VIII. 對…講究 *to be discerning, discriminating, particular about* 🎧 04-12

 英譯 p.94

Function: The use of this pattern indicates that the subject is very particular about the object of 對 and wants nothing but the best.

① 鈴木先生沒想到台南人對吃這麼講究。

② 高先生對住的環境非常講究，不但要離車站近，附近還要有公園。

③ 小張對吃東西不怎麼講究，常常吃麵包或是超商的速食。

④ 李小姐對衣服的品質很講究，總是買有名的牌子的。

⑤ 對吃很講究的人，不一定都胖。

練習 Exercise

Please complete the following sentences, by detailing S2 as an elaboration of S1.

1 他對吃很講究，＿＿＿＿＿＿＿＿＿＿＿＿＿＿＿＿＿＿。

2 我對穿不講究，＿＿＿＿＿＿＿＿＿＿＿＿＿＿＿＿＿＿。

3 他對家裡用的東西很講究，＿＿＿＿＿＿＿＿＿＿＿＿。

4 日本人對啤酒很講究，＿＿＿＿＿＿＿＿＿＿＿＿＿＿。

5 他對手機的功能非常講究，＿＿＿＿＿＿＿＿＿＿＿＿。

語法例句英譯
Grammar Examples in English

I. 不但…，還… *not only…, but also*

Function:

1 The coat he bought yesterday is not only light, but also very warm.

2 Chen Minxuan's Chinese is not only spot on in terms of tones; she speaks very fluently.

3 The cell phone I just got not only has low monthly fees; I get unlimited internet usage.

4 It's not only raining outside; it's also very windy. Don't go out.

5 In ancient times, during the Dragon Boat Festival, Chinese people not only wore fragrant sachets but also drank realgar liquor.

Usage:

1 Not only is the style of his coat attractive, the price is really low.

2 Not only is the dish he made visually attractive, it tastes great too.

III. …不是…，而是… *not…; rather…*

Function:

1 The one that An Desi likes isn't Miss Wang; rather, it's Miss Bai.

2 It's not that I don't want to take part in the field trip; rather, it's because I've been really busy lately.

3 You didn't purchase this garment with cash. You bought it with a credit card, so the money can't be refunded immediately.

4 He didn't come to Taiwan to travel around; rather, he came to study Chinese.

5 I changed jobs, not because the salary is higher; rather, it's because the new company is closer.

IV. 從來 + Negation *never*

Function:

1 Although he's Taiwanese, he has never had authentic Tainan food.

2 I've never taken part in a New Year's countdown. It's nice that I have the opportunity to go this year.

3 Luo Shandi has never checked out a bookstore that's open 24/7, so I'm going to take her today.

4 I've never had realgar liquor before. Today, I would like to drink some and see what it tastes like.

5 I've never worked in a restaurant. I don't know if it's tiring work.

6 My little sister is still too little. Mom never lets her leave the house alone.

7 He says that riding a motorcycle in the mountains isn't all that safe, so he never does like that.

8 For the sake of his health, he never eats fried foods.

V. Various Meanings of the Verb 上

Function:

1 In the spring, many people go up Yangming Mountain to soak in the hot springs and enjoy the cherry blossoms.

2 After class, I'm going upstairs to discuss homework with classmates.

3 The bus is here. Hurry up and get on.

4 Get to sleep a little earlier. You have to board the plane at 6:00 am tomorrow.

5 He usually goes to the supermarket on the weekend to buy groceries.

6 For your health, it's best to get to bed before 11:00 pm.

7 When going to work, there are lots of people on the MRT. It's really crowded.

8 He goes to church every Saturday.

9 The Taipei 101 New Year's fireworks display was on the news last night.

VI. 非…不可 *it is imperative that…*

Function:

1 My big brother hasn't been back from abroad in two years. My mom says this year, he absolutely must come back and get together with the family on Chinese New Year's Eve.

2 If you want to get a good job, it is absolutely imperative that you hone your professional skills.

3 Taipei is so humid; my shoes have grown mildew. I really have to buy a dehumidifier.

4 A lot of bad things have happened lately. I have to go to the temple and worship.

5 I had no idea that this English contract was so complicated. The company has to find somebody to translate it into Chinese.

VII. 對…來說 *as far as...is concerned, for*

Function:

1 For the people of Tainan, breakfast is very important.

2 For people who like Chinese culture, the National Palace Museum is a place worth visiting.

3 For me, NT$8,000 for a wool coat is too expensive.

4 For Japanese, writing Chinese characters is not hard.

5 For the Chinese, the Spring Festival, the Dragon Boat Festival, and the Mid-Autumn Moon Festival are days that families get together.

VIII. 對…講究 *to be discerning, discriminating, particular about*

Function:

1 Mr. Lingmu had no idea that the people of Tainan were so particular about foods.

2 Mr. Gao is very particular about where he lives. Not only does it have to be close to the public transportation, it also has to have a park nearby.

3 Xiao Zhang isn't all that fussy about what he eats. He often has bread or fast food from convenience stores.

4 Miss Li is very particular about the quality of her clothes and always buys famous brand names.

5 People who care a great deal about eating aren't necessarily all over-weight.

課室活動 Classroom Activities

I. The Friendliness of Taiwan (or A Country)

Goal: Learning to use lists to provide information.

Task: Ask students to give examples from their experience of situations showing the friendliness of the Taiwanese (or a country), for example, assistance they received or other anecdotes when at the airport, asking directions, taking the MRT, or at a hotel.

Try to use the following sentence patterns and vocabulary words:

從來…	不是…而是…	對…來說

II. A City I Want to Visit

Goal: Learning to clearly explain what I like about a city.

Task: Interview three classmates. Ask them if they would like to visit old cities or modern cities. After interviews, report your findings to the class.

同學	城市的名字	特色一	特色二	特色三
❶				
❷				
❸				

III. Recommending a Place

Goal: Learning to explain the special characteristics of a place.

Task: Divide the class into two groups. Recommend an unforgettable place, listing reasons and emphasis and provide further information explaining what makes that place so special and hard to forget.

Try to use the following sentence patterns and vocabulary words:

對…來說	不但…還…	非…不可	算是

文化 *Bits of Chinese Culture*

Ghost Money

When foreigners come to Taiwan and see people burning paper at the side of the road, they might think that these plain pieces of yellow paper would be great for making homemade cards to give to friends and family. But these slips of paper are actually "冥紙"（míngzhǐ, ghost money）, money used by gods and ghosts. To a Chinese who is still alive, a gift of ghost money isn't a blessing at all; rather, it's a curse. A "gift" of ghost money means that the giver has a deep hatred for the recipient.

▲ 《聯合報》陳易辰 攝影

"冥紙", also known as "紙錢"（zhǐqían, paper money）, can generally be divided into two categories. The kind with a square of goldleaf affixed to it is called "金紙"（jīnzhǐ, gold paper）. It is used for venerating gods. Paper with pieces of silverleaf on it is called "銀錢"（yínzhǐ, silver paper）. It is burned to give to friends and family that have passed away as well as to ghosts to spend as money in the netherworld.

It is said that the Chinese custom of burning ghost money finds its origins deep in antiquity when jade and other treasures were placed in the graves of the deceased. By the Tang Dynasty, paper money was burnt for the dead. Some people believe that the burning in China of ghost money for the dead comes from Buddhism, but only Chinese societies have this custom.

▲ 《聯合報》鄭超文 攝影

▲ Burning paper money to venerate gods or the dead.

Whenever there is a festival or holiday, you can always see people burning ghost money in temples, in front of businesses, or in front of their homes.

▲ Ghost money for the dead.

▲ Gold paper money for venerating gods.

Self-Assessment Checklist

I can discuss with my friends leisure activities that I enjoy.

20%   40%   60%   80%   100%

I can tell others about Taiwan's culture and provide travel information for different destinations.

20%   40%   60%   80%   100%

I can emphasize, give examples, and provide further information.

20%   40%   60%   80%   100%

I can talk about the unique characteristics and culture of small towns.

20%   40%   60%   80%   100%

LESSON 5

第五課

現在流行什麼？

What Are the Trends Now?

....

學習目標 Learning Objectives

Topic: 流行文化 Popular Culture

- Learning to talk about trends.
- Learning to explain in detail the merits of your hobbies and activities.
- Learning to provide various reasons refuting the views of others.
- Learning to describe a live concert.

現在流行什麼？

What Are the Trends Now?

對話 Dialogue 05-01

〈倔強〉3DNA LIVE 版 音樂提供／相信音樂
（詞．曲／五月天阿信、演唱人／五月天、OP ／認真工作室、SP ／相信音樂國際股份有限公司）

陳 敏 萱 ：你怎麼了？怎麼那麼沒精神？

高橋健太：唉！氣死了！昨天我上網買五月天演唱會的票。沒想到網路塞車，我試了兩、三個鐘頭，等我上線成功，票已經賣完了。真倒楣！

陳 敏 萱 ：你別生氣了。買不到就算了。為什麼非聽不可？

羅 珊 蒂 ：五月天是誰？什麼演唱會啊？

高橋健太：（拿出手機）妳聽。這就是他們的歌。五月天是華人世界最受歡迎的樂團。下個月他們的演唱會，我當然不能錯過。

陳 敏 萱 ：我朋友去聽了他們的跨年演唱會。她說，那天體育館擠滿了人，大家都站在椅子上又唱又叫，興奮極了。

羅 珊 蒂 ：他們很帥嗎？為什麼這麼多人迷他們？

高橋健太 ：大家喜歡他們是因為他們的歌詞不但都寫得很美，而且能說出年輕人心裡的話。高興的時候，要聽；難過的時候，更要聽。

陳 敏 萱 ：演唱會人那麼多，票又不好買，不如在家上網看舒服。

高橋健太 ：聽演唱會當然要去現場，大家一起唱，一起跳，整個體育館都在震動。這樣的感覺沒去過的人是不能了解的。

陳 敏 萱 ：聲音那麼大，吵死了。還是在家好。

高橋健太 ：妳整天在家不會太無聊嗎？

陳 敏 萱 ：怎麼會呢？有那麼多有趣的漫畫，怎麼會覺得無聊呢？

羅 珊 蒂 ：我媽媽說租書店的漫畫內容都太色情，不適合我們看。

高橋健太 ：現在誰去租書店啊？大家都用平板電腦跟智慧型手機上網看了。

羅 珊 蒂 ：我媽也說他朋友的孩子因為迷漫畫，花了太多時間，影響了功課，所以她不讓我們看。

高橋健太 ：不會啊，好的漫畫也很多啊。看漫畫除了可以放鬆心情，還可以學到很多歷史、文化和傳統。

陳 敏 萱 ：沒錯。我也是看了漫畫才知道壽司是怎麼做的。

羅 珊 蒂 ：看漫畫就是為了殺時間。你們想太多啦。

陳 敏 萱 ：幾點了？這麼晚啦？我跟朋友約了去看漫畫展，他們在捷運站等我，再不走就來不及了。改天再聊吧。

陈 敏 萱：你怎么了？怎么那么没精神？

高桥健太：唉！气死了！昨天我上网买五月天演唱会的票。没想到网路塞车，我试了两、三个钟头，等我上线成功，票已经卖完了。真倒楣！

陈 敏 萱：你别生气了。买不到就算了。为什么非听不可？

罗 珊 蒂：五月天是谁？什么演唱会啊？

高桥健太：（拿出手机）妳听。这就是他们的歌。五月天是华人世界最受欢迎的乐团。下个月他们的演唱会，我当然不能错过。

陈 敏 萱：我朋友去听了他们的跨年演唱会。她说，那天体育馆挤满了人，大家都站在椅子上又唱又叫，兴奋极了。

罗 珊 蒂：他们很帅吗？为什么这么多人迷他们？

高桥健太：大家喜欢他们是因为他们的歌词不但都写得很美，而且能说出年轻人心里的话。高兴的时候，要听；难过的时候，更要听。

陈 敏 萱：演唱会人那么多，票又不好买，不如在家上网看舒服。

高桥健太：听演唱会当然要去现场，大家一起唱，一起跳，整个体育馆都在震动。这样的感觉没去过的人是不能了解的。

陈 敏 萱：声音那么大，吵死了。还是在家好。

高桥健太：妳整天在家不会太无聊吗？

陈 敏 萱：怎么会呢？有那么多有趣的漫画，怎么会觉得无聊呢？

罗 珊 蒂：我妈妈说租书店的漫画内容都太色情，不适合我们看。

高桥健太：现在谁去租书店啊？大家都用平板电脑跟智慧型手机上网看了。

罗 珊 蒂：我妈也说他朋友的孩子因为迷漫画，花了太多时间，影响了功课，所以她不让我们看。

高桥健太：不会啊，好的漫画也很多啊。看漫画除了可以放松心情，还可以学到很多历史、文化和传统。

陈 敏 萱：没错。我也是看了漫画才知道寿司是怎么做的。

罗 珊 蒂：看漫画就是为了杀时间。你们想太多啦。

陈 敏 萱：几点了？这么晚啦？我跟朋友约了去看漫画展，他们在捷运站等我，再不走就来不及了。改天再聊吧。

課文英譯 Text in English

Chen Minxuan : What's wrong? Why so listless?

Gaoqiao Jiantai: Argh! I'm so angry that I could just die! Yesterday, I went online to buy tickets to the Mayday concert. I had no idea the internet would be so congested. I tried for two or three hours, and by the time I got connected the tickets were all sold out. What rotten luck!

Chen Minxuan : Don't be angry. If you couldn't get tickets then just forget about it. Why do you have to go?

Luo Shandi : Who is Mayday? What concert?

Gaoqiao Jiantai: (*Takes out his cell phone*) Listen. This is one of their songs. Mayday is the most popular band among Chinese speaking people. I simply can't miss their concert next month.

Chen Minxuan : One of my friends went to listen to their New Year's Eve concert. She said that the stadium was packed with people that day. Everybody was standing on their seats singing and screaming. It was really exciting.

Luo Shandi : Are they handsome? Why do so many people like them?

Gaoqiao Jiantai: Everybody likes them because their lyrics are not only all written beautifully; they resonate with young people. They are great to listen to when you're happy, even better when you're sad.

Chen Minxuan : With so many people at the concert and tickets so hard to get, it would be better to watch them online from the comfort of your own home.

Gaoqiao Jiantai: Concerts, of course, have to be seen live. When everybody is singing and dancing, it's like the entire stadium shakes. Somebody who has never gone wouldn't understand.

Chen Minxuan : It's so loud; the noise would drive me crazy. I'd rather stay at home.

Gaoqiao Jiantai: Don't you get bored staying at home all day?

Chen Minxuan : No way. With so many interesting comic books, how could I feel bored?

Luo Shandi : My mom says that the content of book rental store comics are too pornographic and aren't appropriate for us to read.

Gaoqiao Jiantai: Who goes to book rental stores nowadays? Everybody reads them online using tablets and smartphones.

Luo Shandi : My mom says that her friend's kid is obsessed with comic books and spends so much time reading them that it has affected his school work. That's why my mom won't let us read any.

Gaoqiao Jiantai: That's not true. There are also a lot of good comic books. Not only do they help you relax, reading comic books allows you to learn a lot of history, culture, and traditions.

Chen Minxuan : That's right. I didn't know how to make sushi until I read about it in a comic book.

Luo Shandi : Reading comic books is for killing time. You're reading too much into it.

Chen Minxuan : What's the time? That late? I am meeting up with friends to go see a comic exhibition. They're at the MRT station waiting for me. If I don't leave now, I'll be late. Let's catch up another day.

生詞一 Vocabulary I 🎧 05-02

Vocabulary

1	流行	liúxíng	ㄌㄧㄡˊ ㄒㄧㄥˊ	(Vst)	popular
2	唉	āi	ㄞ	(Ptc)	Oh no! Oh boy!
3	演唱會	yǎnchànghuì	ㄧㄢˇ ㄔㄤˋ ㄏㄨㄟˋ	(N)	concert
4	塞車	sāichē	ㄙㄞ ㄔㄜ	(Vs)	net congestion, jam
5	上線	shàngxiàn	ㄕㄤˋ ㄒㄧㄢˋ	(V-sep)	to log in, go online
6	成功	chénggōng	ㄔㄥˊ ㄍㄨㄥ	(Vp)	to succeed
7	倒楣	dǎoméi	ㄉㄠˇ ㄇㄟˊ	(Vs)	out of luck, down on one's luck
8	樂團	yuètuán	ㄩㄝˋ ㄊㄨㄢˊ	(N)	(music) band
9	唱	chàng	ㄔㄤˋ	(V)	to sing
10	興奮	xīngfèn	ㄒㄧㄥ ㄈㄣˋ	(Vs)	excited
11	迷	mí	ㄇㄧˊ	(Vst)	to be enamored with, be into, be enchanted by, be obsessed with
12	歌詞	gēcí	ㄍㄜ ㄘˊ	(N)	lyrics
13	難過	nánguò	ㄋㄢˊ ㄍㄨㄛˋ	(Vs)	sad
14	不如	bùrú	ㄅㄨˋ ㄖㄨˊ	(Vst)	inferior to

15	現場現場	xiànchǎng	ㄒㄧㄢˋ ㄔㄤˇ	(N)	live; lit. on-site
16	跳跳跳跳	tiào	ㄊㄧㄠˋ	(Vi)	to jump
17	整整整	zhěng	ㄓㄥˇ	(Det)	entire, whole
18	震動震動震	zhèndòng	ㄓㄣˋ ㄉㄨㄥˋ	(Vi)	to vibrate, to shake
19	漫畫漫畫漫	mànhuà	ㄇㄢˋ ㄏㄨㄚˋ	(N)	comics
20	內容內容內容	nèiróng	ㄋㄟˋ ㄖㄨㄥˊ	(N)	content
21	色情色情色情	sèqíng	ㄙㄜˋ ㄑㄧㄥˊ	(Vs)	pornographic; obscene
22	放鬆放鬆放	fàngsōng	ㄈㄤˋ ㄙㄨㄥ	(Vst)	to relax
23	心情心情心情	xīnqíng	ㄒㄧㄣ ㄑㄧㄥˊ	(N)	mood

Names

| 24 | 五月天 | Wǔyuètiān | ㄨˇ ㄩㄝˋ ㄊㄧㄢ | | Mayday (name of a Taiwanese rock band) |

Phrases

25	算了算了	suàn le	ㄙㄨㄢˋ ㄌㄜ	forget it; let it be!
26	受歡迎	shòu huānyíng	ㄕㄡˋ ㄏㄨㄢ ㄧㄥˊ	well-received; well-liked; popular
27	擠滿擠滿擠	jǐmǎn	ㄐㄧˇ ㄇㄢˇ	crowded with, packed with
28	租書店	zūshū diàn	ㄗㄨ ㄕㄨ ㄉㄧㄢˋ	book rental store
29	平板電腦	píngbǎn diànnǎo	ㄆㄧㄥˊ ㄅㄢˇ ㄉㄧㄢˋ ㄋㄠˇ	tablet computer
30	智慧型手機	zhìhuìxíng shǒujī	ㄓˋ ㄏㄨㄟˋ ㄒㄧㄥˊ ㄕㄡˇ ㄐㄧ	smartphone
31	殺時間殺	shā shíjiān	ㄕㄚ ㄕˊ ㄐㄧㄢ	to kill time
32	漫畫展	mànhuà zhǎn	ㄇㄢˋ ㄏㄨㄚˋ ㄓㄢˇ	comic (book) exhibition
33	來不及	lái bù jí	ㄌㄞˊ ㄅㄨˋ ㄐㄧˊ	not be in time for, not make it on time

短文 Reading 05-03

撞衫

何雅婷昨天晚上去上西班牙文課的時候，發現班上有個同學穿著一件跟她一模一樣的淺藍色外套。何雅婷馬上脫掉外套，把它塞進背包裡。她覺得怎麼會發生這種事情呢？這件外套是當季款式，她看到連續劇裡的女主角穿了這件衣服看起來很甜美，所以才特別請朋友從國外寄來的。沒想到居然撞衫，害她整個晚上心情都很不好。

今天中午下了課以後，何雅婷跟陳敏萱和安德思見面的時候，談到了這件事。陳敏萱覺得不需要為了這種事不高興。既然是最流行的款式，當然會有很多人穿。服裝公司在各種媒體上用不同的方式做廣告，吸引大家去買，撞衫就很難避免。只要能穿出不同的感覺就好了。

安德思不懂為什麼有人怕撞衫。他認為何雅婷太小題大作了。衣服、包包跟別人一樣有什麼關係。商人為了賺錢，每年都要推出新的產品，新的款式，像電子產品，如果市場上有了最新型的，自己沒有，就落伍了。如果別人有跟自己一樣的新產品，一定會說個不停，像碰到了知音。既然這樣，女人為什麼怕撞衫呢？

何雅婷覺得他說的沒錯，是很難想像如果自己穿著喇叭褲去上課，會給別人什麼印象。再說，如果不懂流行，不看最受歡迎的連續劇，不去最熱門的餐廳，不玩最流行的電腦遊戲，不知道現在流行化什麼樣的妝，大概就沒什麼朋友了。

撞衫

何雅婷昨天晚上去上西班牙文课的时候，发现班上有个同学穿着一件跟她一模一样的浅蓝色外套。何雅婷马上脱掉外套，把它塞进背包里。她觉得怎么会发生这种事情呢？这件外套是当季款式，她看到连续剧里的女主角穿了这件衣服看起来很甜美，所以才特别请朋友从国外寄来的。没想到居然撞衫，害她整个晚上心情都很不好。

今天中午下了课以后，何雅婷跟陈敏萱和安德思见面的时候，谈到了这件事。陈敏萱觉得不需要为了这种事不高兴。既然是最流行的款式，当然会有很多人穿。服装公司在各种媒体上用不同的方式做广告，吸引大家去买，撞衫就很难避免。只要能穿出不同的感觉就好了。

安德思不懂为什么有人怕撞衫。他认为何雅婷太小题大作了。衣服、包包跟别人一样有什么关系。商人为了赚钱，每年都要推出新的产品，新的款式，像电子产品，如果市场上有了最新型的，自己没有，就落伍了。如果别人有跟自己一样的新产品，一定会说个不停，像碰到了知音。既然这样，女人为什么怕撞衫呢？

何雅婷觉得他说的没错，是很难想象如果自己穿着喇叭裤去上课，会给别人什么印象。再说，如果不懂流行，不看最受欢迎的连续剧，不去最热门的餐厅，不玩最流行的电脑游戏，不知道现在流行化什么样的妆，大概就没什么朋友了。

Wardrobe Clash

Last night, when He Yating went to Spanish class, she discovered that a classmate was wearing a light blue coat exactly like hers. He Yating immediately took off her coat and stuffed it in her backpack. She thought to herself, how could something like this happen? The coat was the latest fashion. She saw the leading lady in a television series wearing it and she looked lovely, so she made it a point to ask a friend to mail one to her from abroad. She never expected that somehow she would have a "wardrobe clash" with somebody else and this put her into a funk the entire evening.

At noon today after class, when He Yating met with Chen Minxuan and An Desi, this episode came up in their conversation. Chen Minxuan felt that there was no need to be upset about things like that. Since it is a popular style, obviously, a lot of people are wearing it. Clothing companies advertise using many different methods across various types of media to attract a lot of people to buy their products, so wardrobe clashes are hard to avoid. As long as you are able to exude a different feeling when you wear yours, that's what matters.

An Desi doesn't understand why some people are afraid of wardrobe clashes. He thinks that He Yating is making a big deal out of nothing. What does it matter if your clothes or bag are the same as other people's? To make money, every year, businesspeople introduce new products and new styles. Take electronics, for example. If the latest style comes out and you don't have it, then you're "uncool". If somebody has the same new product as you, you're bound to talk non-stop about it. It's like running into a close friend. That being the case, why are women so afraid of running into someone with duplicate clothing?

He Yating concedes it certainly would be hard to imagine what kind of impression you would give others if you wore bell-bottom pants to class. Besides, if you don't understand what's in fashion, don't watch the most popular TV series, don't go to the hottest restaurants, don't play the most popular computer games, and don't know what the latest make-up trends are, you probably won't have any friends.

生詞二 Vocabulary II 🎧 05-04

Vocabulary

1	撞衫	zhuàngshān	ㄓㄨㄤˋ ㄕㄢ	(Vs)	"wardrobe clash", more than one person unintentionally wearing duplicate garments
2	它	tā	ㄊㄚ	(N)	it
3	塞	sāi	ㄙㄞ	(V)	to stuff, cram, squeeze (into)
4	當季	dāngjì	ㄉㄤ ㄐㄧˋ	(N)	in season
5	款式	kuǎnshì	ㄎㄨㄢˇ ㄕˋ	(N)	style (of clothes)
6	連續劇	liánxùjù	ㄌㄧㄢˊ ㄒㄩˋ ㄐㄩˋ	(N)	TV series
7	主角	zhǔjiǎo	ㄓㄨˇ ㄐㄧㄠˇ	(N)	leading role, leading actor
8	甜美	tiánměi	ㄊㄧㄢˊ ㄇㄟˇ	(Vs)	sweet and cute, lovely

9	寄	jì	ㄐㄧˋ	(V)	to mail
10	居然	jūrán	ㄐㄩ ㄖㄢˊ	(Adv)	unexpectedly, counter to assumption
11	害	hài	ㄏㄞˋ	(V)	adversely impacting somebody so that they...
12	既然	jìrán	ㄐㄧˋ ㄖㄢˊ	(Conj)	since, given that...
13	服裝	fúzhuāng	ㄈㄨˊ ㄓㄨㄤ	(N)	clothing, garments
14	媒體	méitǐ	ㄇㄟˊ ㄊㄧˇ	(N)	the media
15	方式	fāngshì	ㄈㄤ ㄕˋ	(N)	method, ways
16	吸引	xīyǐn	ㄒㄧ ㄧㄣˇ	(Vst)	to attract, to draw
17	避免	bìmiǎn	ㄅㄧˋ ㄇㄧㄢˇ	(V)	to avoid
18	包包	bāobāo	ㄅㄠ ㄅㄠ	(N)	bag, purse
19	商人	shāngrén	ㄕㄤ ㄖㄣˊ	(N)	businessperson
20	產品	chǎnpǐn	ㄔㄢˇ ㄆㄧㄣˇ	(N)	product
21	電子	diànzǐ	ㄉㄧㄢˋ ㄗˇ	(N)	electronics
22	市場	shìchǎng	ㄕˋ ㄔㄤˇ	(N)	market
23	新型	xīnxíng	ㄒㄧㄣ ㄒㄧㄥˊ	(Vs-attr)	new style
24	落伍	luòwǔ	ㄌㄨㄛˋ ㄨˇ	(Vs)	behind the times, passé, old-fashioned
25	知音	zhīyīn	ㄓ ㄧㄣ	(N)	bosom buddy, confidant
26	想像	xiǎngxiàng	ㄒㄧㄤˇ ㄒㄧㄤˋ	(V)	to imagine
27	喇叭褲	lǎbākù	ㄌㄚˇ ㄅㄚ ㄎㄨˋ	(N)	bell-bottom pants
28	印象	yìnxiàng	ㄧㄣˋ ㄒㄧㄤˋ	(N)	impression
29	遊戲	yóuxì	ㄧㄡˊ ㄒㄧˋ	(N)	game
30	化妝	huàzhuāng	ㄏㄨㄚˋ ㄓㄨㄤ	(V-sep)	to apply cosmetics, to make up

Phrases

31	一模一樣	yìmó yíyàng	ㄧˋ ㄇㄛˊ ㄧˊ ㄧㄤˋ		identical
32	淺藍色	qiǎn lánsè	ㄑㄧㄢˇ ㄌㄢˊ ㄙㄜˋ		light blue
33	脫掉	tuōdiào	ㄊㄨㄛ ㄉㄧㄠˋ		to take off (clothing)

| 34 | 小題大作 | xiǎotí dàzuò | ㄒㄧㄠˇ ㄊㄧˊ ㄉㄚˋ ㄗㄨㄛˋ | to make a mountain out of a molehill, to make a big deal of nothing |
| 35 | 推出 | tuīchū | ㄊㄨㄟ ㄔㄨ | to introduce, to roll out (products) |

文法 Grammar

I. Verb Plus Complement V + 滿 *crowded with* 05-05   英譯 p.121

Function: The state verb 滿 'full' serves as a result complement in this pattern. This pattern employs exaggeration to indicate a large number of items in a given location. See Lesson 6 of Vol. 1 or Lesson 7 of Vol. 2.

① 街道的兩邊蓋滿了新的大樓。

② 101 大樓前面擠滿了看跨年煙火的年輕人。

③ 客廳牆上掛滿了他去花蓮拍的照片。

④ 不到八點,教室裡就坐滿了學生。

⑤ 這個袋子裡怎麼塞滿了垃圾?

Usage: This type of existential sentence indicates the existence of a noun at a location.

練習 Exercise

Please complete the dialogues below with V + 滿.

① A:聽說這棟宿舍大樓裡住了很多外國人,真的嗎?

　　B:是真的,這裡面＿＿＿＿＿＿了從各個國家來的人。

② A:來海邊,不去沙灘上玩,多可惜啊。

　　B:沙灘上＿＿＿＿＿＿了曬太陽的人,太擠了。還是坐在這裡看風景舒服。

❸ A：展覽館門口為什麼＿＿＿＿＿＿＿＿了人？今天有活動嗎？

B：是啊，今天有電腦展。來參觀的人很多。

❹ A：喝完的空杯子，為什麼不放進資源回收桶去呢？

B：放不進去了。＿＿＿＿＿＿＿＿＿＿＿＿＿＿＿＿＿＿＿。

❺ A：你的背包怎麼這麼快就破了？

B：我背包裡每天都＿＿＿＿＿＿了書。破了，一點也不奇怪。

II. Verb Particle 出 *to have emerged* 05-06　　　

Function: When the verb particle 出 is attached to an action verb, it carries the meaning of something coming into existence or consciousness.

❶ 我不好意思說出的話，他都幫我說了。

❷ 一樣的衣服，他穿起來，總是能穿出跟別人完全不同的感覺。

❸ 他用有機商店買回來的材料做出又酸又辣的泡菜。

❹ 我寫不出這麼讓人感動的歌。

❺ 那位教授花了十年的時間才研究出這種新藥。

Usage:

1. We already studied two other uses of 出 in Vol. 2, where it was a main verb, not a particle:

   (1) 出 indicates spatial movement from inside to outside, as V_1 in V_1V_2 (e.g., 出來 'come out'、出去 'go out').

   (2) 出 as V_2 in $V_1V_2V_3$ (e.g., 拿出去 'take it out and away'、走出去 'walk out of'、跑出來 'run out towards me'、把書拿出房間去 'get the books out of this room').

2. 來 is needed informing $V_1V_2V_3$, when the particle 出 appears with 把 or when the object is moved to the front, e.g., 你應該把心裡的話說出來。or 心裡的話，你應該說出來。'You should speak out what's on your mind.' In other situations, 來 is optional, e.g., 他研究了很久，才研究出（來）新的做法。'He researched it for a long time before he thought (out) a new way.'

3. The pattern '出（來）' can also be used in the potential form. E.g.,

   A：你想得出辦法嗎？ 'Can you think out a way?'

   B：我想不出來。 'I can't think one out.'

4. Watch out for the differences between the particles 出 and 起 (Vol. 2, Lesson. 3, Grammar point 4). The first refers to the emergence of something out of nowhere, while the second refers to something that used to be known but returns to his consciousness or awareness. Compare the examples below:

   (1) 我想了很久才想出一個辦法來。 'I thought for a long time before I thought of a way.' (出 = from nothing to something, out of thin air)

   (2) 他說過一個不錯的辦法，我差一點忘了。幸虧現在想起來了。 'I almost forgot. He mentioned a good method. Luckily, I thought of it just now.' (起 = already in existence, new awareness)

練習 Exercise

Answer the following questions with V 出（來）. Pay attention to the difference between potential form and actual form.

❶ A：這次考試，你的成績怎麼這麼不理想？（寫）

   B：考試的時候我頭痛，很多我都念過，可是＿＿＿＿＿＿＿＿。

❷ A：告訴我，是誰讓你不開心的？（說）

   B：我不想說。我怕＿＿＿＿＿＿＿＿有人會不高興。

❸ A：你那麼喜歡連續劇女主角穿的外套，我們就上網訂，再請我朋友從國外帶回來啊。（想）

   B：這麼好的辦法，你是怎麼＿＿＿＿＿＿＿＿的？

❹ A：這是我媽做的素餃子，請你嚐嚐。（包）

   B：真沒想到沒有肉，也＿＿＿＿＿＿＿＿這麼好吃的餃子。

❺ A：壽司很好吃，可是有一點貴。我去學做壽司，改天自己做，你覺得怎麼樣？（做）

   B：做壽司看起來容易，但是要＿＿＿＿＿＿＿＿好吃的壽司比你想像的要難得多。

III. 不如 *not as good as*   05-07

Function: The transitive state verb 不如 introduces a comparison between two items. The first noun is inferior to, or less desirable, than the second.

1. 這件衣服的品質不如那件的好。
2. 這家火鍋店的海鮮不如那家的新鮮。
3. 搭捷運得轉兩趟車，不如坐公車方便。
4. 考試以前才熬夜念書，不如平常就做好準備。
5. 太陽這麼大，躺在沙灘上，不如回房間看電視舒服。

Usage:

1. The state verb at the end of a sentence with 不如 must indicate a desirable property. E.g., you cannot say *這支手機不如那支手機舊。

2. If the context of a sentence using a state verb is clear, then the state verb can be omitted. For example:

   A：我的手機壞了。你知道哪裡可以修理嗎？

   B：你的手機已經那麼舊了。修理不如買一支新的（好）。

3. 不如 and 沒有⋯那麼⋯ are similar, but there are differences:

   (1) 不如 is frequently used in literary Chinese. 沒有⋯那麼⋯ is more colloquial.

   (2) The state verb at the end of a sentence using 不如 can be omitted. The same is not true of 沒有⋯那麼⋯. E.g., 坐巴士不如坐高鐵（快）'Taking the HSR is faster than taking a bus.'; But you cannot say *坐巴士沒有坐高鐵那麼。

練習 Exercise

Answer the following questions by making a comparison with 不如.

1. A：夏天到了，天氣又濕又熱。你想我買除濕機好還是買冷氣機好？

   B：＿＿＿＿＿＿＿＿＿＿＿＿＿＿＿＿＿＿＿＿＿＿＿＿。

❷ A：我的手機最近不知道為什麼總是收不到訊號。我想拿去門市修理。

B：你那支手機已經用了四年了，＿＿＿＿＿＿＿＿＿＿＿。

❸ A：你原來念的會計系很熱門，以後應該會有不錯的發展。為什麼要轉系呢？

B：我對會計一點興趣也沒有，＿＿＿＿＿＿＿＿＿＿＿。

❹ A：這條魚很新鮮，炸一炸味道一定好得不得了。

B：炸的魚比較不健康，＿＿＿＿＿＿＿＿＿＿＿。

❺ A：我父母考慮搬到鄉下住，可是我有一點擔心。

B：對年紀大的人來說，＿＿＿＿＿＿＿＿＿＿＿。

IV. Urgent Conditional with 再不⋯就⋯了 🎧 05-08 🔍英譯 p.121

Function: This pattern presents a condition first, and if the condition is not met, an undesirable consequence follows. 就 and 了 can be omitted in some contexts.

❶ 已經四個月沒下雨了。再不下雨，我們就沒水喝了。

❷ 天氣這麼潮濕，再不買除濕機，衣服就要發霉了。

❸ 五月天演唱會很熱門。今天再不訂票，就訂不到了。

❹ 上次考試我只有 60 分。再不用功，恐怕會被當。

❺ 發生什麼事了？你快說。你再不說清楚，我就要生氣了。

Usage: It is common to have such words as 就, 會, 要 to be used in the 2nd sentence, and it's also common to precede this pattern with conjunctions such as 如果 or 要是, e.g.,

❶ 他已經發燒好幾天了。要是再不去看醫生、吃藥，恐怕會越來越嚴重。

❷ 知道這些傳統風俗的人已經越來越少了。如果我們再不重視，恐怕以後就沒有人能懂了。

練習 Exercise

Please complete the 再不 clauses below.

❶ 麵包在桌上放了兩天了。再不＿＿＿＿＿＿＿＿＿＿＿＿。

❷ 他約了我八點見面。現在已經快八點半了。他再不

＿＿＿＿＿＿＿＿＿＿＿＿＿＿＿＿＿＿＿＿＿＿。

❸ 這個月你已經花了兩萬多塊了。再不＿＿＿＿＿＿＿＿。

❹ 已經十點多了。功課那麼多，你再不＿＿＿＿＿＿＿。

❺ 你看起來很累。快躺下來休息。你再不＿＿＿＿＿＿。

V. Verb Particle 掉 *separated from* 05-09   英譯 p.122

Function: The verb particle 掉 expresses the meaning that a noun is disposed of, separated from where it was before. Its precise meaning is determined by the main verb.

❶ 廚房裡的垃圾，我拿出去丟掉了。(away)

❷ 誰把我的咖啡喝掉了？(up and gone)

❸ 他每次一走進房間，就把鞋子踢掉。(off)

❹ 桌子上的茶，我還沒喝呢，他怎麼拿去倒掉了？(out and away)

❺ 他上個月把舊車賣掉，買了新車。(off)

Usage：

1. 'V + 掉' can also be used in the potential pattern, i.e., V + 得 + 掉；V + 不 + 掉. For example, 衣服上的咖啡洗得掉嗎？'Can the coffee on the clothes be washed out?'

2. Because 掉 indicates 'separation from', therefore, only action verbs that can 'be removed' in some way can be used with 掉. Usable verbs have an 'outward' direction, e.g., 丟、脫、忘、賣 , etc. Most verbs that indicate the obtaining of something cannot be used. For example, *他把車買掉 isn't good Chinese.

3. If the verb used in this pattern is an outward transitive action verb, like 喝、吃、忘、賣、脫、倒 (Please see the explanation for 把 in Vol. 1, Lesson. 15,

Grammar point 2), the 掉 is often omitted. E.g., Both 他上個月把機車賣掉
了。and 他上個月把機車賣了。are good sentences. 'Last month, he sold his
motorcycle.'

4. The semantic meaning of the verb particles 掉 and 走 overlaps a bit. Both
suggest that an 'object' is removed in some way from the 'main body'. When
using 掉, the agent does not accompany the object when it leaves the main
body. Use of 走, on the other hand, indicates that the agent leaves with the
object. E.g., 他離開的時候，不小心把我的悠遊卡帶走了。'When he left,
he inadvertently brought my EasyCard with him.' But *他離開的時候，不小
心把我的悠遊卡帶掉了。isn't good Chinese.

練習 Exercise

Please complete the following dialogues using the V + 掉 options given below.

踢掉、脫掉、拿掉、跑掉、丟掉、倒掉、弄掉、賣掉、放掉、當掉、吃掉

❶ A：安德思今天怎麼這麼用功？我從來沒看過他熬夜念書。

　 B：他上次考試成績很不理想，讓他覺得壓力很大，擔心被
　　　＿＿＿＿＿＿＿＿＿＿＿＿。

❷ A：我從來沒放過天燈，不知道怎麼做才對。

　 B：別擔心，等一下我說「放」，你就＿＿＿＿＿＿＿＿＿。

❸ A：門口這個袋子裡裝的是什麼東西？為什麼放在這裡？

　 B：那是垃圾，先放在那裡，等一下我出去的時候再順便
　　　＿＿＿＿＿＿＿＿＿＿＿。

❹ A：王先生是做什麼的？他的工作好像很輕鬆。

　 B：他原來是一家公司的老闆，後來把公司＿＿＿＿＿＿＿，
　　　開始到處旅行。生活快樂得不得了。

❺ A：你衣服上紅紅的是什麼？

　 B：我也不知道。你幫我＿＿＿＿＿＿＿＿＿吧。

⑥ A：我買回來的牛肉麵怎麼不見了？

B：我剛剛還看見。不知道是被誰＿＿＿＿＿＿的。

VI. 居然 *to one's surprise* 🎧 05-10

Function: The adverb 居然 expresses the speaker's surprise that something happened like the way it did. Compare the pair below.

A. 今天氣溫只有十度，可是羅珊蒂沒穿外套。
（A plain and factual statement.）

B. 今天氣溫只有十度，可是羅珊蒂居然沒穿外套。
（An unexpected exception to a rule.）

① 他是韓國人，居然不吃辣。

② 語言中心主任約他今天早上面談，他居然忘了。

③ 我們看電影的時候，大家都感動得哭（kū, cry）了，只有他居然睡著了。

④ 安德思收到帳單的時候才發現，吃到飽居然只是網路，不包括打電話。

⑤ 他好不容易才找到一件品質不錯、價錢合適的外套，居然不買了。

Usage:

1. 居然 is an adverb and is generally placed after the subject and in front of the verb.

2. It frequently appears together with 沒想到. Reinforcement is a common strategy in Chinese. E.g., 今天天氣這麼冷，沒想到羅珊蒂居然沒穿外套。 'It's so cold today. I never imagined that Luo Shandi would (surprisingly) not wear a coat.'

練習 Exercises

1. Please insert 居然 where appropriate in the following sentences to add an element of great surprise.

❶ 公車路線那麼複雜，他第一次搭，沒迷路。

_____。

❷ 我原來以為談茶文化很無聊，沒想到這麼有趣。

_____。

❸ 台灣人的婚禮上，新娘要換三次禮服。

_____。

❹ 大家都羨慕他念熱門科系，沒想到他覺得很痛苦。

_____。

❺ 我來台北以後才知道，有的書店是二十四小時營業的。

_____。

2. Please complete the following sentences using 居然.

❶ 他平常對穿衣服並不講究，沒想到_____。

❷ 這麼熱的天，他居然_____。

❸ 這麼有名的餐廳，居然_____。

❹ 最好的朋友結婚，_____。

❺ 我以為羊毛外套很貴，沒想到_____。

VII. Concession with 既然…（就）… since... (then)...   🎧 05-11   🔍 英譯 p.122

Function: This pattern presents the speaker's acceptance of the circumstances and his or her subsequent plans.

1. 既然天氣這麼不穩定，我們就別去海邊了吧。
2. 既然網路塞車，那就先去運動，晚一點再上網。
3. 既然刷 Visa 卡可以再打九五折，當然要刷 Visa 卡。
4. 既然吃素對保護地球環境有幫助，以後我們就常吃素食。
5. 既然你整天都會待在這裡，我就先去一趟銀行，再回來找你。

Usage: Like all conjunctions, 既然 can be placed before or after the subject. E.g., 既然你不去，我就不去了。 or 你既然不去，我就不去了。 'Since you're not going, I'm not going either.'

練習 Exercise

Please complete the following dialogues using 既然…，（就）…, indicating a subsequent plan.

1. A：網路上說，這家商店沒有招牌，恐怕不好找。

   B：既然＿＿＿＿＿＿＿＿＿＿＿＿＿＿＿＿＿＿＿＿＿＿。

2. A：朋友告訴我，有一所（suǒ, measure for locations）高中在找中文老師。我想去試試。

   B：既然＿＿＿＿＿＿＿＿＿＿＿＿＿＿＿＿＿＿＿＿＿＿。

3. 顧客：這兩個款式我都喜歡，真的很難決定。

   店員：既然＿＿＿＿＿＿＿＿＿＿＿＿＿＿＿＿＿＿＿＿＿。

4. A：我覺得選科系的時候，一定得考慮到將來的發展。

   B：既然這樣，＿＿＿＿＿＿＿＿＿＿＿＿＿＿＿＿＿＿＿。

5. A：老闆說國外的分公司有一個機會，問我想不想去。我很想試試，可是，我的家人怎麼辦？

   B：既然＿＿＿＿＿＿＿＿＿＿＿＿＿＿＿＿＿＿＿＿＿＿。

VIII. V + 個不停 *keep on...* 05-12 英譯 p.122

Function: This pattern stresses the incessant happening of an event, much to the displeasure of the speaker.

① 雨下個不停，真不知道什麼時候天氣才會變好。

② 什麼事讓你這麼生氣，罵個不停？

③ 她一走進百貨公司就買個不停，連跟我說話的時間都沒有。

④ 我感冒了，鼻水流個不停，真討厭。

⑤ 你不是已經吃過晚飯了嗎？怎麼一看到蛋糕，還是吃個不停？

Usage:

1. This pattern only uses action verbs that can continue for a while. State verbs (Vs) and process verbs (Vp) don't work. The following two examples are not good Chinese: *他高興個不停。 or *這件事結束個不停。

2. In this pattern, 個 is not the measure word it usually is; rather, it's an 'event marker'.

練習 Exercise

Please complete the following sentences, indicating an incessant action using V 個不停.

① 火鍋很好吃嗎？他怎麼一坐下來就＿＿＿＿＿＿＿＿＿＿？

② 我知道他很熱心，想給我介紹台灣的風俗習慣，可是他每次一說起話來，就＿＿＿＿＿＿＿＿，有時候讓我很受不了。

③ 他低著頭在寫什麼，＿＿＿＿＿＿＿？他打算把我說的話都寫下來嗎？

④ 他們兩個＿＿＿＿＿＿＿＿＿＿＿＿，都不跟我說話。

⑤ 她又在唱歌了！整天＿＿＿＿＿＿＿＿＿＿，吵死了。

I. Verb Plus Complement V + 滿 *crowded with*

Function:

1 Both sides of the road are bristling with new buildings.

2 The area in front of Taipei 101 was packed with young people watching the New Year's Eve fireworks.

3 The living room wall was packed with photographs he took while in Hualian.

4 It's not even eight o'clock yet and the classroom is filled with students.

5 Why is this bag stuffed full of garbage?

II. Verb Particle 出 *to have emerged*

Function:

1 The things I was too embarrassed to say, he said for me.

2 When he wears the same garment as someone else, he always exudes a totally different feeling.

3 He made sour and spicy kimchi out of ingredients purchased at an organic shop.

4 I could never write such a powerful song.

5 That professor spent a decade on research before coming up with this type of new medicine.

III. 不如 *not as good as*

Function:

1 The quality of this garment is not as good as that one.

2 The seafood in this hot pot restaurant is not as fresh as that one.

3 Taking the MRT, you have to transfer twice. It's not as convenient as taking the bus.

4 Staying up all night to study just before the test isn't as good as being prepared on a general basis.

5 The sun is scorching. Lying on the beach isn't as comfortable as returning to the room and watching TV.

Usage:

2.   A: My cell phone is broken. Do you know where I can get it fixed?
     B: Your cell phone is already so old. Rather than fix it, get a new one.

IV. Urgent Conditional with 再不… 就…了

Function:

1 It hasn't rained in four months. If it doesn't rain soon, we won't have any water to drink.

2 It's so humid. If we don't buy a dehumidifier now, our clothes are going to mildew.

3 Mayday concerts are always a popular event. If you don't book tickets today, there won't be any left.

4 On the last test, I only got 60 points. If I don't start studying hard, I'm afraid I'll be flunked.

5 What happened? Tell me right now. If you don't explain yourself, I'm going to be mad.

Usage:

1 He's had a fever for quite a few days. If he doesn't see a doctor or take medicine soon, I'm afraid it's going to get increasingly serious.

2 Fewer and fewer people know these traditional customs. If we don't attach greater importance to them now, I'm afraid nobody will understand them.

V. Verb Particle 掉 *separated from*

Function:

1. I removed the garbage from the kitchen.
2. Who drank my coffee?
3. Every time, as soon as he walks into a room, he kicks off his shoes.
4. The tea on the table, I hadn't drunk it yet. Why did he take it and pour it out?
5. Last month, he sold his old car and bought a new one.

VI. 居然 *to one's surprise*

Function:

A. It's only 10 degrees today, but Luo Sandi isn't wearing a jacket.
B. It's only 10 degrees today, but Luo Sandi surprisingly isn't wearing a coat.
1. He's Korean but, surprisingly, doesn't like spicy food.
2. The language center director made an appointment to interview him this morning. He surprisingly forgot.
3. When we were watching the movie, everybody was moved to tears, except for him. Surprisingly, he fell asleep.
4. When An Desi got his bill, to his surprise, he realized that only internet access was unlimited, not phone calls.
5. He finally managed to find a good quality coat at a reasonable price and, to my surprise, he didn't buy it.

VII. Concession with 既然…（就）… *since... (then)...*

Function:

1. Since the weather is so unpredictable, let's not go to the seaside.
2. Since the internet is congested, let's go exercise first and go online later.
3. Since I can get 5% off if I use a Visa Card, then, of course, I'll use my Visa Card.
4. Since eating vegetarian food helps protect the earth's environment, we should eat vegetarian food more often.
5. Since you'll be here all day, I'll go to the bank and come back later.

VIII. V + 個不停 *keep on...*

Function:

1. It just keeps raining. I have no idea when the weather will change for the better.
2. You keep harping on and on. What's got you so pissed off?
3. As soon as she stepped into the department store, she just kept buying. She didn't even have time to talk to me.
4. I have a cold and my nose keeps running. What a pain.
5. Haven't you already eaten dinner? How is it that as soon as you see cake, you just keep shoveling it in?

Classroom Activities

I. Describe Your Favorite Performers

Goal: Learning to talk about trendy things as well as what you like.

Task: Please find a video clip of your favorite performer(s) (e.g., band, stage performer, pop singer, actor) to share with your class. Explain in Chinese the reasons you like the performer(s) and their position in their field.

Try to use the following sentence patterns and vocabulary words:

受歡迎	非…不可	V 滿	V 個不停	心情
迷	錯過	V 出	印象	流行

II. The Internet and Grades

Goal: Learning to express rhetorical questions and to refute views in Chinese.

Task: A girl's parents feel that she plays online video games too much and that playing is affecting her grades. They tell their daughter... (What might her parents tell her?) But the girl feels that there is no relationship at all between playing online games and grades. After talking for a while, they start arguing. Pair up. One student play the mother. The other play the daughter. Write down the conversation.

Try to use the following sentence patterns and vocabulary words:

有什麼關係	小題大作	怎麼會呢？	不會太…嗎
算了	不如	是不能了解的	還是…好
為什麼非…不可	你想太多了	不會啊	誰 V 啊

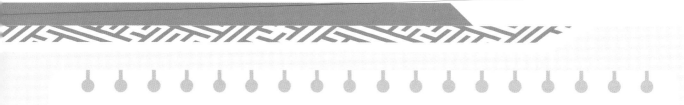

III. Culture and Trends

Goal: Learning to describe and discuss trends.

Task: In the culture of your country, are there any things that started out as pop culture, but later became part of the culture? Examples might include movie dialogues, ad slogans ("Trust me. You can make it."), fashion designs (Chanel coat), a folk song, or other music. Please think of an example. Explain where it came from, its meaning, and its significance in the culture.

文化 *Bits of Chinese Culture*

Japanese Words Borrowed into Chinese

Do you eat a lot of 便當（biàndāng, boxed lunches）like many Taiwanese? Was the 便當 you had for lunch today prepared by an 歐巴桑（ōubāsāng, middle-aged women）in a 便當 shop? Or did you buy it at a convenience store from a super 萌（méng, cute）cashier? If you frequently visit convenience stores, then you're sure to know which is the most 人氣（rénqì, popular）便當 right now and which convenience store has the most 經濟（jīngjì, economical, i.e., least expensive）便當.

▲ A 便當 shop.《經濟日報》陳致畬／攝影

What you might not know, however, is that the terms in Chinese characters above were borrowed into Taiwanese Mandarin from Japanese during three major periods: during the Qing Dynasty, when Taiwan was a colony of Japan, and since the 1990s. With the westernization of China under the Qing Dynasty, such words as 經濟 and 教授 entered the lexicon. They are such a part of the language that many native speakers of Chinese don't even realize that they are borrowed words.

便當（lunch box）and 歐巴桑（middle-aged women）were first borrowed into Taiwanese when Japan governed Taiwan and were later transliterated into Mandarin. 便當 is from the Japanese 弁当（べんとう, Japanese pronunciation: bento）. 歐巴桑（おばさん, Japanese pronunciation: obasan）is also used in Taiwan, but it means middle-aged women in general as opposed to the original meaning of 伯母 and 嬸嬸（bómǔ and shěnshen, aunt）. Most Japanese words borrowed into Taiwanese when Taiwan was a colony of Japan came into the language verbally and weren't transliterated until later.

▲ 便當 (boxed lunch) is borrowed from Japanese.《聯合報》侯永全 攝影

▲ 達人 (experts) is borrowed from Japanese.

▲ 元氣 (vitality) is borrowed from Japanese.

Driven by Japanese pop culture since the 1990s, including TV shows and manga, most of the borrowed words have been in the form of kanji, but with Mandarin pronunciation, such as 達人（dárén, expert）or 萌（méng, cute）. These new words make the language a bit more exotic and witty. Interestingly, after words are borrowed into Mandarin in Taiwan, they frequently develop new meanings or become different parts of speech. Take the words 元氣（yuánqì）in the Japanese sentence お元氣ですか。（Roughly: How are you?）for example. In Taiwan, you can see stores with signs that sell "元氣早餐"（Roughly: energy breakfast）and people even say "他今天很有元氣",（He has a lot of 元氣, i.e., vitality, today）.

▲ 人氣 (popular) is borrowed from Japanese.

▲ 萌 (cute) is borrowed from Japanese.

▲《聯合報》／提供

Self-Assessment Checklist

I can talk about trends.

20%   40%   60%   80%   100%

I can explain in detail the merits of own hobbies and activities.

20%   40%   60%   80%   100%

I can provide various reasons refuting the views of others.

20%   40%   60%   80%   100%

I can describe a live concert.

20%   40%   60%   80%   100%

LESSON 6

第六課

到鄉下住一晚！
Spending the Night in the Countryside

學習目標 **Learning Objectives**

Topic: 台灣農業 Taiwan's Agricultural Industry

- Learning to discuss the cultivation of agricultural crops.
- Learning to explain your reasons for choosing something.
- Learning to talk about changes in society, including values and lifestyle.
- Learning to discuss food safety issues with friends.

對話 Dialogue 🎧 06-01

（李文彥帶朋友安德思、羅珊蒂去鄉下表哥家）

表　　哥：歡迎、歡迎。大家隨便坐。這是剛摘下來的芒果，大家嚐嚐。

李 文 彥：很好吃吧？我表哥除了芒果以外，還種了很多有機蔬菜。他是現代農夫。

安 德 思：為什麼說他是現代農夫？

李 文 彥：因為他跟傳統農夫很不一樣。為了減少對環境的汙染，他不用農藥，而且只用天然堆肥，大家可以放心地吃。

安 德 思：當農夫不是很辛苦嗎？你為什麼要當農夫？

表　　哥：我本來在大學教書，因為看到父母年紀大了，做不動了，才決定回來幫忙的。

羅珊蒂：你家人不反對你回來嗎？

表　　哥：當然反對。農夫在台灣的社會地位不高，工作辛苦不說，收入也不穩定，父母都希望孩子有更好的發展。

羅珊蒂：怎麼會呢？超市的有機蔬菜都貴得不得了。

表　　哥：賣給超市，農夫的利潤很低，可是自己賣的話，問題更多。今天不談這個。天氣這麼好，別一直待在屋子裡，我們出去走走吧。

（到了屋外）

安德恩：這些番茄真漂亮！

表　　哥：這不是基因改造的，是新品種。今年氣候特別好，再加上沒有颱風，所以青菜水果都長得很好。

安德恩：這些番茄熟了嗎？

表　　哥：熟了，熟了，摘下來就可以吃了。這些番茄都是有機的，不必洗。

安德恩：這麼大的一片田，你一個人照顧，忙得過來嗎？

表　　哥：平常還好，可是收成的時候，很難找到人幫忙。

李文彥：這幾年，回鄉下種田的年輕人不是很多嗎？

表　　哥：忙的時候，大家都一樣，連自己的事都做不完，怎麼有時間幫別人的忙？

羅珊蒂：你怎麼不找個太太來幫你？

李文彥：妳這問題問得真好。我表哥什麼都有，就是少了一個太太。

表　　哥：別開玩笑了。農夫看天吃飯，收入這麼不穩定，怎麼敢結婚？

羅珊蒂：表哥，你條件這麼好，我給你介紹一個，怎麼樣？

表　　哥：以後再說吧！天黑了，我們快回去吃飯。

課文簡體字版 Text in Simplified Characters

（李文彦带朋友安德思、罗珊蒂去乡下表哥家）

表　　哥：欢迎、欢迎。大家随便坐。这是刚摘下来的芒果，大家尝尝。

李 文 彦：很好吃吧？我表哥除了芒果以外，还种了很多有机蔬菜。他是现代农夫。

安 德 思：为什么说他是现代农夫？

李 文 彦：因为他跟传统农夫很不一样。为了减少对环境的污染，他不用农药，而且只用天然堆肥，大家可以放心地吃。

安 德 思：当农夫不是很辛苦吗？你为什么要当农夫？

表　　哥：我本来在大学教书，因为看到父母年纪大了，做不动了，才决定回来帮忙的。

罗 珊 蒂：你家人不反对你回来吗？

表　　哥：当然反对。农夫在台湾的社会地位不高，工作辛苦不说，收入也不稳定，父母都希望孩子有更好的发展。

罗 珊 蒂：怎么会呢？超市的有机蔬菜都贵得不得了。

表　　哥：卖给超市，农夫的利润很低，可是自己卖的话，问题更多。今天不谈这个。天气这么好，别一直待在屋子里，我们出去走走吧。

（到了屋外）

安 德 思：这些番茄真漂亮！

表　　哥：这不是基因改造的，是新品种。今年气候特别好，再加上没有台风，所以青菜水果都长得很好。

安 德 思：这些番茄熟了吗？

表　　哥：熟了，熟了，摘下来就可以吃了。这些番茄都是有机的，不必洗。

安 德 思：这么大的一片田，你一个人照顾，忙得过来吗？

表　　哥：平常还好，可是收成的时候，很难找到人帮忙。

李 文 彦：这几年，回乡下种田的年轻人不是很多吗？

表　　哥：忙的时候，大家都一样，连自己的事都做不完，怎么有时间帮别人的忙？

罗 珊 蒂：你怎么不找个太太来帮你？

李 文 彦：妳这问题问得真好。我表哥什么都有，就是少了一个太太。

表　　哥：别开玩笑了。农夫看天吃饭，收入这么不稳定，怎么敢结婚？

罗 珊 蒂：表哥，你条件这么好，我给你介绍一个，怎么样？

表　　哥：以后再说吧！天黑了，我们快回去吃饭。

課文英譯 Text in English

(Li Wenyan takes his friends An Desi and Luo Shandi to his cousin's house in the country.)

Cousin : Welcome, welcome. Sit wherever you like. These are freshly picked mangoes. Have a taste.

Li Wenyan : Really tasty, right? In addition to mangoes, my cousin has planted a lot of organic vegetables. He's a modern farmer.

An Desi : Why do you say he's a modern farmer?

Li Wenyan : Because he's very different from traditional farmers. In order to reduce environmental pollution, he doesn't use pesticides and only uses natural compost. People can eat with their minds at ease.

An Desi : Isn't being a farmer tough? Why did you want to become a farmer?

Cousin : I used to teach in university. It was only because I saw that my parents were old and couldn't work that I decided to come back and help out.

Luo Shandi: Your family didn't oppose you returning?

Cousin : Of course they were against it. The social status of farmers in Taiwan isn't high. The hard work aside, you don't have a stable income. Parents all hope that their children have better careers than themselves.

Luo Shandi: How is that possible? Organic vegetables in the supermarket are all incredibly expensive.

Cousin : Farmers' profits are low when they sell to supermarkets, but if you sell them yourself, you have even more problems. Let's not talk about this today. The weather is so good; we shouldn't stay inside all day. Let's go out and walk around.

(outside)

An Desi : These tomatoes are really pretty!

Cousin : These aren't genetically modified. It's a new variety. The climate has been especially good this year, plus there haven't been any typhoons, so the vegetables and fruit have grown really well.

An Desi : Are these tomatoes ripe?

Cousin : Yes, they're ripe. You can eat them right off the plant. These tomatoes are organic, no need to wash them.

An Desi : Such a large plot of land. Can you manage it all alone?

Cousin : Generally, it's not a problem, but during harvest time, it's hard to find people to help.

Li Wenyan : Over the past few years, haven't a lot of young people been returning to the countryside to till the land?

Cousin	: When it's busy, everybody's the same. You can't even finish your own work. How can you have time to help others?
Luo Shandi:	Why don't you get married and have your wife help you?
Li Wenyan :	This is a really good question. My cousin has everything, except a wife.
Cousin	: Kidding aside, a farmer's livelihood depends on the whims of nature and the income is so unpredictable. How can one even think about getting married?
Luo Shandi:	Cousin, you've got so much going for you. I'll introduce a girl to you. What do you think?
Cousin	: Maybe later. It's getting dark. Let's go back and eat.

生詞一 Vocabulary I   06-02

People in the Dialogue

1	李文彥	Lǐ Wényàn	ㄌㄧ ㄨㄣˊ ㄧㄢˋ		an American-born Chinese

Vocabulary

2	表哥	biǎogē	ㄅㄧㄠˇ ㄍㄜ	(N)	cousin (older male cousin, from a female lineage)
3	隨便	suíbiàn	ㄙㄨㄟˊ ㄅㄧㄢˋ	(Adv)	as one pleases oneself, to act freely
4	種	zhòng	ㄓㄨㄥˋ	(V)	to grow (plants)
5	蔬菜	shūcài	ㄕㄨ ㄘㄞˋ	(N)	vegetable
6	農夫	nóngfū	ㄋㄨㄥˊ ㄈㄨ	(N)	farmer
7	減少	jiǎnshǎo	ㄐㄧㄢˇ ㄕㄠˇ	(V)	to reduce, to decrease
8	農藥	nóngyào	ㄋㄨㄥˊ ㄧㄠˋ	(N)	pesticide
9	天然	tiānrán	ㄊㄧㄢ ㄖㄢˊ	(Vs-attr)	natural
10	堆肥	duīféi	ㄉㄨㄟ ㄈㄟˊ	(N)	compost
11	辛苦	xīnkǔ	ㄒㄧㄣ ㄎㄨˇ	(Vs)	tough, hard, bitter (life, work, etc.)
12	地位	dìwèi	ㄉㄧˋ ㄨㄟˋ	(N)	position, status

13	收入收入	shōurù	ㄕㄡ ㄖㄨˋ	(N)	income
14	利潤	lìrùn	ㄌㄧˋ ㄖㄨㄣˋ	(N)	profit
15	屋子	wūzi	ㄨ ㄗ	(N)	house
16	番茄	fānqié	ㄈㄢ ㄑㄧㄝˊ	(N)	tomato
17	品種	pǐnzhǒng	ㄆㄧㄣˇ ㄓㄨㄥˇ	(N)	variety, species
18	氣候	qìhòu	ㄑㄧˋ ㄏㄡˋ	(N)	climate
19	長	zhǎng	ㄓㄤˇ	(Vi)	to grow
20	熟	shóu	ㄕㄡˊ	(Vp)	to be ripe, to ripen
21	片	piàn	ㄆㄧㄢˋ	(M)	measure word for a stretch, swath (of land)
22	田	tián	ㄊㄧㄢˊ	(N)	field, plot of land, paddy
23	照顧照顧照顧	zhàogù	ㄓㄠˋ ㄍㄨˋ	(V)	to take care of
24	敢	gǎn	ㄍㄢˇ	(Vaux)	to dare
25	條件	tiáojiàn	ㄊㄧㄠˊ ㄐㄧㄢˋ	(N)	terms, conditions, (here) good qualities (in a prospective spouse)
26	黑	hēi	ㄏㄟ	(Vp)	dark, black

Phrases

27	摘下來	zhāi xiàlái	ㄓㄞ ㄒㄧㄚˋ ㄌㄞˊ	to pluck, to pick (e.g., fruit from a tree)
28	做不動	zuò bú dòng	ㄗㄨㄛˋ ㄅㄨˊ ㄉㄨㄥˋ	to be unable to physically function due to old age
29	基因改造	jīyīn gǎizào	ㄐㄧ ㄧㄣ ㄍㄞˇ ㄗㄠˋ	genetically modified
30	忙得過來	máng de guòlái	ㄇㄤˊ ㄉㄜ ㄍㄨㄛˋ ㄌㄞˊ	to be able to manage everything
31	開玩笑	kāi wánxiào	ㄎㄞ ㄨㄢˊ ㄒㄧㄠˋ	to joke, to kid
32	看天吃飯	kàntiān chīfàn	ㄎㄢˋ ㄊㄧㄢ ㄔ ㄈㄢˋ	livelihood depends on the whims of nature

短文 Reading 🎧 06-03

現代小農

　　星期天一大早，何雅婷就陪著媽媽到農夫市集去買菜。最近食品安全出了好幾次問題，何雅婷的媽媽為了家人的健康，開始注意食材的產地，也盡量到有機商店和農夫市集買菜。雖然這些地方賣的東西種類沒有市場那麼多，價錢也比較高，可是媽媽常跟農夫聊天，了解小農用友善的方式對待土地和環境，很信任他們，所以寧可每個星期跑一趟，多花一點錢，也要支持小農。

　　像何雅婷媽媽這樣關心小農的人越來越多。有人寫文章介紹小農種的蔬菜水果，有人到處幫小農推銷，其中最有名的是一位麵包師傅。他從小在農村長大，了解農夫的辛苦。為了幫助小農，也為了幫自己的產品找更好的食材，他常常拜訪小農，用他們出產的食材做出受歡迎的麵包。

　　由於報紙、網路的介紹，許多住在城市裡的人開始羨慕小農的生活。他們利用放假的時候，帶著孩子到農村去，一方面可以讓孩子在田裡跑跑跳跳，接近自然，一方面自己也可以放鬆心情。到鄉下住一晚變成了現在熱門的休閒活動。

　　隨著小農越來越受重視，到農村來觀光的人也慢慢地多起來了，連便利商店都來了。以前當地人習慣自己做飯，或是到傳統的小商店和小吃店消費，現在便利商店更方便也更吸引他們。傳統的小店生意受到了影響，原來安靜的農村有了很大的變化。現在農人擔心的是傳統的生活方式會不會消失。

现代小农

　　星期天一大早，何雅婷就陪着妈妈到农夫市集去买菜。最近食品安全出了好几次问题，何雅婷的妈妈为了家人的健康，开始注意食材的产地，也尽量到有机商店和农夫市集买菜。虽然这些地方卖的东西种类没有市场那么多，价钱也比较高，可是妈妈常跟农夫聊天，了解小农用友善的方式对待土地和环境，很信任他们，所以宁可每个星期跑一趟，多花一点钱，也要支持小农。

　　像何雅婷妈妈这样关心小农的人越来越多。有人写文章介绍小农种的蔬菜水果，有人到处帮小农推销，其中最有名的是一位面包师傅。他从小在农村长大，了解农夫的辛苦。为了帮助小农，也为了帮自己的产品找更好的食材，他常常拜访小农，用他们出产的食材做出受欢迎的面包。

　　由于报纸、网路的介绍，许多住在城市里的人开始羡慕小农的生活。他们利用放假的时候，带着孩子到农村去，一方面可以让孩子在田里跑跑跳跳，接近自然，一方面自己也可以放松心情。到乡下住一晚变成了现在热门的休闲活动。

　　随着小农越来越受重视，到农村来观光的人也慢慢地多起来了，连便利商店都来了。以前当地人习惯自己做饭，或是到传统的小商店和小吃店消费，现在便利商店更方便也更吸引他们。传统的小店生意受到了影响，原来安静的农村有了很大的变化。现在农人担心的是传统的生活方式会不会消失。

Small Farmers in Modern Times

　　Early Sunday morning, He Yating accompanied her mom to the farmer's market to buy produce. Lately, there have been a lot of problems with food safety. For the sake of the family's health, He Yating's mom has begun to pay attention to the place of origin of food. She does her best to go to organic shops and farmers' markets to buy produce. These places don't have the variety that markets do, and the prices are higher, but her mom likes to chat with the farmers and familiarize herself with the environmentally friendly methods they employ in their treatment of the land. She trusts them, so she'd rather support the small farmer, even if it means going once a week and spending a little more money.

More and more people, like He Yating's mom, are concerned for the small farmer. Some people write articles on the fruits and vegetables grown by small farmers. Others go around helping small farmers promote their products. Of these, the most famous is a master baker. He grew up in a farming village, and understands the hard life of a farmer. To help small farmers and to find better ingredients for his own products, he frequently visits small farmers and uses their produce to make popular breads.

Due to media attention in newspapers and on the internet, many people living in cities have begun to envy the way small farmers live. They use days off from work to bring their children to farming villages, on the one hand, to let their kids run around in the fields and be close to nature, while on the other, they themselves can relax. Spending a night in the countryside has become a popular leisure activity.

As more and more importance is placed on small farmers, a steadily increasing number of people are arriving in farming villages for sightseeing. Even convenience stores are popping up. In the past, locals were accustomed to cooking for themselves or spending money at traditional shops and small eateries. Now, the ease of convenience stores has started drawing them in, and the business of traditional shops has been impacted. There have been big changes in what were once quiet farming villages. Now, farmers are worried about whether traditional ways of living will disappear.

生詞二 Vocabulary II 🎧 06-04

Vocabulary

1	小農 農農農	xiǎonóng	ㄒㄧㄠˇ ㄋㄨㄥˊ	(N)	small farmer
2	市集 市集集	shìjí	ㄕˋ ㄐㄧˊ	(N)	bazaar, market
3	食材食材食材 shícái 食材		ㄕˊ ㄘㄞˊ	(N)	food materials, ingredients
4	產地產地 chǎndì 產地		ㄔㄢˇ ㄉㄧˋ	(N)	place of origin
5	盡量盡	jìnliàng	ㄐㄧㄣˋ ㄌㄧㄤˋ	(Adv)	to do one's best to
6	友善	yǒushàn	ㄧㄡˇ ㄕㄢˋ	(Vs)	friendly
7	對待	duìdài	ㄉㄨㄟˋ ㄉㄞˋ	(V)	to treat
8	土地	tǔdì	ㄊㄨˇ ㄉㄧˋ	(N)	land
9	信任任	xìnrèn	ㄒㄧㄣˋ ㄖㄣˋ	(Vst)	to trust
10	寧可寧寧寧 níngkě		ㄋㄧㄥˊ ㄎㄜˇ	(Vst)	would rather

泡

11	跑 跑	pǎo	ㄆㄠˇ	(Vi)	to run
12	支持	zhīchí	ㄓ ㄔˊ	(V)	to support
13	文章文章章 wénzhāng		ㄨㄣˊ ㄓㄤ	(N)	article
14	推銷推銷推 tuīxiāo 銷		ㄊㄨㄟ ㄒㄧㄠ	(V)	to promote, to market
15	其中	qízhōng	ㄑㄧˊ ㄓㄨㄥ	(N)	of these, of which, amongst which
16	師傅師傅	shīfù	ㄕ ㄈㄨˋ	(N)	master (of a trade)
17	農村 農	nóngcūn	ㄋㄨㄥˊ ㄘㄨㄣ	(N)	farming village
18	長大	zhǎngdà	ㄓㄤˇ ㄉㄚˋ	(Vi)	to grow up
19	幫助幫助	bāngzhù	ㄅㄤ ㄓㄨˋ	(V)	to help
20	拜訪拜	bàifǎng	ㄅㄞˋ ㄈㄤˇ	(V)	to pay someone a visit
21	出產	chūchǎn	ㄔㄨ ㄔㄢˇ	(V)	to produce
22	由於由方於 yóuyú 於		ㄧㄡˊ ㄩˊ	(Conj)	due to, because of
23	許多	xǔduō	ㄒㄩˇ ㄉㄨㄛ	(Det)	many
24	接近	jiējìn	ㄐㄧㄝ ㄐㄧㄣ	(Vst)	to come close to, to approach
25	自然自然然 zìrán 然		ㄗˋ ㄖㄢˊ	(N)	nature
26	變成變成	biànchéng	ㄅㄧㄢˋ ㄔㄥˊ	(Vpt)	to become
27	休閒休閒	xiūxián	ㄒㄧㄡ ㄒㄧㄢˊ	(Vs)	leisure
28	隨著隨	suízhe	ㄙㄨㄟˊ ㄓㄜ	(Prep)	along with, with the happening of
29	觀光	guānguāng	ㄍㄨㄢ ㄍㄨㄤ	(Vi)	to tour, to sightsee
30	消費消費費 xiāofèi 費費		ㄒㄧㄠ ㄈㄟˋ	(Vi)	to be a consumer, to purchase things
31	安靜	ānjìng	ㄢ ㄐㄧㄥˋ	(Vs)	quiet
32	消失消失	xiāoshī	ㄒㄧㄠ ㄕ	(Vp)	to disappear

Phrases

33	出問題	chū wèntí	ㄔㄨ ㄨㄣˋ ㄊㄧˊ		to go wrong, to have problems
34	一方面	yì fāngmiàn	ㄧˋ ㄈㄤ ㄇㄧㄢˋ		on the one hand

文法 Grammar

I. 因為…才… *only because...* 🎧 06-05 英譯 p.146

Function: This pattern stresses that an event happened only because of a particular reason. This is a typical cause-effect construction.

① 因為賣保險，收入不穩定，她才想換工作的。
② 因為這個沙拉是用表哥種的有機蔬菜做的，我才吃的。
③ 美美條件很好，因為工作一直很忙，才到現在還沒有結婚。
④ 因為工作壓力太大，健康出了問題，他才決定回鄉下種田的。
⑤ 因為他不但熱心，而且成績好，才拿到獎學金的。

Usage: 才 can only be used in a sentence that describes a past event. The 因為…所以 pattern is used to indicate cause and effect. It is not necessarily used for events that have already happened.

① A：你不是最喜歡看煙火的嗎？怎麼沒去？
   B：因為我不舒服，才沒去看煙火的。
② A：你明天為什麼不去看煙火了？
   B：因為要去女朋友家，所以不能去看煙火了。

練習 Exercise

Complete the following dialogues using 因為…才…, detailing the reason for something.

---

① A：你怎麼沒去聽五月天的跨年演唱會？
   B：＿＿＿＿＿＿＿＿＿＿＿＿＿＿＿＿＿＿＿＿＿。

② A：你為什麼不買基因改造的食品？不是比較便宜嗎？
   B：＿＿＿＿＿＿＿＿＿＿＿＿＿＿＿＿＿＿＿＿＿。

---

❸ A：為什麼很多人喜歡到農夫市集買菜？價錢不是比較貴嗎？

B：＿＿＿＿＿＿＿＿＿＿＿＿＿＿＿＿＿＿＿＿＿。

❹ A：你為什麼要買他推銷的產品？你信任他嗎？

B：＿＿＿＿＿＿＿＿＿＿＿＿＿＿＿＿＿＿＿＿＿。

❺ A：你為什麼喜歡去古老的城市？現代城市不吸引你嗎？

B：＿＿＿＿＿＿＿＿＿＿＿＿＿＿＿＿＿＿＿＿＿。

II. Complaining with …S1…不說，S2 也… *not merely, but also*

06-06

英譯 p.146

Function: This pattern is used to indicate a complaint about two issues, the second of which is more serious than the first.

❶ 那個地方吵不說，環境也很複雜。

❷ 他現在的工作是推銷產品。薪水低不說，也很辛苦。

❸ 那家店賣的商品種類少不說，價錢也很貴，難怪客人不多。

❹ 小林最近常遲到不說，功課也不寫。他怎麼了？

❺ 週年慶的時候，擠死了不說，也常常因為便宜買了一些沒有用的東西回家。

Usage: Both …不說，也… and 不但…，還… patterns are incremental, i.e., they add one fact on top of another, but the 不但…，還… of Lesson 4 can be used with either positive or negative events, whereas …不說，也… can only be used in the negative. E.g., you can say: 他不但成績好，還很熱心。 'His grades are not only good, he is also very enthusiastic.', but *他成績好不說，也很熱心 isn't good Chinese.

練習 Exercise

Please complete the dialogues below by using the pattern …不說，也…, referring to two undersirable things.

❶ A：你為什麼不想租那間房子？（光線不好；很舊）

   B：_____。

❷ A：你新買的手機為什麼要拿回去退換？
    （聽不清楚；常常自動關機）

   B：_____。

❸ A：你喜歡吃薯條嗎？（太鹹；太油膩）

   B：不喜歡。_____。

❹ A：你想當翻譯嗎？（辛苦；收入不穩定）

   B：不想，_____。

❺ A：你喜歡住在鄉下嗎？（蚊蟲多；生活不方便）

   B：不喜歡。_____。

III. 再加上 *furthermore* 🎧 06-07　　　　 英譯 p.146

Function: The phrase 再加上 adds a further item. The sentence can be an approval or a criticism, on the part of the speaker.

❶ 那件衣服的款式比較舊，顏色也太淺，再加上穿起來不舒服，所以雖然打五折，我也沒買。

❷ 陽明山上有很多很好的餐廳，再加上夜景很美，他決定帶女朋友上陽明山吃晚飯。

❸ 當老師生活穩定，再加上薪水比一般工作高，難怪他每天熬夜念書，準備考試。

❹ 在鄉下，孩子可以接近土地，在田裡跑跑跳跳，再加上可以
吃到最新鮮的蔬菜，所以父母週末都喜歡帶孩子到鄉下去玩。

❺ 大家都很信任他，再加上他的麵包都是用最好的食材做的，
所以很多人住得再遠也要去他的店買麵包。

練習 Exercise

Complete the sentences below, with the phrase 再加上…, which adds another element to what has already been stated.

....

❶ 表哥種的番茄是新品種，顏色很漂亮，
再加上_____，所以賣得很好。

❷ 這件羊毛外套又輕又暖和，再加上_____，
我就買了。

❸ 王小姐很甜美，再加上_____，
所以喜歡她的人很多。

❹ 這個款式的手機是最新型的，功能好，再加上_____，
買的人很多。

❺ 去台南可以看到很多台灣人傳統的風俗習慣，
再加上_____，所以我一有機會就去。

IV. 什麼都…，就是… *everything but...* 06-08　　　 英譯 p.146

Function: This pattern presents an exception to what has been said previously.

❶ 她什麼都買了，就是忘了買鹽。

❷ 這家商店今天什麼都打八折，就是我要買的東西不打折。

❸ 他對什麼都不講究，就是講究吃。

❹ 這條街上什麼店都有，就是沒有電信公司的門市。

❺ 他做什麼他父母都支持，就是不讓他休學去工作。

練習 Exercise

Please complete the dialogues below, indicating an exception using 什麼都…，就是….

❶ A：聽說墾丁有很多水上活動，你去潛水了嗎？

B：＿＿＿＿＿＿＿＿＿＿＿＿＿＿＿＿＿＿＿＿＿。

❷ A：他對電子產品那麼有興趣，一定有平板電腦吧？

B：＿＿＿＿＿＿＿＿＿＿＿＿＿＿＿＿＿＿＿＿＿。

❸ A：你怎麼不點海鮮呢？你吃素嗎？

B：＿＿＿＿＿＿＿＿＿＿＿＿＿＿＿＿＿＿＿＿＿。

❹ A：你週末請客，飲料準備好了嗎？

B：＿＿＿＿＿＿＿＿＿＿＿＿＿＿＿＿＿＿＿＿＿。

❺ A：你還留著買手機的發票嗎？沒丟掉吧。

B：丟掉了。＿＿＿＿＿＿＿＿＿＿＿＿＿＿＿＿＿＿＿＿＿。

V. 寧可… ，也要… *would rather…, in order to…* 06-09 英譯 p.147

Function: In this pattern, 寧可 presents what the subject is willing to put up with, so that something more important could be accomplished.

❶ 父母寧可自己辛苦一點，也要讓孩子快樂。

❷ 小農寧可收成少，也要種出安全、健康的食材。

❸ 她寧可薪水少，也要做自己有興趣的工作。

❹ 表哥寧可不睡覺，也要把報告寫完。

❺ 美美寧可餐餐吃麵包，也要買漂亮的衣服。

練習 Exercise

Please complete the dialogues below, using 寧可…，也要… indicating a compromise required for a certain outcome.

❶ A：你不是沒時間睡覺嗎？為什麼還在玩電腦遊戲？

B：_____ 。

❷ A：你總是說錢不夠，不能跟我們去玩。為什麼買這麼貴的智慧型手機？

B：_____ 。

❸ A：你買不買有機產品？聽說有機的貴很多。

B：買啊！為了健康，_____ 。

❹ A：他為什麼那麼熱心，熬夜幫朋友找資料。

B：他就是這樣的人，_____ 。

❺ A：他對吃真講究，可以為了一碗鹹粥跑一趟台南。

B：他喜歡美食，_____ 。

VI. 像…的 + **noun** *such (nouns) as* 06-10

Function: This pattern adds special properties to either the subject or object of a sentence.

❶ 像小籠包、炸雞排、擔仔麵這樣的小吃，他都喜歡。

❷ 像你這樣喜歡古蹟的人，一定要去台南看看。

❸ 像她那樣有語言天分的人，一定能很快地學好中文。

❹ 像他這樣友善對待土地的小農越來越多。

❺ 像她這樣在農村長大的人都喜歡接近自然。

Usage: This pattern is not related to 像…一樣 (Lesson 9, Vol.2), which compares two nouns, e.g., 他在鄉下買了一片田，每天吃的都是自己種的新鮮蔬菜，我羨慕他，希望能像他一樣。'He bought a piece of farmland in the country and now his meals consist of the fresh vegetables he planted himself. I admire him. I wish I could do that.'

Please complete the following 像…的 + Noun sentences.

❶ 像_____,美美都喜歡吃。

❷ 像手機、平板電腦_____,她都要買最新型的。

❸ 像_____開演唱會的時候,美美都要去聽。

❹ 美美喜歡流行的東西,像_____,她都要買當季款式。

❺ 像_____,都能讓我們放鬆心情。

VII. 一方面… , 一方面… *on the one hand, …, on the other* 🎧 06-11 🔍 英譯 p.147

Function: This pattern presents two different perspectives on an event.

❶ 她去聽五月天的演唱會,一方面想放鬆心情,一方面也想了解為什麼五月天這麼受歡迎。

❷ 她暑假去打工,一方面想賺點錢,一方面也想學一些社會經驗。

❸ 這個款式的包包賣得這麼好,一方面是因為連續劇裡的女主角拿過,一方面是價錢也不太貴。

❹ 去農夫市集買菜,一方面可以吃到最新鮮的蔬菜、水果,一方面也可以幫助小農。

❺ 過節的時候回家鄉,一方面可以跟家人團聚,一方面還可以看看老同學。

Usage: This is a somewhat literary construction, rarely used in colloquial speech.

練習 Exercise

Please complete the dialogues below, presenting two different perspectives using 一方面… , 一方面….

❶ A:你為什麼不參加校外教學?

B:_____。

❷ A：大明為什麼轉到會計系？

B：＿＿＿＿＿＿＿＿＿＿＿＿＿＿＿＿＿＿＿＿＿＿＿＿。

❸ A：媽媽為什麼不讓孩子看漫畫？

B：＿＿＿＿＿＿＿＿＿＿＿＿＿＿＿＿＿＿＿＿＿＿＿＿。

❹ A：你表哥為什麼用天然堆肥種蔬菜？

B：＿＿＿＿＿＿＿＿＿＿＿＿＿＿＿＿＿＿＿＿＿＿＿＿。

❺ A：父母為什麼不喜歡孩子當農夫？

B：＿＿＿＿＿＿＿＿＿＿＿＿＿＿＿＿＿＿＿＿＿＿＿＿。

VIII. 隨著 S_1…，S_2 也… *as a consequence of...* 06-12    英譯 p.147

Function: This pattern means that S_1 contributes significantly to the realisation of S_2.

❶ 隨著中國的經濟越來越好，中國在國際上的地位也越來越重要。

❷ 隨著她的中文越來越好，她參加的活動也越來越多。

❸ 隨著大家對農藥越來越了解，買有機產品的人也越來越多了。

❹ 隨著研究所考試的時間越來越近，他的壓力也越來越大。

❺ 隨著年紀越來越大，她也越來越想在美國工作的孩子。

Usage: This pattern is not used in daily conversation. It is rather formal.

練習 Exercise

Please complete the sentences below, building a sequence using 隨著…，…也…。

❶ 隨著收入越來越高，＿＿＿＿＿＿＿＿＿＿＿＿＿＿＿＿＿。

❷ 隨著大家越來越重視健康，＿＿＿＿＿＿＿＿＿＿＿＿＿＿。

❸ 隨著使用網路的人越來越多，＿＿＿＿＿＿＿＿＿＿＿＿＿。

❹ 隨著到農村來觀光的人越來越多，＿＿＿＿＿＿＿＿＿＿＿。

❺ 隨著她推銷的經驗越來越多，＿＿＿＿＿＿＿＿＿＿＿＿＿。

Grammar Examples in English •

I. 因為…才… *only because…*

Function:

❶ She only wants to change jobs because she sells insurance and her income isn't stable.

❷ I'm only eating this salad because it's made from organic vegetables raised by my cousin.

❸ Meimei is a great catch. She's still unmarried only because she's always been busy at work.

❹ Stress from work caused him to have health issues, so he decided to go back to his village and work the fields.

❺ He got a scholarship because he is both enthusiastic and has good grades.

Usage:

❶ A: Don't you love fireworks? Why didn't you go?
   B: I didn't go, because I didn't feel well.

❷ A: Why aren't you going to see the fireworks tomorrow?
   B: I'm not going, because I'm going to my girlfriend's house.

II. Complaining with …S1…不說，S2 也… *not merely, but also*

Function:.

❶ Aside from the fact that the place is noisy, it's also a bit seedy.

❷ His current job is selling products. The low salary aside, it's hard work.

❸ That shop has poor selection, not to mention high prices. It's no wonder they don't have many customers.

❹ Xiao Lin has been late a lot recently; not to mention, he hasn't been doing his homework. What's up with him?

❺ During anniversary sales the stores are overcrowded; not to mention, you often buy and bring home a lot of useless things just because they're cheap.

III. 再加上 *furthermore*

Function:

❶ The style of that garment was relatively old and the color too light. In addition, it was uncomfortable, so even though it was half off, I didn't buy it.

❷ Yangming Mountain has a lot of good restaurants. What's more, the view at night is beautiful, so he decided to take his girlfriend there for dinner.

❸ A teacher's life is stable. In addition, the pay is higher than most jobs. No wonder he's staying up nights studying in preparation for the test.

❹ In the country, kids can be close to the land and they can run and jump about in the fields. Furthermore, the vegetables there are the freshest you can get. That's why parents like to take their children to the countryside on weekends.

❺ Everybody trusts him. What's more, he uses the best ingredients in his bread, so a lot of people, no matter how far away they live, go to his shop to buy bread.

IV. 什麼都…，就是… *everything but…*

Function:

❶ He bought everything except for salt.

❷ This shop has 20% off on everything except the things I want to buy today.

❸ He's not fussy about anything except food.

❹ This street has any kind of shop you could possibly need except a phone company retail outlet.

❺ His parents support everything he does, but they won't let him take time off school to work.

V. 寧可⋯，也要⋯ *would rather..., in order to...*

Function:

❶ Parents would rather work a little harder, in order that their kids can be happy.

❷ Small farmers would rather the harvest be small, as long as they can raise safe and healthy food.

❸ She would rather receive less money, if it means doing a job that she's interested in.

❹ My cousin would rather not sleep, so that he can finish writing his report.

❺ Meimei would prefer eating bread for every meal, if it means she can buy pretty clothes.

VI. 像⋯的 + **noun** *such (nouns) as*

Function:

❶ He likes all kinds of light snacks, like steamed dumplings, fried chicken fillet, and danzai noodles.

❷ A person like you who likes historical sites really must go check out Tainan.

❸ A person talented in languages like her will most certainly learn Chinese quickly.

❹ Small farmers like him who work the land in an environmentally conscious way are increasing in number.

❺ People who, like her, grew up in a farming village all like to be close to nature.

VII. 一方面⋯，一方面⋯ *on the one hand, ..., on the other*

Function:

❶ She went to the Mayday concert, on the one hand, to kick back and relax, on the other, to figure out why the band is so popular.

❷ She's working part time during the summer, on the one hand, to make a little money, on the other, to get a little experience in society.

❸ This style of bag sells really well, because, on the one hand, the female lead in a TV series had one, and on the other, it's not all that expensive.

❹ Going to the farmer's market, on the one hand, allows you to eat really fresh vegetables and fruit; on the other, it helps the small farmer.

❺ Going back to your hometown during holidays allows you to, on the one hand, get together with your family, and on the other, see old schoolmates.

VIII. 隨著 S₁⋯，S₂ 也⋯ *as a consequence of...*

Function:

❶ As a consequence of China's improving economy, the country's international position has been increasing in importance.

❷ As her Chinese improves, she is taking part in more and more activities.

❸ As people come to better understand pesticides, an increasing number of people are buying organic products.

❹ As the date for the grad school entrance test drew nearer, he grew increasingly stressed out.

❺ As she got older, she thought more and more about her child working in the US.

Classroom Activities

I. Do You Choose Organic or Non-organic Agricultural Products?

Goal: Learning to explain your reasons for choosing something.

Task: Pair up and compare organic and non-organic agricultural products and fill out the following form. Then explain why you generally buy organic or non-organic foods.

	有機農產品 **organic agricultural products**	非有機農產品 **non-organic agricultural products**
優點 Pros	不用農藥	菜又大又漂亮，菜上沒有蟲
缺點 Cons	價錢很貴	使用農藥，不安全

II. The Ups and Downs of Work

Goal: Learning to compare differences between two occupations.
Task: Student form into two groups and discuss the differences between being a farmer and a teacher. Complete the form below.

農夫	
樂（**Advantages**）	苦（**Disadvantages**）
每天運動，身體好	看天吃飯

老師	
樂（**Advantages**）	苦（**Disadvantages**）
薪水穩定	作業很多改不完 （Endless correcting to do）

III. Opening up a Convenience Store in a Rural Area

Goal: Learning to give reasons supporting or opposing the opening up of a convenience store in the countryside.

Task: Students form into two groups. One group doesn't welcome a convenience store in the countryside. Explain the merits of mom and pop stores and traditional small eateries in the countryside. The other group welcomes the idea of a convenience store in the countryside. Explain the merits of a convenience store.

Try to use the following sentence patterns and vocabulary words:

一方面…，一方面…	再加上	…不說，…也…	寧可…，也…

鄉下小店／小吃店	便利商店
當地傳統文化、建築	用悠遊卡付錢很方便

Hu, Fan, and Yang

A student asked me today, "Why doesn't the 番（fān）in 番茄（fānqié, tomato）have a grass radical above it? Aren't tomatoes plants?" His question shows how advanced his Chinese is. The problem is 番 has more to do with history, so it's understandable why he asked the question. Chinese terms with the characters 胡（hú）, 番, and 洋（yáng）describe things produced or invented outside of China. They were introduced from abroad.

Of these three terms, 胡 has the longest history. During the Qin and Han Dynasties (221BC-220AD), the 胡人（húrén）were China's strongest enemy. The term indicated either the Beidi or the Huns, both ethnic minorities in the north. Later, Zhang Qian of the Han Dynasty was sent as an envoy to the Western Region, thereby opening up a road to the West known as the Silk Road and with it frequent exchange between East and West. According to historical documents, Eastern Han Emperor Ling（東漢靈帝）was fond of foreign clothes（胡服 hú fú）, foreign beds（胡床 hú chuáng）, foreign food（胡飯 hú fàn）, and the like. China saw the "foreignization" of society with Chinese wearing foreign clothes and integrating foreign foods into their diet. Worth noting, the foreign "beds" （胡床）were actually seats invented by foreigners, which brought to an end the Chinese custom of sitting on the floor. Other things that came from the Western Region include black pepper（胡椒 hújiāo）, walnuts（胡桃 hútáo）, sesame（胡麻 húmá）, cucumbers（胡瓜 húguā）, carrots（胡蘿蔔 húluóbo）, and huqin（胡琴 húqín） which are two-stringed bowed instruments.

When ethnic groups from China's north invaded the country's Central Plains, many people fled southward. The people coming down from the north no longer used 胡 to refer to imported items; rather, they employed 番. Things like tomatoes（番茄）, sweet potatoes（番薯 fānshǔ）, corn（番麥 fānmài）, hot peppers（番椒 fānjiāo）, and guava（番石榴 fānshíliú）, which arrived in China indirectly from the New World via Europe during the Age of Discovery, were all prefixed with the character 番. This is why the 番 in tomato is not written with a grass radical.

洋 was the latest character used in the naming of imported items. As the name suggests（洋 means ocean）, items prefixed with this character crossed the ocean to get to China. Examples include onions（洋蔥 yángcōng）, western mushrooms （洋菇 yánggū）, potatoes（洋芋 yángyù）, and western orchids （洋蘭 yánglán）. Of the three characters, 洋 is the least derogatory. For example, one might say of a scholar, "他喝過洋墨水，見識比較廣"（ Lit. He has drunk of western ink, i.e., he studied abroad, and has a wide range of knowledge and experience）. Or of an adorable child, "他的孩子好可愛，真像洋娃娃"（His child is lovely. He looks like a doll.）胡, when used in phrases, never means anything good. Examples include poppycock （胡說 húshuō）, run wild （胡鬧 húnào）, and act wildly in defiance of the law or practices （胡作非為 húzuò-fēiwéi）. The same is true of 番. In the past, indigenous peoples were divided into two types—savage tribes （生番 shēngfān） and assimilated border tribes （熟番 shóufān）. During the period of colonization, Westerners were called Red-haired Foreigners （紅毛番 hóngmáofān）, while their books were referred to as foreign books （番仔書 fānzǎishū）.

胡

▲ Carrot, pepper, cucumber, and walnut are words that include the character 胡, indicating that they originated in the Western Region (today's Western China).

番

▲ Corn, tomato, hot pepper, sweet potato, and guava are words that include the character 番, indicating that they originated among ethnic groups of China's north.

洋

▲ Onion, potato, and mushroom are words that include the character 洋, indicating that they were brought across the ocean to China.

Self-Assessment Checklist

I can discuss the cultivation of agricultural crops.

20%   40%   60%   80%   100%

I can explain my reasons for choosing something.

20%   40%   60%   80%   100%

I can talk about changes in society, including values and lifestyle.

20%   40%   60%   80%   100%

I can discuss food safety issues with friends.

20%   40%   60%   80%   100%

第七課

我最親的家「人」

My Closest "Family"

. . . .

學習目標 Learning Objectives

Topic: 家庭 Family

- Learning to talk about the merits and shortcomings of different family makeups.

- Learning to describe in detail the various family makeups of your friends and relatives.

- Learning to state reasons and arguments methodically and sum up your thoughts.

- Learning to talk about the relationship between people and pets in modern society.

我最親的家「人」

My Closest "Family"

 對話 Dialogue　　07-01

羅珊蒂　：何雅婷，昨天我們去打籃球，妳怎麼沒去？

何雅婷　：我媽說我爺爺跌倒，叫我去看他。

羅珊蒂　：妳爺爺還好吧？

何雅婷　：還好。幸虧鄰居聽見狗一直叫，很快地過來幫忙，所以沒什麼關係。

羅珊蒂　：妳爺爺一個人住啊？

何雅婷　：嗯，奶奶過世以後，爺爺就一個人住。我爸擔心爺爺，所以領養了一隻狗陪他。

羅珊蒂　：幸虧有這隻可愛的狗，要不然就太孤單了。

何雅婷　：我爺爺很愛牠，把牠當成家人一樣，晚上還讓牠睡在自己的床上。

（李文彥走過來）

李 文 彥 ：什麼？睡在他床上？狗不髒嗎？不怕牠把床
弄髒嗎？

何 雅 婷 ：我爺爺常給狗洗澡，牠乾淨得很。

李 文 彥 ：以前我女朋友養了一隻狗，整天亂叫、亂咬
東西。有一天，我忍不住打了牠，我女朋友
氣得要跟我分手。

羅 珊 蒂 ：你怎麼可以打狗？狗是人最好的朋友。很多
研究報告都說，人緊張的時候，摸摸狗會減
輕壓力。

李 文 彥 ：不過台灣人對狗太好了。不但送狗去美容院，
還帶狗去餐廳慶祝生日。現在狗連路都不必
走了，坐在推車裡讓主人推著逛街。

羅 珊 蒂 ：對狗好有什麼不對？現代社會大家各忙各的，
常常回到家就只有一個人。人跟狗相處的時
間有時候比家人還長呢。

何 雅 婷 ：是啊，現在有些人覺得生活壓力太大，養不
起孩子，就算結了婚也不生孩子，寧可養寵
物。還有很多單身的人，他們一個人住，寵
物對他們來說，比家人還親。

李 文 彥 ：不管怎麼說，狗不是人。你生病的時候，牠
不能照顧你，幫你買晚飯，陪你去醫院。而
且，你有問題的時候，也不能問牠的意見。
人還是應該建立跟人的關係。

羅 珊 蒂 ：可是狗可以幫你建立跟別人的關係。

何 雅 婷 ：是啊，我爺爺養狗以後，快樂多了。每天帶
著狗去散步，認識了很多朋友。他們有說不
完的話，回家以後還上網繼續聊。

李 文 彥 ：妳們說的也對。可是我還是覺得一個人應該
有家庭，更應該有孩子，一家人熱熱鬧鬧地
一起生活才是真正的幸福。

課文簡體字版 Text in Simplified Characters

罗 珊 蒂 ：何雅婷，昨天我们去打篮球，妳怎么没去？

何 雅 婷 ：我妈说我爷爷跌倒，叫我去看他。

罗 珊 蒂 ：妳爷爷还好吧？

何 雅 婷 ：还好。幸亏邻居听见狗一直叫，很快地过来帮忙，所以没什么关系。

罗 珊 蒂 ：妳爷爷一个人住啊？

何 雅 婷 ：嗯，奶奶过世以后，爷爷就一个人住。我爸担心爷爷，所以领养了一只狗陪他。

罗 珊 蒂 ：幸亏有这只可爱的狗，要不然就太孤单了。

何 雅 婷 ：我爷爷很爱牠，把牠当成家人一样，晚上还让牠睡在自己的床上。

（李文彦走过来）

李 文 彦 ：什么？睡在他床上？狗不脏吗？不怕牠把床弄脏吗？

何 雅 婷 ：我爷爷常给狗洗澡，牠干净得很。

李 文 彦 ：以前我女朋友养了一只狗，整天乱叫、乱咬东西。有一天，我忍不住打了牠，我女朋友气得要跟我分手。

罗 珊 蒂 ：你怎么可以打狗？狗是人最好的朋友。很多研究报告都说，人紧张的时候，摸摸狗会减轻压力。

李 文 彦 ：不过台湾人对狗太好了。不但送狗去美容院，还带狗去餐厅庆祝生日。现在狗连路都不必走了，坐在推车里让主人推着逛街。

罗 珊 蒂 ：对狗好有什么不对？现代社会大家各忙各的，常常回到家就只有一个人。人跟狗相处的时间有时候比家人还长呢。

何 雅 婷 ：是啊，现在有些人觉得生活压力太大，养不起孩子，就算结了婚也不生孩子，宁可养宠物。还有很多单身的人，他们一个人住，宠物对他们来说，比家人还亲。

李 文 彦 ：不管怎么说，狗不是人。你生病的时候，牠不能照顾你，帮你买晚饭，陪你去医院。而且，你有问题的时候，也不能问牠的意见。人还是应该建立跟人的关系。

罗 珊 蒂 ：可是狗可以帮你建立跟别人的关系。

何 雅 婷 ：是啊，我爷爷养狗以后，快乐多了。每天带着狗去散步，认识了很多朋友。他们有说不完的话，回家以后还上网继续聊。

李 文 彦 ：妳们说的也对。可是我还是觉得一个人应该有家庭，更应该有孩子，一家人热热闹闹地一起生活才是真正的幸福。

課文英譯 Text in English

Luo Shandi : He Yating, yesterday we went to play basketball. Why didn't you go?

He Yating : My mom said my grandpa had a fall and told me to go see him.

Luo Shandi : Is your grandpa OK?

He Yating : He's all right. Luckily, the neighbors heard his dog's non-stop barking and quickly went over to help, so it wasn't a big deal.

Luo Shandi : Does your grandpa live alone?

He Yating : Uh-huh. Since my grandma died, my grandpa has been living alone. My dad is worried about him, so he adopted a dog to keep him company.

Luo Shandi : Luckily he has the cute dog. Otherwise, he would be really lonely.

He Yating : My grandpa loves it and considers it family. At night, he even lets it sleep with him in his own bed.

(Li Wenyan walks over.)

Li Wenyan : What?! Sleep in his bed? Aren't dogs dirty? Isn't he afraid it'll get the bed dirty?

He Yating : My grandpa often washes the dog. It's extremely clean.

Li Wenyan : My girlfriend once had a dog. It barked all day long and chewed everything up. One day my patience ran out and I hit it. My girlfriend was so angry that she wanted to break up with me.

Luo Shandi : How could you hit a dog? Dogs are a man's best friend. Many studies say that when a person is tense, patting a dog can reduce stress.

Li Wenyan : But Taiwanese are too good to dogs. Not only do they take them to beauty salons, they even bring them to restaurants to celebrate their birthdays. Dogs today don't even have to walk. They sit in dog strollers that their owners push as they window shop.

Luo Shandi : What's wrong with treating dogs well? Nowadays, everybody's busy with their own things and often when they get home, they are alone. Sometimes, people spend more time with dogs than with family.

He Yating : That's right. Some people today feel that life is filled with stress. They can't afford to raise children and even if they do get married, they don't have any. They'd rather raise pets. There are also many single people who live alone. To them, pets are closer than family.

Li Wenyan : In any case, a dog isn't a person. When you're sick, it can't take care of you, buy dinner for you, or go with you to the hospital. And when you have problems, you can't ask its opinion. People should still build relationships with people.

Luo Shandi : But dogs can help you build relationships with others.

He Yating : That's right. After my grandfather started raising a dog, he was much happier. Every day, he took the dog on walks where he made many friends. They had a lot to talk about and after they got home, they would continue chatting online.

Li Wenyan : You're probably right. But I still think that people should have families and more importantly, they should have children. True happiness is a family living together, full of life.

生詞一 Vocabulary I 🎧 07-02

Vocabulary

1	親親親親親qīn親	ㄑㄧㄣ	(Vs)	close (as of familial relationship)
2	爺爺爺爺爺 yéye	ㄧㄝˊㄧㄝ	(N)	grandpa (father's side)
3	鄰居鄰居鄰 línjū 鄰居鄰居	ㄌㄧㄣˊㄐㄩ	(N)	neighbor
4	狗狗狗狗 gǒu	ㄍㄡˇ	(N)	dog
5	叫叫叫叫 jiào	ㄐㄧㄠˋ	(Vi)	to bark
6	嗯嗯嗯嗯 en	ㄣ˙	(Ptc)	an interjection indicating the speaker's agreement
7	奶奶 nǎinai	ㄋㄞˇㄋㄞ	(N)	grandma (father's side)
8	過世 guòshì	ㄍㄨㄛˋㄕˋ	(Vp)	to die, pass away (honorific)
9	領養領養領 lǐngyǎng 養	ㄌㄧㄥˇㄧㄤˇ	(V)	to adopt
10	隻 zhī	ㄓ	(M)	measure word for animals
11	可愛 kě'ài	ㄎㄜˇㄞˋ	(Vs)	cute
12	孤單孤單孤 gūdān 單	ㄍㄨ ㄉㄢ	(Vs)	lonely
13	牠 tā	ㄊㄚ	(N)	it (animals)
14	髒 zāng 髒髒	ㄗㄤ	(Vs)	dirty
15	洗澡洗澡洗 xǐzǎo 澡	ㄒㄧˇㄗㄠˇ	(V-sep)	to take a bath
16	養 yǎng	ㄧㄤˇ	(V)	to raise, to keep

17	亂	luàn	ㄌㄨㄢˋ	(Adv)	arbitrarily, without rhyme or reason
18	咬咬咬	yǎo	ㄧㄠˇ	(V)	to bite
19	打	dǎ	ㄉㄚˇ	(V)	to hit, beat, smack, slap
20	分手	fēnshǒu	ㄈㄣ ㄕㄡˇ	(Vp)	to break up (said of romantic relationships)
21	緊張	jǐnzhāng	ㄐㄧㄣˇ ㄓㄤ	(Vs)	tense
22	減輕	jiǎnqīng	ㄐㄧㄢˇ ㄑㄧㄥ	(V)	to reduce
23	送	sòng	ㄙㄨㄥˋ	(V)	to take to
24	美容院	měiróngyuàn	ㄇㄟˇ ㄖㄨㄥˊ ㄩㄢˋ	(N)	beauty salon
25	推車	tuīchē	ㄊㄨㄟ ㄔㄜ	(N)	stroller
26	主人	zhǔrén	ㄓㄨˇ ㄖㄣˊ	(N)	master, owner
27	相處	xiāngchǔ	ㄒㄧㄤ ㄔㄨˇ	(Vi)	to get along (with), to spend time together
28	生	shēng	ㄕㄥ	(V)	to give birth, to bear
29	寵物	chǒngwù	ㄔㄨㄥˇ ㄨˋ	(N)	pet
30	單身	dānshēn	ㄉㄢ ㄕㄣ	(Vs)	to be single
31	醫院	yīyuàn	ㄧ ㄩㄢˋ	(N)	hospital
32	意見	yìjiàn	ㄧˋ ㄐㄧㄢˋ	(N)	suggestion, opinion
33	建立	jiànlì	ㄐㄧㄢˋ ㄌㄧˋ	(V)	to establish
34	散步	sànbù	ㄙㄢˋ ㄅㄨˋ	(V-sep)	to take a walk
35	家庭	jiātíng	ㄐㄧㄚ ㄊㄧㄥˊ	(N)	family
36	真正	zhēnzhèng	ㄓㄣ ㄓㄥˋ	(Vs-attr)	real, true, genuine
37	幸福	xìngfú	ㄒㄧㄥˋ ㄈㄨˊ	(N)	happiness, blessing

Phrases

38	跌倒	diédǎo	ㄉㄧㄝˊ ㄉㄠˇ		to fall down
39	當成	dāng chéng	ㄉㄤ ㄔㄥˊ		to consider, view as, regard
40	忍不住	rěn bú zhù	ㄖㄣˇ ㄅㄨˊ ㄓㄨˋ		to be beyond the limits of endurance

短文 Reading 07-03

多元家庭

李文彥的阿姨一個人帶著孩子住在台北。她的先生因為工作的關係，大部分的時間都在國外。阿姨白天在學校教書，下了班，接了孩子回家，就忙著做飯、陪孩子做功課。好不容易等孩子睡了，才能開始改學生的作業，準備第二天上課的資料。週末的時候，還要上市場幫公公買一個星期的菜。家裡大大小小的事全靠她一個人。她常說，她雖然不是單親媽媽，可是生活比單親媽媽更辛苦。

阿姨很羨慕她的同學——美真。美真是一個單身貴族。大學時代，在學校就是一個風雲人物，不但人長得美，而且能力強，追她的人多得不得了。可是她一直不想結婚，一來怕結了婚不自由，不能發展自己的興趣，二來，她的經濟獨立，可以把自己的生活安排得很好。雖然大部分的時候她都很享受單身生活，但是一個人旅行的時候，她也常想，要是身邊有個伴也不錯。

美真的朋友——家華，也不願意結婚。他雖然跟女朋友已經同居好幾年了，但是一想到成家以後，得負擔起養家的責任，他就下不了決心。而且，要是結了婚，就會有生孩子的壓力。現在社會這麼亂，怎麼教養孩子？他想來想去，覺得還是現在的生活比較好。雖然女朋友跟他說過幾次，年紀不小，應該結婚了，他還是沒答應。

現在社會慢慢地接受了各種家庭的組成方式。同居不再被認為是不道德的事了，一個人也能是一個「單身家庭」。因此，只要有愛，愛自己、愛家人，就是一個完整的家。

課文簡體字版 Text in Simplified Characters

多元家庭

　　李文彦的阿姨一个人带着孩子住在台北。她的先生因为工作的关系，大部分的时间都在国外。阿姨白天在学校教书，下了班，接了孩子回家，就忙着做饭、陪孩子做功课。好不容易等孩子睡了，才能开始改学生的作业，准备第二天上课的资料。周末的时候，还要上市场帮公公买一个星期的菜。家里大大小小的事全靠她一个人。她常说，她虽然不是单亲妈妈，可是生活比单亲妈妈更辛苦。

　　阿姨很羡慕她的同学——美真。美真是一个单身贵族。大学时代，在学校就是一个风云人物，不但人长得美，而且能力强，追她的人多得不得了。可是她一直不想结婚，一来怕结了婚不自由，不能发展自己的兴趣，二来，她的经济独立，可以把自己的生活安排得很好。虽然大部分的时候她都很享受单身生活，但是一个人旅行的时候，她也常想，要是身边有个伴也不错。

　　美真的朋友——家华，也不愿意结婚。他虽然跟女朋友已经同居好几年了，但是一想到成家以后，得负担起养家的责任，他就下不了决心。而且，要是结了婚，就会有生孩子的压力。现在社会这么乱，怎么教养孩子？他想来想去，觉得还是现在的生活比较好。虽然女朋友跟他说过几次，年纪不小，应该结婚了，他还是没答应。

　　现在社会慢慢地接受了各种家庭的组成方式。同居不再被认为是不道德的事了，一个人也能是一个「单身家庭」。因此，只要有爱，爱自己、爱家人，就是一个完整的家。

課文英譯 Text in English

Diversified Families

　　Li Wenyan's aunt lives in Taipei alone with her children. Due to work-related reasons, her husband is abroad most of the time. His aunt teaches in the school during the day. After work, she picks up her children and goes home where she cooks and monitors them as they do their homework. She can't start checking her students' homework and preparing for class the next day until after her kids have finally fallen asleep. On weekends, she also has to go to the market to buy a week's worth of groceries for her father-in-law. All household affairs, both large and small, have to be done by her alone. She often says that although she's not a single mother, her life is tougher than that of a single mother.

Wenyan's auntie envies her classmate Meizhen. Meizhen is a "single aristocrat" (i.e., single, eligible, and well off). In college she was popular and influential. Not only was she beautiful, she was very capable, and there were any number of suitors chasing after her. But she never wanted to get married. First of all, she was afraid that if she married, she would have to give up being free and pursuing her own interests. Secondly, she was financially independent and she could plan her own life the way she wanted. Although most of the time, she enjoys the single life, when she travels alone, she often thinks, if she had a companion by her side, that would be nice, too.

Meizhen's friend Jiahua is also unwilling to get married. He has lived with his girlfriend for many years, but the very thought of marrying and supporting a family is enough to deter the commitment. What's more, if he gets married, he'll be pressured to have kids. With society today in such turmoil, how are you supposed to raise kids? After much deliberation, he believes that his current life is better. Although his girlfriend has told him a few times that they are no longer young and should get married, he has still not agreed to do so.

Society today is gradually accepting different kinds of family structures. Living together is no longer thought of as immoral. An individual can be a "single person family". Therefore, a complete family is a one wherever there is love—love of self and love of other family members.

生詞二 Vocabulary II　🎧 07-04

Vocabulary

1	多元	duōyuán	ㄉㄨㄛ ㄩㄢˊ	(Vs-attr)	diverse, diversified
2	阿姨	āyí	ㄚ ㄧˊ	(N)	aunt (mother's sisters)
3	先生	xiānshēng	ㄒㄧㄢ ㄕㄥ	(N)	husband
4	下班	xiàbān	ㄒㄧㄚˋ ㄅㄢ	(V-sep)	to get off work
5	改 改改	gǎi	ㄍㄞˇ	(V)	correct, check (homework)
6	公公	gōnggōng	ㄍㄨㄥ ㄍㄨㄥ	(N)	father-in-law (of a female)
7	全	quán	ㄑㄩㄢˊ	(Adv)	completely, entirely
8	靠	kào	ㄎㄠˋ	(V)	to depend on, rely on
9	單親	dānqīn	ㄉㄢ ㄑㄧㄣ	(Vs-attr)	single parent
10	貴族	guìzú	ㄍㄨㄟˋ ㄗㄨˊ	(N)	nobility, aristocrat
11	時代	shídài	ㄕˊ ㄉㄞˋ	(N)	period, time of
12	強 強	qiáng	ㄑㄧㄤˊ	(Vs)	strong

13	追	zhuī	ㄓㄨ	(V)	to go after someone trying to establish a relationship of love, to chase
14	自由	zìyóu	ㄗˋ ㄧㄡˊ	(Vs)	free
15	獨立	dúlì	ㄉㄨˊ ㄌㄧˋ	(Vs)	independent
16	安排	ānpái	ㄢ ㄆㄞˊ	(V)	to handle, to arrange
17	享受	xiǎngshòu	ㄒㄧㄤˇ ㄕㄡˋ	(Vst)	to enjoy
18	身邊	shēnbiān	ㄕㄣ ㄅㄧㄢ	(N)	by one's side
19	伴	bàn	ㄅㄢˋ	(N)	companion
20	同居 同居 同居 tóngjū 同居	tóngjū	ㄊㄨㄥˊ ㄐㄩ	(Vi)	to live together (as a couple), to cohabit
21	成家	chéngjiā	ㄔㄥˊ ㄐㄧㄚ	(Vp)	to set up a family, to marry (from the male's perspective)
22	負擔 負擔	fùdān	ㄈㄨˋ ㄉㄢ	(V)	to bear (a burden, responsibility)
23	養家	yǎngjiā	ㄧㄤˇ ㄐㄧㄚ	(V-sep)	to support one's family
24	責任	zérèn	ㄗㄜˊ ㄖㄣˋ	(N)	responsibility
25	亂	luàn	ㄌㄨㄢˋ	(Vs)	to be in turmoil, be in chaos
26	教養	jiàoyǎng	ㄐㄧㄠˋ ㄧㄤˇ	(V)	to raise, bring up, train, educate (one's children)
27	接受	jiēshòu	ㄐㄧㄝ ㄕㄡˋ	(V)	to accept
28	組成 組成 組 zǔchéng 成	zǔchéng	ㄗㄨˇ ㄔㄥˊ	(V)	to form
29	道德	dàodé	ㄉㄠˋ ㄉㄜˊ	(Vs)	moral
30	因此	yīncǐ	ㄧㄣ ㄘˇ	(Conj)	therefore, so
31	完整	wánzhěng	ㄨㄢˊ ㄓㄥˇ	(Vs)	complete, integral, whole

Names

| 32 | 美真 | Měizhēn | ㄇㄟˇ ㄓㄣ | female person's name |
| 33 | 家華 | Jiāhuá | ㄐㄧㄚ ㄏㄨㄚˊ | male person's name |

Phrases

| 34 | 風雲人物 | fēngyún rénwù | ㄈㄥ ㄩㄣˊ ㄖㄣˊ ㄨˋ | mover and shaker, popular and influential person |
| 35 | 下決心 | xià juéxīn | ㄒㄧㄚˋ ㄐㄩㄝˊ ㄒㄧㄣ | to resolve oneself, make up one's mind (to do something) |

163

文法 Grammar

I. 亂 + V *to do something in an irresponsible manner,*
risking undersirable consequences 🎧 07-05

Function: 亂 is an adverb and refers to doing some action in a disorderly,
irresponsible, destructive manner, risking undersirable consequences.

Note the range of possible meanings through the translations. (p.171)

1 你不能亂倒垃圾，得等垃圾車來才能倒。

2 功課要好好地寫，不能亂寫。

3 這些座位都有人坐，不能亂坐。

4 你的感冒雖然不嚴重，可是不能自己亂買藥吃。

5 媽媽怕孩子亂花錢，不敢給孩子太多錢。

Usage:

1. 亂 is always negative in nature.
   E.g., 亂寫、亂做、亂選、亂走、亂翻譯、亂交朋友、亂打電話… these
   phrases suggest a negative, halfhearted, or haphazard attitude or way of doing
   something. 亂, however, differs from 隨便 in 隨便走走、隨便拿一個、隨便
   坐. 隨便 does not have the negative connotations.

2. 亂 + V is also sometimes used in self-deprecation, often used to suggest
   humility.
   E.g.,

   (1) A：妳真會穿，你的衣服都很講究。

   B：哪裡，我是亂穿的。

   (2) A：妳的報告寫得真好，拿到 A。

   B：哪裡，我亂寫的，只是運氣好。

練習 **Exercise**

Please complete the following sentences using the options given below.

亂改、亂貼、亂寫、亂選、亂拿、亂想、亂放、亂填、亂罵、亂掛

❶ 這張申請表要是你不知道怎麼填，就別_____。填錯就麻煩了。

❷ 考試的時候別_____，成績不好會被當的。

❸ 你們店的招牌不能_____，鄰居會生氣的。

❹ 你一定能畢業的，別_____。有問題就給我打電話。

❺ 這些資料很重要，別_____。要是找不到就麻煩了。

II. 各 V 各的 *each doing her/his own...* 🎧 07-06 🔍英譯 p.171

Function: This pattern refers to each member of a given group engaged in her/his own pursuit.

❶ 他們結婚以後，因為在不同的城市上班，還是各住各的。

❷ 他們各說各的，沒辦法一起討論。

❸ 我們雖然一起去故宮博物院，可是我們的興趣不同，各看各的。

❹ 他們同居好幾年了，可是晚飯常常是各吃各的。

❺ 他們一起去夜市，可是各逛各的。

練習 **Exercise**

Please complete the dialogues below, indicating individual pursuit with 各 V 各的 .

❶ A：你常常跟同學一起去玩嗎？

　 B：我們興趣不同，平常都是_____。

❷ A：你覺得早一點結婚好，還是晚一點結婚好？

　 B：_____。

3 A：妳常常跟妳姐姐交換包包用嗎？

B：我們喜歡的款式不一樣，我們都_____。

4 A：你今天跟同學一起吃飯，誰請客？

B：沒有人請客。我們_____。

5 A：你跟你弟弟都賣寵物。你們一起在媒體上做廣告嗎？

B：我們各賣各的，所以也_____。

III. 就算…，也… *even if... (S₁)..., would...(S₂)...* 🎧 07-07 🔍 英譯 p.172

Function: The pattern indicates that even if a condition (S₁) is met, (S₂) would still be true.

1 我爸爸常說：就算我做不動了，也不要靠孩子。

2 就算你的能力比老闆強，你也應該聽老闆的意見。

3 就算男人有養家的責任，家庭經濟也不能完全讓男人負擔啊。

4 他的婚禮，我就算再忙，也要參加。 *jīngjì economy*

5 就算你覺得孤單，也不能隨便打擾別人。

Usage: This is a highly colloquial pattern. The subject can appear before or after 就算. E.g., pre-subject in **1** above and post-subject in **4** above.

練習 Exercise

Answer the following questions with 就算…，也…, insisting on own ideas.

1 A：聽說妳的男朋友以前結過婚，妳還要跟他結婚嗎？

B：_____。

2 A：你喜歡狗，聽說領養手續很簡單，你想領養一隻嗎？

B：_____。

3 A：美美說在網路上交朋友，也能找到幸福。你要不要試試？

B：_____。

④ A：大明的爸爸幫他安排了一份不錯的工作。我羨慕死了。

B：我喜歡自己找工作，_____。

⑤ A：現代社會進步得很快，原住民文化恐怕會消失了。

B：不會吧，_____。

IV. 因為 **NP**，**S**… *because of NP, S...* 🎧 07-08

Function: This pattern presents an NP (a reason, an explanation or a motivation), for the subsequent clause. 因為 in this pattern is a preposition, not a conjuction, and is thus used with an NP.

① 因為氣溫的變化，今年的芒果熟得比較早。

② 因為工作的關係，我需要懂越南語的翻譯人員。

③ 因為成家晚的關係，他的孩子年紀還很小。

④ 因為週年慶的關係，百貨公司裡擠滿了人。

⑤ 因為連續劇的影響，街上賣韓國炸雞的店越來越多。

Usage: As indicated in the description above, 因為 in this pattern is a preposition but can be followed by a sentence with its own conjunction, e.g., 因為氣溫的變化，因此 (or 所以) 今年的芒果熟得比較早。'Changes in weather conditions have caused mangoes to ripen earlier this year.'

練習 Exercise

Please provide explanations to the questions below as suggested in the parentheses.

① A：他的錢怎麼這麼快就花光了？（喜歡享受的關係）

B：_____。

② A：你爺爺為什麼答應搬到台北來跟你們一起住？（奶奶過世的關係）

B：_____。

③ A：為什麼迷網路遊戲的人越來越多？（社會環境的影響）

   B：_____。

④ A：現代人為什麼越來越晚結婚？（時代的變化）

   B：_____。

⑤ A：為什麼最近很多人感冒？（季節的變化）

   B：_____。

V. 一來⋯，二來⋯ *on the one hand…, and on the other…;*
first…, second… 🎧 07-09

Function: This pattern offers two reasons or explanations for a statement already presented.

① 我不信任他，一來我們認識不久，二來聽說他會騙人。

② 我不跟你們到綠島去玩，一來我怕坐船，二來我不會游泳，去了沒意思。

③ 我最近吃素，一來天氣太熱，吃不下油膩的東西，二來吃青菜對健康比較好。

④ 我們今年的收成不錯，一來天氣好，沒有颱風，二來我種的是新品種。

⑤ 養寵物，一來讓我們不孤單，二來給我們很多快樂。所以現在養寵物的人越來越多。

Usage: The usage of this pattern is the same as 一方面⋯，一方面⋯, but 一來⋯，二來⋯ can be used to offer more reasons. For example, 一來⋯，二來⋯，三來⋯. In addition, 一來⋯，二來⋯ is more colloquial than 一方面⋯，一方面⋯.

練習 Exercise

Please answer the questions below using 一來⋯，二來⋯, giving two points of argument.

① A：為什麼到鄉下住一晚變成了現在熱門的休閒活動？

   B：_____。

2 A：你認為鄉下有便利商店好不好？

B：_____。

3 A：現代人為什麼晚結婚？

B：_____。

4 A：你認為結婚以前應該先同居嗎？

B：_____。

5 A：你買東西喜歡刷卡嗎？為什麼？

B：_____。

VI. Repetitively, Back and Forth with V 來 V 去   07-10

Function: This pattern is used with action verbs and indicates repetitive execution, oftentimes in vain.

1 孩子總是喜歡打來打去，你別擔心。

2 他很講究吃，他說吃來吃去，還是台南的牛肉湯最好喝。

3 他們想來想去，最後決定帶狗去旅行，不送牠去狗旅館住。

4 他想換班，可是換來換去都不適合，最後只好回到原來的班。

5 小孩子逛市場喜歡摸來摸去，讓老闆很不高興。

Usage:

1. If there is an object, it must be moved to the front of the sentence, as a topic.
   E.g.,

   (1) 電腦，我不想帶來帶去，累死了。

   (2) 他寫的文章，看來看去都跟吃有關。

2. The V 來 V 去 structure is often followed by some kind of comments by the speaker.
   E.g.,

   這幾個辦法，他想來想去，都覺得不好。

練習 Exercise

Please complete the dialogues below with V 來 V 去 , indicating repetitive attempts.

❶ A：你畢業以後打算念研究所，還是找工作？決定了沒有？

　　B：＿＿＿＿＿＿＿＿＿＿＿＿＿＿＿＿＿＿＿＿＿。

❷ A：鞋這麼舊了，你怎麼還留著？丟掉吧。

　　B：不行，＿＿＿＿＿＿＿＿＿＿＿＿＿＿＿＿＿。

❸ A：上次你請客，今天應該我請你了。

　　B：我們還是各付各的吧。＿＿＿＿＿＿＿＿＿＿＿。

❹ A：好多人給他介紹女朋友，他選了誰？

　　B：＿＿＿＿＿＿＿＿＿＿＿＿＿＿＿＿＿＿＿＿＿。

❺ A：你最近為什麼不上網玩遊戲了？

　　B：沒什麼新遊戲，＿＿＿＿＿＿＿＿＿＿＿＿＿＿。

VII. 不再…了 *not…any more* 🎧 07-11　　🔍 英譯 p.173

Function: The use of this structure indicates that the subject abandons an old routine/habit/belief.

❶ 他覺得自己長大了，可以獨立了，就不再接受父母的幫助了。

❷ 我已經跟我男朋友分手了，我們不再見面了。

❸ 那家店的東西品質不是很好，而且價錢很貴，我不再去了。

❹ 漫畫不再吸引我了。現在我喜歡看談歷史的書。

❺ 他現在越來越喜歡狗了，覺得養狗很快樂，不再是負擔了。

練習 Exercise

Complete the following dialogues, indicating a discontinuation with 不再…了.

❶ A：他在公司裡還受老闆重視嗎？

　　B：＿＿＿＿＿＿＿＿＿＿＿＿＿＿＿＿＿＿＿＿＿。

❷ A：在你的國家幾歲的孩子可以獨立不靠父母？

B：＿＿＿＿＿＿＿＿＿＿＿＿＿＿＿＿＿＿＿＿＿＿＿＿＿＿＿。

❸ A：以前教養孩子只是媽媽的責任，現在還一樣嗎？

B：＿＿＿＿＿＿＿＿＿＿＿＿＿＿＿＿＿＿＿＿＿＿＿＿＿＿＿。

❹ A：美美大學時代是學校的風雲人物，念研究所的時候還是嗎？

B：＿＿＿＿＿＿＿＿＿＿＿＿＿＿＿＿＿＿＿＿＿＿＿＿＿＿＿。

❺ A：這家公司的產品出問題以後，大家還信任他們嗎？

B：＿＿＿＿＿＿＿＿＿＿＿＿＿＿＿＿＿＿＿＿＿＿＿＿＿＿＿。

語法例句英譯
Grammar Examples in English

I. 亂＋V *to do something in an irresponsible manner, risking undersirable consequences*

Function:

❶ You can't just dump your garbage anywhere. You need to wait for the garbage truck before you can dump it.

❷ You need to do a good job on your homework. You can't just do it haphazardly.

❸ These seats are all occupied. You can't just sit anywhere you please.

❹ Your cold isn't serious, but you can't just go and buy any meds you want.

❺ Moms are afraid their kids will spend money like there's no tomorrow, so they don't dare give them too much.

Usage:

2. (1) A: You really know how to dress. You have very refined tastes when it comes to clothes.

B: Not at all. It's just something I threw on.

(2) A: Your report was written really well. You got an A.

B: It was nothing. I just threw it together. It was just luck.

II. 各V各的 *each doing her/his own…*

Function:

❶ Since they've been married, because they work in different cities, each lives his or her own life.

❷ Everyone was talking past each other. There was no way to get any discussion done.

❸ Although we went to the Palace Museum together, each of us has his own interest, so each visited what he wanted to see.

❹ They have lived together for many years, but they often eat their meals on their own.

❺ They went to the night market together, but split so each could check out what they wanted to see.

III. 就算…，也… *even if… (S₁)…, would…(S₂)…*

Function:

❶ My dad often says, 'Even if I can't move anymore, I don't want to depend on my kids.'

❷ Even if you're more capable than the boss, you should still listen to his suggestions.

❸ Even if men have the responsibility of taking care of their families, the household finances cannot be the sole responsibility of the man.

❹ No matter how busy I am, I will be at his wedding.

❺ Even if you feel lonely, you can't go around bothering others.

IV. 因為 NP，S… *because of NP, S…*

Function:

❶ Due to changes in the temperature, mangoes are ripening relatively early this year.

❷ For the sake of my job, I need a translator in Vietnamese.

❸ Because he didn't get married until later in life, his kids are still very young.

❹ The department stores are packed with people because the anniversary sale is on.

❺ Because of the influence of the TV series, an increasing numbers of street shops are selling Korean-style fried chicken.

V. 一來…，二來… *on the one hand…, and on the other…; first…, second…*

Function:

❶ I don't trust him. First, we have not known each other for very long. Second, I've heard that he cheats.

❷ I'm not going to go with you to Green Island. On the one hand, I'm afraid of boat rides. On the other, I can't swim. It'll be boring if I go.

❸ I've been eating vegetarian food a lot lately. First of all, it's been too hot out; I can't handle oily food. Second, eating vegetables is better for health.

❹ Our harvest this year was pretty good. On the one hand, the weather was good--no typhoons. On the other, I planted a new strain of crops.

❺ Keeping pets, on the one hand, takes away loneliness, and on the other, brings us a lot of joy, so an increasing number of people are keeping pets.

VI. Repetitively, Back and Forth with V 來 V 去

Function:

❶ Kids are always hitting each other. It's nothing to worry about.

❷ He's very particular about what he eats. He says he's eaten around and he still feels that the beef soup in Tainan is the best.

❸ After thinking about it for a while, they decided to bring their dog along with them on their trip and not put him in a dog hotel.

❹ He wanted to change classes, but he changed several times and none of them were a good fit. In the end, he had no choice but to return to his original class.

❺ Kids like to touch things when they're wandering about markets, making the vendors really unhappy.

Usage:

1. (1) I don't want to carry my computer around. It's exhausting.

   (2) After reading a lot of his articles, it turns out they're all about eating.

2. After tossing the solutions about in his mind for a while, he feels that none of them are any good.

VII. 不再…了 *not...any more*

Function:

❶ He feels that he has grown up and can be independent, so he doesn't accept his parents' help anymore.

❷ I have broken up with my boyfriend. We no longer see each other.

❸ The quality of the products in that store isn't all that good and the prices are expensive. I no longer go there.

❹ Comics no longer have the draw on me than they used to. I now like to read books on history.

❺ He likes dogs more and more. He feels that raising dogs is a joy and no longer a burden.

Classroom Activities

I. I Want to Raise a Pet

Goal: Learning to present reasons supporting your views and refuting those of others.

Task 1: Five-year old Xiaomin tells her mother that she wants a pet, but her mother says, "Wait until you're older." Do you think raising a pet is a good thing? Pair up and complete the following form.

Task 2: Do you agree with the mother's view that her daughter should wait until she's older? Separate the class into two groups to discuss the results.

Try to use the following sentence patterns and vocabulary words:

就算…，也…	V 來 V 去	不管怎麼說
一來…，二來…	有什麼不對	

養寵物的好處	養寵物的壞處
可以陪伴人	很髒

養寵物的好處	養寵物的壞處

II. My Views on Different Kinds of Family Makeups

Goal: Learning to explain the pros and cons of different types of family makeups.

Task: Separate the class into three groups to discuss ❶ marriage, ❷ cohabitation, and ❸ being single. Assign one topic to each group. After discussions, choose one person from each group to report the findings to the rest of the class.

Try to use the following sentence patterns and vocabulary words:

辛苦	自由	經濟獨立	享受	負擔
養家	因此	各V各的	溫馨	幸福

175

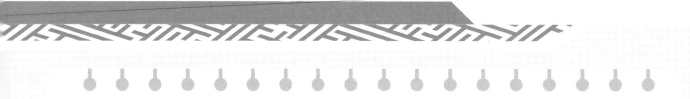

III. What Should This Mother Do?

A 30-year old man, who is an only child, just started to work. In order to save money, he is living at home with his parents. The young man has a girlfriend who he brought home to live with him. All the housework, including cooking, dishes, and laundry, is done by the parents. The mother thinks her son should move out and live on his own, but she's also afraid that bringing the subject up with her son will adversely impact their relationship. What should the mother do?

Each group is to select a person from their group and report the group's findings to the class.

Try to use the following sentence patterns and vocabulary words:

靠	負擔	責任	就算…也…
各 V 各的	不再…了	因為	亂＋V

文化 *Bits of Chinese Culture*

Visiting the Parents

People born in the 1950's and 1960's can remember going to their grandparents (on their mother's side of the family) when they were kids and how warm and inviting it was when they offered their grandparents Chinese New Year's greetings. Not only did they receive red envelopes and enjoy Grandma's wonderful cooking, they also got to play all kinds of games with their cousins. What's more, at Grandma's house, they could bend the rules a bit without getting scolded, but the same wasn't true of their cousins. Grandma said that this was because grandkids on her daughter's side of the family were "guests" and should be treated with hospitality.

▲ A daughter returning home to see her family.

At that time, Taiwan was still a paternalistic society in which males enjoyed higher status than females. The portion of the Civil Code regulating family relations even stipulated that a wife must move into her husband's home. When a woman married, her mother would tell her, "A married daughter is water poured out." From that time forward, she no longer had any relationship with her parents and needed to do her best to bring prosperity to her husband's family.

▲ According to custom, when a daughter marries, she is "water poured out."

Whenever a daughter returned to her parents' home, she would do so only as a guest. Her husband's home was now her only true home.

Despite the difficulties that women experienced, however, society still offered them a token of warmth--the custom of wives returning to their parents' home on the second day of the lunar New Year. According to tradition, in ancient times, marriages generally took place between men and women of different villages and when they married, women would often move far from home. Parents would be concerned that their daughter might be mistreated by her in-laws... sometimes, not even knowing if she were alive or dead. The custom of returning home during the Chinese New Year's holiday was established, so parents could stay informed with what was happening in their daughter's life in her new home. With this custom in place, in-laws could make no excuses to prevent their daughter-in-law from going home to see her family. This was a way of protecting women's rights in ancient China.

The Women's Rights Movement in Taiwan began in the 1960s, giving women the opportunity to become independent. Regulations regarding women's rights began to be added to the Civil Code. Men and women now had equal rights under the law. Daughters, like sons, were now first tier relatives with their parents. Daughters were no longer outsiders with no relationship with their parents and now, when they return home to see their parents during the Chinese New Year, they are no longer "guests".

Self-Assessment Checklist

I can talk about the merits and shortcomings of different family makeups.

20%　　40%　　60%　　80%　　100%

I can describe in detail the various family makeups of my friends and relatives.

20%　　40%　　60%　　80%　　100%

I can state reasons and arguments methodically and sum up my thoughts.

20%　　40%　　60%　　80%　　100%

I can talk about the relationship between people and pets in modern society.

20%　　40%　　60%　　80%　　100%

LESSON 8

第八課

我想做自己

I Just Want to Be Myself

學習目標 **Learning Objectives**

Topic: 教育 Education

- Learning to explain in detail classes that you are currently taking and your future plans.

- Learning to talk about study and work experience.

- Learning to discuss differences in traditional and modern ideas and values.

- Learning the names of university departments and graduate school programs.

我想做自己

I Just Want to Be Myself

對話 Dialogue 🎧 08-01

陳敏萱 ：早，李文彥。欸？你怎麼看起來不太有精神？
怎麼回事？

李文彥 ：別說了。我那個室友，最近不是整夜開著燈
打電玩，就是熬夜看球賽，激動的時候，還
大喊大叫，害我睡不著覺。

陳敏萱 ：他不是在準備公職人員考試嗎？怎麼有時間
打電玩？

李文彥 ：其實他對當公務員一點興趣都沒有，是他媽媽
叫他去考的。他覺得很煩，所以最近常打電玩。

陳敏萱 ：既然沒興趣就別去考啊。為什麼要那麼聽話？

李文彥 ：因為他媽媽說，現在大學生的失業率很高。
考上公職的話，薪水不錯，工作又穩定。這
樣父母才放心。算了，算了，不說這個。妳
最近怎麼樣？

陳敏萱 ：快要期中考了，我壓力好大啊！這學期我在
大學選了好幾門課，還在語言中心上密集班，
每天忙得連睡覺的時間都不夠。

李文彥 ：這樣一來，妳不是就沒時間參加學校的社團
活動了嗎？

陳敏萱 ：那有什麼關係。我來台灣是來讀書的，不是
來玩的。我希望早一點把中文系的學分修完，
回國以後專心修輔系的課，這樣明年才能畢
業。

李文彥 ：妳還修輔系啊？為什麼要把自己弄得這麼
累？如果我是妳，恐怕早就瘋了。

陳敏萱 ：你太誇張了。沒那麼嚴重吧。

李文彥 ：妳應該趁著在台灣的時候，到處走走，多了
解這裡的文化。

陳敏萱 ：旅行的機會以後還很多。為了將來的發展，
現在我應該好好利用時間，充實自己。

（何雅婷走過來）

何雅婷 ：你們都在這裡啊？在聊什麼？

李文彥 ：我們在聊畢業以後的計畫。對了，妳男朋友
的畢業展什麼時候舉行？

何雅婷 ：下個月五號。到時候歡迎大家來看。

陳敏萱 ：他爸媽會去嗎？我聽妳說過，他爸媽很反對
他念服裝設計。現在還是這樣嗎？

何雅婷 ：他父母到現在還覺得很遺憾，兒子沒去念醫
學系。他從小功課就很好，父母對他的期望
一直很高，選服裝設計讓他們很失望。

李文彥 ：為什麼要失望？行行出狀元。不管做什麼，
只要有興趣，願意努力就好了。

陈 敏 萱 ： 早，李文彦。欸？你怎么看起来不太有精神？怎么回事？

李 文 彦 ： 别说了。我那个室友，最近不是整夜开着灯打电玩，就是熬夜看球赛，激动的时候，还大喊大叫，害我睡不着觉。

陈 敏 萱 ： 他不是在准备公职人员考试吗？怎么有时间打电玩？

李 文 彦 ： 其实他对当公务员一点兴趣都没有，是他妈妈叫他去考的。他觉得很烦，所以最近常打电玩。

陈 敏 萱 ： 既然没兴趣就别去考啊。为什么要那么听话？

李 文 彦 ： 因为他妈妈说，现在大学生的失业率很高。考上公职的话，薪水不错，工作又稳定。这样父母才放心。算了，算了，不说这个。妳最近怎么样？

陈 敏 萱 ： 快要期中考了，我压力好大啊！这学期我在大学选了好几门课，还在语言中心上密集班，每天忙得连睡觉的时间都不够。

李 文 彦 ： 这样一来，妳不是就没时间参加学校的社团活动了吗？

陈 敏 萱 ： 那有什么关系。我来台湾是来读书的，不是来玩的。我希望早一点把中文系的学分修完，回国以后专心修辅系的课，这样明年才能毕业。

李 文 彦 ： 妳还修辅系啊？为什么要把自己弄得这么累？如果我是妳，恐怕早就疯了。

陈 敏 萱 ： 你太夸张了。没那么严重吧。

李 文 彦 ： 妳应该趁着在台湾的时候，到处走走，多了解这里的文化。

陈 敏 萱 ： 旅行的机会以后还很多。为了将来的发展，现在我应该好好利用时间，充实自己。

（何雅婷走过来）

何 雅 婷 ： 你们都在这里啊？在聊什么？

李 文 彦 ： 我们在聊毕业以后的计画。对了，妳男朋友的毕业展什么时候举行？

何 雅 婷 ： 下个月五号。到时候欢迎大家来看。

陈 敏 萱 ： 他爸妈会去吗？我听妳说过，他爸妈很反对他念服装设计。现在还是这样吗？

何 雅 婷 ： 他父母到现在还觉得很遗憾，儿子没去念医学系。他从小功课就很好，父母对他的期望一直很高，选服装设计让他们很失望。

李 文 彦 ： 为什么要失望？行行出状元。不管做什么，只要有兴趣，愿意努力就好了。

課文英譯 Text in English

Chen Minxuan : Good morning, Li Wenyan. Hey? Why do you look so listless? What's the problem?

Li Wenyan : Don't get me started. That roommate of mine… Lately, if he's not playing video games all night with the lights on, then he's up all night watching ball games. When he gets real excited he even cheers at the top of his lungs, keeping me from falling asleep.

Chen Minxuan : Isn't he preparing for the civil servants exam? How does he have time to play computer games?

Li Wenyan : He actually has no interest in the civil servants exam at all. It was his mother who wanted him to take it. He finds the whole situation a drag, so he's been playing a lot of video games lately.

Chen Minxuan : Since he's not interested, then he shouldn't go take it. Why does he do what he's told like that?

Li Wenyan : Because his mom says the unemployment rate among university students today is high. If he can test into the civil service, the salary isn't bad and the work is stable. Doing so would put his parents' minds at ease. Forget it. Let's not talk about it. How have you been?

Chen Minxuan : Mid-terms are almost here. I'm under a great deal of stress. This semester, I am taking a number of courses at the university and I'm taking an intensive class at the language center. Every day, I'm so busy that I don't get enough sleep.

Li Wenyan : If that's the case, you don't have time to take part in school club activities, right?

Chen Minxuan : That doesn't matter. I came to Taiwan to study, not to have fun. I hope to finish taking all the credits in the Chinese department as soon as possible and after I go back to my home country, I'll focus on classes in my minor. That way I can graduate next year.

Li Wenyan : You have a minor? Why do you want to wear yourself out like that? If I were you, I'm afraid I would have gone crazy long ago.

Chen Minxuan : You're making it sound worse than it is. It's not that big a deal.

Li Wenyan : You should use your time in Taiwan to go around and learn more about the culture here.

Chen Minxuan : There'll be more opportunities to travel later. For the sake of my future career, for now, I should make good use of this time to improve myself.

(He Yating walks over.)

He Yating　　: Here you are!! What are you chatting about?

Li Wenyan　　: We're talking about our plans after graduation. By the way, when is your boyfriend holding his graduation exhibition?

He Yating　　: The fifth of next month. When the time comes, you're all welcome to come check it out.

Chen Minxuan : Are his parents going? I heard you say that his parents are really against his studying fashion design. Is that still the case?

He Yating　　: His parents still think it's a shame that their son didn't study in the department of medicine. He has always done well in school, so his parents have always had high expectations for him. His choice of fashion design was a big letdown for them.

Li Wenyan　　: Why would they be disappointed? There are leaders in every industry. It doesn't matter what a person does. As long as they are interested and apply themselves, that's all that matters.

生詞一 Vocabulary I　　🎧 08-02

Vocabulary

1	整夜整夜整	zhěngyè 夜	ㄓㄥˇ ㄧㄝˋ	(N)	all night
2	開開	kāi	ㄎㄞ	(V)	to turn on, to power on
3	燈燈燈	dēng	ㄉㄥ	(N)	light, lamp
4	電玩電玩電	diànwán 玩	ㄉㄧㄢˋ ㄨㄢˊ	(N)	video game
5	球賽	qiúsài	ㄑㄧㄡˊ ㄙㄞˋ	(N)	ball game
6	激動激動	jīdòng 激動激動	ㄐㄧ ㄉㄨㄥˋ	(Vs)	to be excited
7	喊 喊 喊	hǎn	ㄏㄢˇ	(Vi)	to yell, shout
8	公職公職公	gōngzhí 職	ㄍㄨㄥ ㄓˊ	(N)	government posts
9	其實其實其實	qíshí 其實	ㄑㄧˊ ㄕˊ	(Adv)	in fact, actually
10	公務員 務員	gōngwùyuán 公務員	ㄍㄨㄥ ㄨˋ ㄩㄢˊ	(N)	civil servant

11	煩煩煩	fán	ㄈㄢˊ	(Vs)	a "drag", a pain in the neck
12	聽話聽話	tīnghuà 聽話	ㄊㄧㄥ ㄏㄨㄚˋ	(Vs-sep)	to listen, to obey
13	失業率失業率	shīyèlǜ 失業率失業率	ㄕ ㄧㄝˋ ㄌㄩˋ	(N)	unemployment rate
14	門	mén	ㄇㄣˊ	(M)	measure word for academic courses
15	讀書讀書讀	dúshū	ㄉㄨˊ ㄕㄨ	(V-sep)	to study
16	學分	xuéfēn	ㄒㄩㄝˊ ㄈㄣ	(N)	(academic) credits
17	修修	xiū	ㄒㄧㄡ	(V)	to take (courses)
18	專心專心	zhuānxīn	ㄓㄨㄢ ㄒㄧㄣ	(Vs)	to focus on, concentrate
19	修課	xiūkè	ㄒㄧㄡ ㄎㄜˋ	(V-sep)	to take a class
20	輔系輔系	fǔxì 輔系輔系	ㄈㄨˇ ㄒㄧˋ	(N)	minor (in college)
21	瘋瘋瘋瘋	fēng	ㄈㄥ	(Vp)	to go crazy, to be insane
22	誇張誇張	kuāzhāng 誇張	ㄎㄨㄚ ㄓㄤ	(Vs)	to be exaggerated
23	舉行舉行	jǔxíng 舉行	ㄐㄩˇ ㄒㄧㄥˊ	(V)	to hold (a conference, exhibition)
24	遺憾遺憾	yíhàn 遺憾	ㄧˊ ㄏㄢˋ	(Vs)	regretful (that something undesirable happened), a pity, a shame
25	兒子	érzi	ㄦˊ ㄗ	(N)	son
26	期望期望	qíwàng 期望	ㄑㄧˊ ㄨㄤˋ	(N)	expectations
27	狀元狀元狀元	zhuàngyuán	ㄓㄨㄤˋ ㄩㄢˊ	(N)	top-ranking in a public exam (originally the person with the highest marks on the imperial test)
28	努力努力努力	nǔlì	ㄋㄨˇ ㄌㄧˋ	(Vs)	diligent in

Phrases

29	怎麼回事	zěnme huíshì	ㄗㄣˇ ㄇㄜ ㄏㄨㄟˊ ㄕˋ		What's wrong?
30	大喊大叫	dàhǎn dàjiào	ㄉㄚˋ ㄏㄢˇ ㄉㄚˋ ㄐㄧㄠˋ		to yell, yelling, shouting
31	期中考	qízhōng kǎo	ㄑㄧˊ ㄓㄨㄥ ㄎㄠˇ		mid-term exam
32	密集班	mìjí bān	ㄇㄧˋ ㄐㄧˊ ㄅㄢ		intensive course
33	畢業展	bìyè zhǎn	ㄅㄧˋ ㄧㄝˋ ㄓㄢˇ		graduation exhibition

34	服裝設計	fúzhuāng shèjì	ㄈㄨˊ ㄓㄨㄤ ㄕㄜˋ ㄐㄧˋ	fashion design
35	醫學系	yīxué xì	ㄧ ㄒㄩㄝˊ ㄒㄧˋ	department of medicine
36	行行出狀元	hángháng chū zhuàngyuán	ㄏㄤˊ ㄏㄤˊ ㄔㄨ ㄓㄨㄤˋ ㄩㄢˊ	there is a leader in every industry

短文 Reading 🎧 08-03

麵包冠軍吳寶春

　　2013 年三月，世界麵包大賽冠軍吳寶春通過新加坡大學 EMBA（高級管理人員工商管理碩士）研究所的面試，準備從七月起，開始他的學生生活。吳寶春也申請過台灣的 EMBA，卻因為只有國中畢業，學歷太低而被拒絕。「吳寶春要念研究所」在台灣引起了很多人的討論。有人認為學校太沒有彈性。時代已經改變了，制度也應該隨著改變。但是也有人認為他的基礎不夠，如果讓他念研究所，對認真念書的人不公平。

　　吳寶春出生在台灣南部鄉下，他是家裡最小的孩子。他家很窮。父親很早就過世了。母親為了養八個孩子，每天辛苦地工作。吳寶春小時候不了解讀書的重要，不喜歡念書。按照他自己的說法，國中畢業的時候，他認識的字還不到五百個。

　　17 歲那一年，他離開家鄉，一個人到台北一家麵包店當學徒。工作的時候因為書念得不多，吃了很多苦。這時候他才明白讀書的重要。當兵的時候，他利用時間看電視認字。後來他因為想看懂日文烘焙書，去學日文。幾年以後，更因為工作的關係到日本學習，讓他大開眼界，了解到烘焙麵包不但是專業技術，也是一門藝術。

吳寶春經過 20 多年的努力，終於在 2010 年拿到世界麵包大賽
冠軍。回台灣以後，他開了自己的麵包店，一年能做兩億的生意。
他的夢想是成為企業家，能在亞洲各國開分店。新加坡大學也因為
這個原因錄取了他。吳寶春成功的故事鼓勵了很多人做自己。可是，
是不是每個人都能像他在碰到機會以前，做好了百分之百的準備？

shēngyi business/trade

課文簡體字版 Text in Simplified Characters

面包冠军吴宝春

2013 年三月，世界面包大赛冠军吴宝春通过新加坡大学 EMBA（高级管
理人员工商管理硕士）研究所的面试，准备从七月起，开始他的学生生活。
吴宝春也申请过台湾的 EMBA，却因为只有国中毕业，学历太低而被拒绝。
「吴宝春要念研究所」在台湾引起了很多人的讨论。有人认为学校太没有
弹性。时代已经改变了，制度也应该随着改变。但是也有人认为他的基础
不够，如果让他念研究所，对认真念书的人不公平。

吴宝春出生在台湾南部乡下，他是家里最小的孩子。他家很穷。父亲
很早就过世了。母亲为了养八个孩子，每天辛苦地工作。吴宝春小时候不
了解读书的重要，不喜欢念书。按照他自己的说法，国中毕业的时候，他
认识的字还不到五百个。

17 岁那一年，他离开家乡，一个人到台北一家面包店当学徒。工作的
时候因为书念得不多，吃了很多苦。这时候他才明白读书的重要。当兵的
时候，他利用时间看电视认字。后来他因为想看懂日文烘焙书，去学日文。
几年以后，更因为工作的关系到日本学习，让他大开眼界，了解到烘焙面
包不但是专业技术，也是一门艺术。

吴宝春经过 20 多年的努力，终于在 2010 年拿到世界面包大赛冠军。
回台湾以后，他开了自己的面包店，一年能做两亿的生意。他的梦想是成
为企业家，能在亚洲各国开分店。新加坡大学也因为这个原因录取了他。
吴宝春成功的故事鼓励了很多人做自己。可是，是不是每个人都能像他在
碰到机会以前，做好了百分之百的准备？

課文英譯 Text in English

Bread Competition Champion Wu Baochun

In March of 2013, Bakery World Cup champion Wu Baochun passed the interview for the EMBA program at the National University of Singapore and is preparing to start his life as a student from July. Wu Baochun also applied for an EMBA program in Taiwan, but because he only graduated from middle school, his level of education was considered too low, and he was rejected. Wu Baochun's admission to graduate school in Singapore generated much discussion among many people in Taiwan. Some people believe that Taiwan's schools are too inflexible, that the times have changed and systems should change with them. But other people feel that he doesn't have the necessary groundwork laid, and if he were allowed to go to grad school, it wouldn't be fair to others who have had to study hard.

Wu Baochun was born in the country in southern Taiwan, the youngest child in his family. His family was very poor and his father died when he was very young. In order to raise eight children, his mother had to work extremely hard every day. When he was young, Wu Baochun didn't understand the importance of school and didn't enjoy studying. According to him, when he graduated from junior high school, he knew fewer than 500 characters.

When he was 17 he set out on his own, leaving his hometown for Taipei to apprentice in a bakery. He experienced a lot of difficulties at work due to his lack of education. It wasn't until then that he realized the importance of study. During conscription, in his spare time he learned how to read by watching subtitled TV programming. He went on to study Japanese because he wanted to understand Japanese baking books. A few years later, because of his work, he ended up going to Japan to study. It was an eye-opening experience for him. He learned that making bread is not only a specialized skill. It is an art.

More than 20 years of hard work lead to Wu Baochun winning The Bakery World Cup championship in 2010. After returning to Taiwan, he opened up his own bakery, which generates NT$200 million a year. His dream is to become an entrepreneur and open up branches of his bakery in countries around Asia. It is for this reason that The University of Singapore accepted him. Wu Baochun's story of success has inspired many people to follow their dreams. But can each individual make sure that he is 100% ready for the opportunity when it arises?

生詞二 Vocabulary II 08-04

Vocabulary

1	冠軍	guànjūn	ㄍㄨㄢˋ ㄐㄩㄣ	(N)	champion, championship
2	大賽	dàsài	ㄉㄚˋ ㄙㄞˋ	(N)	a major, usually international, competition
3	通過	tōngguò	ㄊㄨㄥ ㄍㄨㄛˋ	(Vpt)	to pass
4	高級	gāojí	ㄍㄠ ㄐㄧˊ	(Vs-attr)	high level, advanced
5	碩士	shuòshì	ㄕㄨㄛˋ ㄕˋ	(N)	master's degree
6	面試	miànshì	ㄇㄧㄢˋ ㄕˋ	(N)	interview
7	卻	què	ㄑㄩㄝˋ	(Adv)	but, yet
8	國中	guózhōng	ㄍㄨㄛˊ ㄓㄨㄥ	(N)	junior middle school
9	學歷	xuélì	ㄒㄩㄝˊ ㄌㄧˋ	(N)	educational background
10	拒絕	jùjué	ㄐㄩˋ ㄐㄩㄝˊ	(V)	to reject
11	引起	yǐnqǐ	ㄧㄣˇ ㄑㄧˇ	(Vpt)	to stir up, generate, cause
12	彈性	tánxìng	ㄊㄢˊ ㄒㄧㄥˋ	(N)	flexibility
13	改變	gǎibiàn	ㄍㄞˇ ㄅㄧㄢˋ	(V)	to undergo change
14	制度	zhìdù	ㄓˋ ㄉㄨˋ	(N)	system
15	基礎	jīchǔ	ㄐㄧ ㄔㄨˇ	(N)	foundation, fundamentals
16	認真	rènzhēn	ㄖㄣˋ ㄓㄣ	(Vs)	earnest, serious
17	公平	gōngpíng	ㄍㄨㄥ ㄆㄧㄥˊ	(Vs)	fair
18	出生	chūshēng	ㄔㄨ ㄕㄥ	(Vp)	to be born
19	窮	qióng	ㄑㄩㄥˊ	(Vs)	poor
20	父親	fùqīn	ㄈㄨˋ ㄑㄧㄣ	(N)	father
21	母親	mǔqīn	ㄇㄨˇ ㄑㄧㄣ	(N)	mother
22	學徒	xuétú	ㄒㄩㄝˊ ㄊㄨˊ	(N)	apprentice
23	吃苦	chīkǔ	ㄔ ㄎㄨˇ	(Vs-sep)	experience tough times
24	明白	míngbái	ㄇㄧㄥˊ ㄅㄞˊ	(Vst)	to understand
25	當兵	dāngbīng	ㄉㄤ ㄅㄧㄥ	(V-sep)	to be a soldier, to do military service
26	認字	rènzì	ㄖㄣˋ ㄗˋ	(Vi)	to learn characters

27	烘焙烘焙烘	hōngbèi	ㄏㄨㄥ ㄅㄟˋ	(V)	to bake
28	學習	xuéxí	ㄒㄩㄝˊ ㄒㄧˊ	(V)	to study
29	技術技術技	jìshù	ㄐㄧˋ ㄕㄨˋ	(N)	skills
30	藝術藝術藝	yìshù	ㄧˋ ㄕㄨˋ	(N)	art
31	經過經過	jīngguò	ㄐㄧㄥ ㄍㄨㄛˋ	(Prep)	after
32	終於終於終	zhōngyú	ㄓㄨㄥ ㄩˊ	(Adv)	finally
33	億億億億	yì	ㄧˋ	(N)	100 million
34	夢想夢想夢	mèngxiǎng	ㄇㄥˋ ㄒㄧㄤˇ	(N)	dream, ideals (not during sleep)
35	成為成為成	chéngwéi	ㄔㄥˊ ㄨㄟˊ	(Vpt)	to become
36	企業家企業家	qìyèjiā	ㄑㄧˋ ㄧㄝˋ ㄐㄧㄚ	(N)	entrepreneur
37	分店分店	fēndiàn	ㄈㄣ ㄉㄧㄢˋ	(N)	branch store, branch office
38	原因原因原因	yuányīn	ㄩㄢˊ ㄧㄣ	(N)	reason
39	錄取錄取錄	lùqǔ	ㄌㄨˋ ㄑㄩˇ	(V)	to accept (application), to admit
40	成功成功成	chénggōng	ㄔㄥˊ ㄍㄨㄥ	(Vs)	successful
41	鼓勵	gǔlì	ㄍㄨˇ ㄌㄧˋ	(V)	to encourage

Names

42	吳寶春	Wú Bǎochūn	ㄨˊ ㄅㄠˇ ㄔㄨㄣ		a famous baker from Taiwan
43	新加坡	Xīnjiāpō	ㄒㄧㄣ ㄐㄧㄚ ㄆㄛ		Singapore
44	日文	Rìwén	ㄖˋ ㄨㄣˊ		Japanese language or writing

Phrases

45	世界麵包大賽	shìjiè miànbāo dàsài	ㄕˋ ㄐㄧㄝˋ ㄇㄧㄢˋ ㄅㄠ ㄉㄚˋ ㄙㄞˋ		The Bakery World Cup
46	EMBA (高級管理人員工商管理碩士)	EMBA (gāojí guǎnlǐ rényuán gōngshāng guǎnlǐ shuòshì)	EMBA (ㄍㄠ ㄐㄧˊ ㄍㄨㄢˇ ㄌㄧˇ ㄖㄣˊ ㄩㄢˊ ㄍㄨㄥ ㄕㄤ ㄍㄨㄢˇ ㄌㄧˇ ㄕㄨㄛˋ ㄕˋ)		EMBA (Executive Master of Business Administration)
47	小時候	xiǎo shíhòu	ㄒㄧㄠˇ ㄕˊ ㄏㄡˋ		in one's childhood

| 48 | 大開眼界 | dàkāi yǎnjiè | ㄉㄚˋ ㄎㄞ ㄧㄢˇ ㄐㄧㄝˋ | to have one's eyes opened |
| 49 | X 分之 Y | X fēn zhī Y | X ㄈㄣ ㄓ Y | pattern for indicating percentages or fractions |

文法 Grammar

I. 不是…就是… *if it's not…, then it's…*   08-05   英譯 p.199

Function: This construction, when used literally, indicates that one of two options offered must be true, and there are no other possibilities. It can also be used for hyperbole when describing a situation, often spoken out of frustration.

1 我新買的手機不是收不到訊號,就是自動關機,我非拿去門市退換不可。

2 桌上這件外套我想不是敏萱的,就是雅婷的。

3 放假的時候,他不是上網玩遊戲,就是在家看漫畫,放鬆心情。

4 他整天不是抱怨工作太多,就是抱怨薪水太少,讓人聽得好煩。

5 暑假,他不是去打工,就是回家照顧爺爺,所以沒時間跟我們玩。

練習 Exercise

Please complete the dialogues below, indicating two options or situations using 不是…就是….

1 A:聽說小王要參加公職人員考試。

　　B:他整天＿＿＿＿＿＿＿＿＿＿＿＿＿＿＿＿＿＿＿＿＿＿,怎麼考得上?

2 A:小王怎麼又遲到了?真討厭。

　　B:你別生氣。我想＿＿＿＿＿＿＿＿＿＿＿＿＿＿＿＿＿＿＿＿＿＿。

③ A：這些豬肉餡兒的水餃樣子很特別，都是雅婷包的嗎？

　　B：不清楚。我想＿＿＿＿＿＿＿＿＿＿＿＿＿＿＿＿＿。

④ A：現在有些年輕人結婚以後，不想生孩子。你知道為什麼嗎？

　　B：我想＿＿＿＿＿＿＿＿＿＿＿＿＿＿＿＿＿＿＿。

⑤ A：為什麼他最近看起來那麼沒有精神？

　　B：＿＿＿＿＿＿＿＿＿＿＿＿＿＿＿＿＿＿＿＿＿。

II. 算了 *forget it, drop it* 🎧 08-06

 英譯 p.199

Function: Use of the idiomatic verb 算了 indicates the speaker's desire to disregard an unpleasant fact.

① A：你不是要跟女朋友去聽五月天的演唱會嗎？怎麼還在這裡？

　　B：氣死我了。她說要準備明天的報告，不去了。

　　A：她不去算了，你不要生氣了。

② A：妳昨天會計的考試，成績怎麼樣？

　　B：真不好。算了，算了。今天不說這個。

③ A：小王說他對唱歌沒興趣，晚上不去 KTV 了。

　　B：那就算了。我自己去。

④ A：沒想到我最喜歡的羊毛外套破了一個大洞。

　　B：既然破了一個大洞，就丟了算了。

⑤ A：我告訴小明炸的東西對身體不好，不要常吃，他總是不聽。

　　B：他不聽算了，你別難過了。

Usage: Note that 算了 can occur at the very front, in the middle or even at the very end of a sentence. This type of grammatical flexibility is rather rare in modern Chinese.

練習 Exercise

Please complete the dialogues below using 算了.

1 A：氣死了，我孩子又把手機弄壞了。

B：算了，別氣了，＿＿＿＿＿＿＿＿＿＿＿＿＿＿＿＿＿＿。

2 A：你不是說週末要去海邊曬太陽，怎麼不去了？

B：算了，＿＿＿＿＿＿＿＿＿＿＿＿＿＿＿＿＿＿＿。

3 A：雖然念會計系比較容易找到工作，但是我一點興趣都沒有。

B：既然沒興趣，就＿＿＿＿＿＿＿＿＿＿＿＿＿＿＿＿。

4 A：去美國念書是難得的機會，妳怎麼不去呢？

B：我是家裡的獨生女，恐怕爸媽捨不得我去那麼遠的地方。

A：要是妳父母捨不得妳去，就＿＿＿＿＿＿＿＿＿＿＿。

5 A：小陳說下星期有考試，所以今天晚上不能來和我們一起過中秋節。

B：＿＿＿＿＿＿＿＿＿＿＿＿＿＿＿＿＿＿＿＿＿。

III. 這樣一來 *that being the case, that way* 08-07　　　　 英譯 p.199

Function: The speaker uses this pattern to present a consequence that could result from the previous statement.

1 A：聽說陳平這個學期有好幾門課被當。

B：這樣一來，他明年恐怕沒辦法畢業了。

2 A：我先生下星期要帶孩子去美國旅行一個月。

B：真的啊。這樣一來，妳就不必天天做飯了。

3 A：電視新聞說這個週末有颱風要來。

B：這樣一來，我們就不能去海邊玩了。

4 A：媽媽建議讓弟弟下課以後去學游泳、書法跟網球。

B：太好了。這樣一來，他就不會整天在家看電視、打電玩了。

5 A：最近三個星期，我住的城市幾乎天天下雨。而且新聞還說，下個禮拜雨還不會停。

B：這樣一來，你的衣服、鞋子不是就都發霉了嗎？

練習 Exercise

Please complete the following dialogues, expanding on what has stated with 這樣一來.

❶ A：小明的爸爸說，如果他要修輔系，就得自己付學費。

　 B：＿＿＿＿＿＿＿＿＿＿＿＿＿＿＿＿＿＿＿＿＿＿＿＿＿＿。

❷ A：我打算今年暑假參加公職人員考試。

　 B：＿＿＿＿＿＿＿＿＿＿＿＿＿＿＿＿＿＿＿＿＿＿＿＿＿＿。

❸ A：聽說從這個學期起，成功的企業家不必參加筆試，只要通過口試就能上研究所。

　 B：這怎麼可以呢？這樣一來，＿＿＿＿＿＿＿＿＿＿＿＿＿＿。

❹ A：小王已經決定念服裝設計系，不念醫學系了。

　 B：＿＿＿＿＿＿＿＿＿＿＿＿＿＿＿＿＿＿＿＿＿＿＿＿＿＿。

❺ A：爸爸答應我，下個月開始，每個月多給我兩千塊錢生活費。

　 B：＿＿＿＿＿＿＿＿＿＿＿＿＿＿＿＿＿＿＿＿＿＿＿。

IV. 早就⋯了 *long since...* 08-08　　　　　🔍英譯 p.199

Function: This construction presents an exaggerated reference to the time in the past that an event took place.

❶ 我只見過陳平幾次面，早就對他沒印象了。

❷ 五月天演唱會的票，我早就買了，你不必擔心。

❸ 那條路上早就沒有日本人留下來的木造房子了。我們還要去嗎？

❹ 你的平板電腦我早就修理好了，你怎麼不記得呢？

❺ 媽媽煮的水餃，早就被弟弟吃光了。你吃別的吧！

練習 Exercise

Please complete the dialogues below, indicating an event that occurred long ago using 早就…了 .

❶ A：小李住在台灣一年了，還沒拿到居留證嗎？

B：他＿＿＿＿＿＿＿＿＿＿＿＿＿＿＿＿＿＿＿＿＿＿＿。

❷ A：你轉系的手續辦得怎麼樣？

B：沒想到轉系的手續那麼麻煩，我＿＿＿＿＿＿＿＿＿＿＿＿。

❸ A：你不是很喜歡王美美嗎？怎麼不追她？

B：追她的人這麼多，我＿＿＿＿＿＿＿＿＿＿＿＿＿＿＿＿＿。

❹ A：你爺爺還在鄉下種水果嗎？

B：小農的利潤那麼低，我爺爺＿＿＿＿＿＿＿＿＿＿＿＿＿＿。

❺ A：王明跟他女朋友同居了好幾年了，怎麼不結婚呢？

B：誰說的。他們＿＿＿＿＿＿＿＿＿，而且還生了一個孩子。

V. 從…起 *starting from…* 08-09 英譯 p.200

Function: This pattern specifies the beginning point of an event.

❶ 學生總是說從明天起，我要好好地念書，不讓父母失望。

❷ 那個語言中心規定從今年秋天起，申請獎學金的學生，成績要有 85 分。

❸ 因為放暑假的關係，學校的圖書館從後天起，上午九點才開門。

❹ 你弄錯了。百貨公司打折活動是從十月十號起，不是十月一號。

❺ 那個展覽館從下星期一起到下個月三十一號，要舉行電腦展。

Usage ： 從…起 is relatively literary and formal. It's more colloquial to say 從…開始 . E.g., 從明天開始，我不再吃炸的東西了。'Starting tomorrow, I'm not eating fried foods.'

練習 Exercise

Please complete the dialogues below, indicating a starting point using 從…起 .

❶ A：她是什麼時候開始在餐廳打工的？

B：＿＿＿＿＿＿＿＿＿＿＿＿＿＿＿，她就在餐廳打工了。

❷ A：小王決定去日本念研究所了嗎？

B：是啊。他終於決定＿＿＿＿＿＿＿去日本念三年的書。

❸ A：你是什麼時候開始學做飯的？

B：＿＿＿＿＿＿＿＿＿＿＿＿＿＿＿，就開始學做飯了。

❹ A：小美網球怎麼打得那麼好？

B：因為她＿＿＿＿＿＿＿＿＿＿＿＿＿，就學打網球了。

❺ A：玉真，妳這次的口頭報告做得不太好。

B：我知道了。＿＿＿＿＿＿＿＿＿＿＿＿，我會認真一點。

VI. 卻 *however* 08-10 　　　　　　　　　英譯 p.200

Function: In sentences indicating events that are contrary to expectation, the adverb 卻 frequently occurs before the verb phrase in the second clause.

❶ 他的成績不錯，可是卻沒通過研究所的面試。

❷ 在那家麵包店當學徒，雖然辛苦，卻讓他大開眼界。

❸ 我昨天買的外套，裡面破了一個洞，但是店員卻不讓我退換。

❹ 早上出門的時候還出太陽，沒想到現在卻下起雨來了。

❺ 那家小吃店雖然沒有招牌，生意卻好得不得了。

Usage: 卻 is often used together with 可是, 但是, or 沒想到.

練習 Exercise

Please complete the sentences below, using 卻 to indicate a circumstance contrary to expectation.

❶ 他想買的鞋子是有名的牌子，可是＿＿＿＿＿＿＿＿＿＿＿。

❷ 我以為媽媽已經答應讓我養寵物了，沒想到＿＿＿＿＿＿＿。

❸ 李明雖然從小在農村長大，＿＿＿＿＿＿＿＿＿＿＿。

❹ 他穿的那件藍色外套，看起來跟我買的一模一樣，
但是＿＿＿＿＿＿＿＿＿＿＿＿＿＿＿＿。

❺ 美真不但長得美，而且能力強，追她的人很多，
她＿＿＿＿＿＿＿＿＿＿＿＿＿＿＿＿＿＿。

VII. 因為…而… *therefore, consequently* 08-11　　 英譯 p.200

Function: The adverb 而 refers to a consequence resulting from a cause given elsewhere in the sentence.

❶ 我奶奶一個人住，因為怕孤單而養了兩隻狗。

❷ 很多人因為想學道地的西班牙文而去西班牙。

❸ 那個小鎮因為今年芒果收成很好而打算舉行慶祝活動。

❹ 她因為衣服、鞋子都發霉了而決定去買除濕機。

❺ 王小姐因為男朋友忘了送她生日禮物而氣得不想跟他說話。

Usage: The structure 因為…而… is frequently used in written documents or in formal venues.

練習 Exercise

Please complete the 而 clauses below.

❶ 他因為爺爺跌倒而＿＿＿＿＿＿＿＿＿＿＿＿＿＿＿。

❷ 他因為想接近自然而＿＿＿＿＿＿＿＿＿＿＿＿＿＿。

❸ 小陳今天因為上課不專心而＿＿＿＿＿＿＿＿＿＿＿＿。

④ 何真真因為想減輕父母的負擔而打算＿＿＿＿＿＿＿＿。

⑤ 王老闆因為明美的口才好而＿＿＿＿＿＿＿＿＿＿。

VIII. 經過 *after* 🎧 08-12

英譯 p.200

Function: 經過 in this usage is a preposition meaning 'after' or 'subsequent to'.

① 經過父母多次的說明，她才明白要成功非努力不可。

② 他的喉嚨經過多天的休息，最近好一點了。

③ 你並沒有經過學校的同意，怎麼可以使用體育館？

④ 我是經過兩年的準備，才考上公務員的。

Usage: 經過 of this usage is followed either by a noun or by a sentence. 經過 can be a verb meaning "to pass a point". E.g., 從台北去高雄，要經過台南。'To get from Taipei to Kaohsiung, you need to pass through Tainan.'

練習 Exercise

Please complete the dialogues below, indicating a process or experience and subsequent outcome using 經過.

① A：那件藍色外套不便宜，何雅婷怎麼就買了？

　 B：＿＿＿＿＿＿＿＿＿＿＿＿才買的。（考慮）

② A：這份合約，你都看懂了嗎？

　 B：＿＿＿＿＿＿＿＿＿＿＿，我終於懂了。（說明）

③ A：你們班畢業旅行要去哪裡？決定了嗎？

　 B：＿＿＿＿＿＿＿＿＿，我們決定去泰國四天。（討論）

④ A：小明的太極拳怎麼打得這麼好？

　 B：＿＿＿＿＿＿＿＿＿，才打得這麼好的。（練習）

⑤ A：你是怎麼見到王老闆的？

　 B：我＿＿＿＿＿＿，才見到王老闆的。（陳先生的安排）

語法例句英譯
Grammar Examples in English •

I. 不是…就是… *if it's not…, then it's…*

Function:

❶ If my new cell phone isn't having problems getting a signal, it's shutting itself off. I'm going to take it back to the store and exchange it if it's the last thing I do.

❷ I think that the coat on the table is either Minxuan or Yating's.

❸ When he's on break, he's either online playing games or reading comic books to relax.

❹ All day long, he's either complaining that he's overworked or underpaid. It's irritating to listen to.

❺ He didn't have any time to go out with us during summer vacation. He was either working or at home taking care of his grandfather.

II. 算了 *forget it, drop it*

Function:

❶ A: Aren't you going with your girlfriend to the May Day concert? Why are you still here?
B: I'm so mad. She said she has to prepare a report for tomorrow, so she's not going.
A: If she's not going then just forget about it. Don't be upset.

❷ A: How did you do on the accounting test yesterday?
B: I did really poorly. Drop it. Let's not talk about it today.

❸ A: Xiao Wang says that he's not a big fan of singing. He's not going to go to KTV tonight.
B: Then, forget it. I'll go myself.

❹ A: I had no idea that my favorite wool coat would get a big hole in it.

B: Since it's got a big hole in it, just toss it and forget about it.

❷ A: I told Xiaoming that fried food is bad for his health, he shouldn't eat it so often, but he never listens.
B: If he doesn't want to listen then just forget it. Don't be upset about it.

III. 這樣一來 *that being the case, that way*

Function:

❶ A: I heard that Chen Ping flunked a number of his classes this semester.
B: That being the case, there's probably no way he'll be able to graduate next year.

❷ A: Next week, my husband is taking the kids to the US for a one-month trip.
B: Really? So I guess you don't have to cook every day.

❸ A: The news on TV said that a typhoon is coming this weekend.
B: In that case, we can't go to the seaside.

❹ A: Mom suggested having my kid brother go to swimming, calligraphy, and tennis classes after school.
B: Great. That way, he won't be in the house all day watching TV and playing video games.

❺ A: Over the past three weeks, it has rained almost every day in the city I live in. And the news says that it's not going to stop next week either.
B: If that's the case, aren't your clothes and shoes going to mildew?

IV. 早就…了 *long since…*

Function:

❶ I only met Chen Ping a few times. I have long since forgotten everything about him.

❷ I bought Mayday concert tickets ages ago. No need to worry.

3 It's been forever since there were any Japanese style wooden houses left on that street. Are we still going to go?

4 I fixed your tablet computer a long time ago. How is it you don't remember?

5 Little brother ate all the dumplings Mom made a long time ago. Go ahead and eat something else.

V. 從…起 *starting from…*

Function:

1 Students always say, "I'll study hard starting tomorrow. I don't want my parents to be disappointed."

2 The language center has stipulated that starting this fall, students applying for scholarships must have a grade average of at least 85.

3 Due to summer vacation, starting tomorrow, the school library won't open until 9:00 in the morning.

4 You've got it wrong. The department store sales start from October 10th, not from October 1st.

5 That exhibition hall will be holding a computer exhibition starting next Monday, until the 31st of next month.

VI. 卻 *however*

Function:

1 His grades are good, but he didn't pass the interview for grad school. (Everyone expected him to pass.)

2 He served as an apprentice in that bakery. It was tough, but it really opened his eyes.

3 The coat I bought yesterday has a hole on the inside, but the store employee wouldn't let me exchange it.

4 It was sunny when I left the house this morning. I never expected it would rain now.

5 That small eatery doesn't even have a sign, but its business is booming.

VII. 因為…而… *therefore, consequently*

Function:

1 My grandma lives by herself. She's afraid of being alone, so she has two dogs.

2 Many people want to learn authentic Spanish, so they go to Spain.

3 Because it had a good mango harvest this year, that town plans to put on some activities in celebration.

4 Because her clothes and shoes mildewed, she decided to go buy a dehumidifier.

5 Because her boyfriend forgot to give her a birthday present, Miss Wang is so angry that she doesn't want to talk to him.

VIII. 經過 *after*

Function:

1 She didn't really understand that to succeed, you must work hard, until after her parents explained it to her numerous times.

2 After several days of rest, his throat has gotten a bit better.

3 You didn't receive permission from the school; thus, you should not be using the gymnasium.

4 I passed the civil service test only after two years of preparation.

課室活動 Classroom Activities

I. What's Happening Now and My Future Plans

Goal: Learning to talk about classes I'm currently taking, what's happening in my life, and my plans for the future.

Task: Interview three classmates. Ask them to tell you about classes they are currently taking, what's happening in their lives, and what plans they have for the future.

同學	修課情形	生活情形	將來的計畫
❶			
❷			
❸			

II. Talking about Somebody's Experience

Goal: Learning to describe study and work experience.

Task: Students, think of an example from your own country of a person who didn't receive a high or complete education, but later had tremendous achievements. Please introduce this person's background to the others.

Try to use the following sentence patterns and vocabulary words:

這樣一來	就算…也…	各 V 各的	早就…了

III. 小高 Wants to Be a Chef

Goal: Learning to explain reasons.

Task: Xiaogao wants to be a renowned chef. Should he go to university and study in a department of culinary arts or should he go work as a chef's assistant? He's not sure what he should do. Students pair up and take turns completing suggestion A or B below. Then, one student from each pair, tells the class what you think Xiaogao should do.

A. 你應該去念餐飲系	為什麼
B. 你應該直接去當大廚的助理	**為什麼**

How Children Are Named

"來弟（lái dì, come little brother）, come here a second!" The first time somebody hears someone call a name like this, they're likely to be taken aback when they see a female walk over instead of the male they were expecting because of the name（弟弟）. This is because the way the Chinese name their children often reveals the hopes and dreams of parents for their children. So almost anybody whose name is 來弟, 引弟（yǐn dì, bring a younger brother）, or 招弟（zhāo dì, beckon a younger brother）is a female. This is due to the traditional Chinese preference of males over females. The parents hope that the next baby will be a male that can carry on the family line, hence, all of these names have something to do with "bringing a younger brother."

▲ People go to fortune tellers to name their children or to change their names to bring better luck.

▲ A great number of people have names like 建宏, because the name is both pleasant to the ear and has a good meaning.

Some parents feel that naming a girl 引弟 or 來弟 is a too obvious and direct expression of their hopes, so they give their daughters names with the character 娣（dì）which brings together 女 and 弟 or they name baby girls 希南（xīnán, a homophone to 希男, "hope for a male"）, expressing the hope that the next child will be a boy. They might even express their hope for a boy using sounds that are close but not exactly the same as an auspicious phrase. For example, 士蘭（shìlán, scholar orchid）sounds a little like 是男（shìnán, it's a boy）. In contrast to females, who are often given names reflecting the wish to have a boy, male babies are often given auspicious names, like 天賜（tiāncì, heaven granted）, 萬福（wànfú, ten thousand blessings）, or 進財（jìncái, bring treasure）.

In addition, fortune tellers in Taiwan divide names into two main categories, auspicious（吉, jí）and inauspicious（凶, xiōng）, based on the total number of pen strokes in the surnames and given names. Some parents believe that the number of strokes in a child's name will influence that for life, so they choose lucky names based on the number of strokes in the name. This is one reason for the great number of people with similar sounding names. Examples include girls' names like 怡君（yíjūn）and 雅婷（yǎtíng）as well as boys' names like 志強（zhìqiáng）and 建宏（jiànhóng）. These names have good sounds and meanings, but it's for these very reasons that a lot of people have the same names.

Parents all hope that their children will get ahead in the world someday, so a couple might name their boy 龍成（lóngchéng）in the hopes that he will 成為龍（become a dragon, i.e., become a mover and shaker）. Somebody else might name their girl 巧玲（qiǎolíng）in the hope that she will be intelligent, sensitive, and skilled in a craft. The loving intentions of parents are evidenced from the names they choose for their children.

Self-Assessment Checklist

I can explain in detail classes that I am currently taking and my future plans.

20%   40%   60%   80%   100%

I can talk about study and work experience.

20%   40%   60%   80%   100%

I can discuss differences in traditional and modern ideas and values.

20%   40%   60%   80%   100%

I can explain the names of university departments and graduate school programs.

20%   40%   60%   80%   100%

LESSON
9

第九課

網購時代

The Age of Online Shopping

....

學習目標 Learning Objectives

Topic: 網路經濟 The Internet Economy

- Learning to talk about online shopping methods and processes.
- Learning to explain the pros and cons of different shopping methods.
- Learning to talk about traditional foods that best represent local cultures.
- Learning to discuss product manufacturing, market share, and market ranking.

網購時代

The Age of Online Shopping

對話 Dialogue 09-01

（在表哥家的客廳）

表　　哥：你們先喝茶聊天，我上網查一下訂單，把明天要寄給客戶的東西準備好。

李文彥：你以前不是都拿到農夫市集去賣嗎？怎麼現在上網賣了？

表　　哥：為了方便客戶訂購，我成立了一個網站，可是現在網路上的客戶不夠多，收入不穩定，所以假日還是到農夫市集去，讓更多的人認識我們的產品。慢慢地，我希望能只靠網路販賣。

羅珊蒂：你的產品種類夠多嗎？一個網站不是得要有很多不同的產品才可以嗎？

表　　哥：我認識的一位老阿嬤種了很多蔬菜。以前她只賣給中間商，利潤很低，所以我幫她上網賣。另外，我也找了一些回鄉下種田的年輕人一起經營網站。

羅 珊 蒂 ： 上網訂購的話，多久可以收到？

表　　哥 ： 在台灣宅配很快，一般來說，下訂單 24 小時後就能收到。客戶能吃到既新鮮又便宜的蔬果。（表哥站起來）不好意思，我得去忙了，你們繼續聊。

安 德 思 ： 網路真的很方便。一天二十四小時，只要你需要，隨時都可以上網訂購。再說，網路商店的商品種類很多，搜尋一下就能找到你要的東西。

李 文 彥 ： 我的冰箱就是在網路上買的。我媽常說，「貨比三家不吃虧」。我利用比價網站，很快就找到了，節省了很多跑來跑去的時間。

何 雅 婷 ： 在網路上買東西也有風險。上次我買了一個皮包，沒想到收到以後，發現跟網站上的照片完全不一樣。更讓人生氣的是，我找不到賣家退錢。

安 德 思 ： 是有這樣的問題。所以網購必須找有信用的網站。這樣的話，萬一不滿意，七天以內還可以退換。而且，一般來說，上網買還是可以便宜一、兩成。

羅 珊 蒂 ： 看起來上網購物越來越普遍。這兩年大家的購物習慣改變了這麼多。將來我開服裝店，還會有客人嗎？

何 雅 婷 ： 別擔心，對很多人來說，買東西的時候，最重要的還是能看到、摸到商品，尤其是服裝，一定要試穿。

李 文 彥 ： 妳說的沒錯，這兩種購物方式各有好處，大家可以按照自己的習慣跟需要選擇適合的購物方式。

羅 珊 蒂 ： 聽你這麼說，我就放心了。

（在表哥家的客厅）

表　　哥：你们先喝茶聊天，我上网查一下订单，把明天要寄给客户的东西准备好。

李 文 彦：你以前不是都拿到农夫市集去卖吗？怎么现在上网卖了？

表　　哥：为了方便客户订购，我成立了一个网站，可是现在网路上的客户不够多，收入不稳定，所以假日还是到农夫市集去，让更多的人认识我们的产品。慢慢地，我希望能只靠网路贩卖。

罗 珊 蒂：你的产品种类够多吗？一个网站不是得要有很多不同的产品才可以吗？

表　　哥：我认识的一位老阿嬷种了很多蔬菜。以前她只卖给中间商，利润很低，所以我帮她上网卖。另外，我也找了一些回乡下种田的年轻人一起经营网站。

罗 珊 蒂：上网订购的话，多久可以收到？

表　　哥：在台湾宅配很快，一般来说，下订单 24 小时后就能收到。客户能吃到既新鲜又便宜的蔬果。（表哥站起来） 不好意思，我得去忙了，你们继续聊。

安 德 思：网路真的很方便。一天二十四小时，只要你需要，随时都可以上网订购。再说，网路商店的商品种类很多，搜寻一下就能找到你要的东西。

李 文 彦：我的冰箱就是在网路上买的。我妈常说，「货比三家不吃亏」。我利用比价网站，很快就找到了，节省了很多跑来跑去的时间。

何 雅 婷：在网路上买东西也有风险。上次我买了一个皮包，没想到收到以后，发现跟网站上的照片完全不一样。更让人生气的是，我找不到卖家退钱。

安 德 思：是有这样的问题。所以网购必须找有信用的网站。这样的话，万一不满意，七天以内还可以退换。而且，一般来说，上网买还是可以便宜一、两成。

罗 珊 蒂：看起来上网购物越来越普遍。这两年大家的购物习惯改变了这么多。将来我开服装店，还会有客人吗？

何 雅 婷：别担心，对很多人来说，买东西的时候，最重要的还是能看到、摸到商品，尤其是服装，一定要试穿。

李 文 彦：妳说的没错，这两种购物方式各有好处，大家可以按照自己的习惯跟需要选择适合的购物方式。

罗 珊 蒂：听你这么说，我就放心了。

課文英譯 Text in English

(In the cousin's living room)

Cousin : You guys have some tea and chat for a bit. I'm going to check orders online and prepare the things that I am going to mail to customers tomorrow.

Li Wenyan : Didn't you used to take it all to the farmer's market to sell? How come you sell online now?

Cousin : I set up a website to make it easy for customers to order, but earnings are a bit unpredictable because I currently don't have enough online customers, so on holidays I still go to the farmers' market for better product exposure. Gradually, we hope that we can sell exclusively online.

Luo Shandi : Do you have enough selection of products? You need to have a wide variety of products to run a website, right?

Cousin : I know an older lady who raises all kinds of vegetables. In the past, she used to only sell to resellers. Her profits were low, so I helped her go online to sell her products. In addition, I also got together with some young people who have returned to the countryside to till the land and together, we operate a website.

Luo Shandi : If someone orders online, how long can they receive their product?

Cousin : In Taiwan, express delivery is very quick. Generally, you can get your products within 24 hours of placing your order. Customers can eat produce that is both fresh and inexpensive. (*The cousin stands up.*) I'm sorry. I have to get busy. You two continue chatting.

An Desi : The internet really is convenient. If you need something, you can go online anytime 24 hours a day to place an order. What's more, online shops have large varieties of products. Simply search and you can find whatever you want.

Li Wenyan : I bought my refrigerator online. My mom likes to say, "Shop around and you won't get ripped off". I used a price comparison website and very quickly found one. It saved me a lot of time running around.

He Yating : Buying things online also comes with risks. Once, I bought a bag. I never expected that when I got it, the bag looked completely different from the picture on the website. What made me even more angry was, I couldn't find the seller to get a refund.

An Desi : These kinds of problems do exist, so when you buy online, you have to find trustworthy sites. That way, if you're not satisfied, you can still make a return within seven days. And usually, buying online you can get things 10 to 20 percent cheaper.

Luo Shandi : It looks like online shopping is becoming increasingly common. Over the past two years, everybody's buying habits have changed so much. Will there still be customers when I open a clothing shop in the future?

He Yating : Don't worry. For many people, being able to see and touch products is still the most important thing when shopping. Clothing, in particular, they definitely want to try on.

Li Wenyan : You're right. Each of these two kinds of shopping methods has its advantages. People can choose the shopping method suited to them based on their own habits and needs.

Luo Shandi : I'm relieved to hear you say that.

生詞一 Vocabulary I 🎧 09-02

Vocabulary

1	訂單	dìngdān	ㄉㄧㄥˋ ㄉㄢ	(N)	an order (trading)
2	客戶	kèhù	ㄎㄜˋ ㄏㄨˋ	(N)	customer, client
3	方便	fāngbiàn	ㄈㄤ ㄅㄧㄢˋ	(V)	to offer convenience
4	訂購	dìnggòu	ㄉㄧㄥˋ ㄍㄡˋ	(V)	to order, place an order
5	成立	chénglì	ㄔㄥˊ ㄌㄧˋ	(V)	to establish, set up
6	假日	jiàrì	ㄐㄧㄚˋ ㄖˋ	(N)	holiday
7	販賣	fànmài	ㄈㄢˋ ㄇㄞˋ	(V)	to sell
8	阿嬤	āmà	ㄚ ㄇㄚˋ	(N)	grandma, older woman (Taiwanese)
9	中間商	zhōngjiānshāng	ㄓㄨㄥ ㄐㄧㄢ ㄕㄤ	(N)	middleman, reseller
10	經營	jīngyíng	ㄐㄧㄥ ㄧㄥˊ	(V)	to operate, run (a business)
11	宅配	zháipèi	ㄓㄞˊ ㄆㄟˋ	(Vi)	express delivery
12	下	xià	ㄒㄧㄚˋ	(V)	to place (an order)
13	既	jì	ㄐㄧˋ	(Adv)	not merely
14	隨時	suíshí	ㄙㄨㄟˊ ㄕˊ	(Adv)	anytime
15	搜尋	sōuxún	ㄙㄡ ㄒㄩㄣˊ	(V)	to search

16	冰箱	bīngxiāng	ㄅㄧㄥ ㄒㄧㄤ	(N)	refrigerator (lit. ice box)
17	吃虧	chīkuī	ㄔ ㄎㄨㄟ	(Vs-sep)	to suffer a loss *chīkuī*
18	比價	bǐjià	ㄅㄧˇ ㄐㄧㄚˋ	(V-sep)	to compare prices, price comparison *bǐ jià*
19	風險	fēngxiǎn	ㄈㄥ ㄒㄧㄢˇ	(N)	risk *fēngxiǎn*
20	賣家	màijiā	ㄇㄞˋ ㄐㄧㄚ	(N)	seller *màijiā*
21	必須	bìxū	ㄅㄧˋ ㄒㄩ	(Vaux)	must, to have to *bì xū*
22	信用	xìnyòng	ㄒㄧㄣˋ ㄩㄥˋ	(N)	credibility *xìnyòng*
23	萬一	wànyī	ㄨㄢˋ ㄧ	(Conj)	in case *wànyì*
24	滿意	mǎnyì	ㄇㄢˇ ㄧˋ	(Vst)	satisfied
25	以內	yǐnèi	ㄧˇ ㄋㄟˋ	(N)	within
26	普遍	pǔbiàn	ㄆㄨˇ ㄅㄧㄢˋ	(Vs)	widespread, common
27	選擇	xuǎnzé	ㄒㄩㄢˇ ㄗㄜˊ	(V)	to choose

Phrases

28	網購	wǎng gòu	ㄨㄤˇ ㄍㄡˋ		online shopping
29	貨比三家 不吃虧	huò bǐ sān jiā bù chīkuī	ㄏㄨㄛˋ ㄅㄧˇ ㄙㄢ ㄐㄧㄚ ㄅㄨˋ ㄔ ㄎㄨㄟ		shop around and you won't get ripped off (lit. Compare products at three stores and you won't be cheated.)
30	兩成	liǎng chéng	ㄌㄧㄤˇ ㄔㄥˊ		20%, literally 2/10

短文 Reading 🎧 09-03

鳳梨酥經濟學

　　鳳梨是台灣很重要的農產品，對台灣的經濟發展一直有很大的幫助。台灣出口的鳳梨曾經占世界第二位，可惜後來因為成本太高，在價格上沒有辦法跟別的國家競爭，很多農夫因為種的鳳梨賣不出去，生活很辛苦。

鳳梨在閩南語叫「旺來」，意思是可以給人帶來好運，所以用鳳梨做成內餡的甜點一直很受歡迎，不但拿來當做喜餅，也是大家喜愛的茶點，更是過年過節最好的禮物。一方面看到了這個商機，一方面希望能讓大家認識最能代表當地文化的傳統美食，台北市政府從 2006 年起年年舉辦鳳梨酥文化節，成功地讓鳳梨酥的產值從每年 19 億提高到現在的 200 多億。

在台灣，早就有很多知名麵包店賣鳳梨酥，但是在 2009 年出現了第一家只賣鳳梨酥的店。老闆本來經營一家科技公司，因為看見家鄉鄰居和親戚朋友種的鳳梨一斤只能賣一塊半，生活非常不容易。他為了提高家鄉鳳梨農的收入，決定賣鳳梨酥。他找來開麵包店的叔叔，用當地出產的鳳梨研究出新口味，結果大受歡迎。因此，他能用穩定的價格跟鳳梨農購買鳳梨，改善了他們的生活。

使用當地的食材，講究品質，並且利用現代的行銷方式，透過網路團購，才一年多這家公司的產品就成為台灣最受歡迎的鳳梨酥，而且在東京、上海開了店，跟 Prada 當了鄰居。一塊小小的鳳梨酥，因為有了網路才能不靠店面，不靠電視廣告，行銷全世界。

課文簡體字版 Text in Simplified Characters

凤梨酥经济学

凤梨是台湾很重要的农产品，对台湾的经济发展一直有很大的帮助。台湾出口的凤梨曾经占世界第二位，可惜后来因为成本太高，在价格上没有办法跟别的国家竞争，很多农大因为种的凤梨卖不出去，生活很辛苦。

凤梨在闽南语叫「旺来」，意思是可以给人带来好运，所以用凤梨做成内馅的甜点一直很受欢迎，不但拿来当做喜饼，也是大家喜爱的茶点，更是过年过节最好的礼物。一方面看到了这个商机，一方面希望能让大家认识最能代表当地文化的传统美食，台北市政府从 2006 年起年年举办凤梨酥文化节，成功地让凤梨酥的产值从每年 19 亿提高到现在的 200 多亿。

在台湾，早就有很多知名面包店卖凤梨酥，但是在 2009 年出现了第一家只卖凤梨酥的店。老板本来经营一家科技公司，因为看见家乡邻居和亲戚朋友种的凤梨一斤只能卖一块半，生活非常不容易。他为了提高家乡凤梨农的收入，决定卖凤梨酥。他找来开面包店的叔叔，用当地出产的凤梨研究出新口味，结果大受欢迎。因此，他能用稳定的价格跟凤梨农购买凤梨，改善了他们的生活。

使用当地的食材，讲究品质，并且利用现代的行销方式，透过网路团购，才一年多这家公司的产品就成为台湾最受欢迎的凤梨酥，而且在东京、上海开了店，跟 Prada 当了邻居。一块小小的凤梨酥，因为有了网路才能不靠店面，不靠电视广告，行销全世界。

課文英譯 Text in English

The Economics of Pineapple Cake

Pineapples are an important agricultural product in Taiwan. They have been a big help to Taiwan's economic development. Taiwan's export of pineapples was once second in the world. Unfortunately, later, because the costs were too high, Taiwan couldn't compete with other countries in terms of price. Many farmers had tough lives, because they couldn't sell their pineapples.

In Taiwanese, pineapples are called "onglai", which sounds like the phrase "to bring good luck", so sweets with pineapple filling have maintained their popularity. They are not only used as pastries given to announce an upcoming wedding, they are also popular tea snacks and even a great present for the Chinese New Year and other holidays. The Taipei City government recognized in Pineapple Cakes a business opportunity on the one hand, and a way of widely promoting a traditional food most representative of the local culture on the other. So starting in 2006 it began holding the Pineapple Cake Culture Festival every year, and succeeded in increasing Pineapple Cake production revenue from 1.9 billion a year to more than 20 billion a year today.

Taiwan has long had many well known bakeries that sell Pineapple Cakes, but in 2009, the first store to sell exclusively Pineapple Cakes opened. The owner originally ran a technology company. He saw that the pineapples raised by neighbors, relatives, and friends in his hometown were only selling for NT$1.5 per catty, making their lives very tough. In order to increase the income of pineapple farmers in his hometown, he decided to take on selling Pineapple Cakes. He contacted an uncle who ran a bakery and developed new flavors using locally produced pineapples. The results were very well received. He used stable prices to purchase pineapples from pineapple farmers, improving their lives.

By using local food materials, devoting particular care to quality, and employing modern marketing methods, such as online group buying, the company's Pineapple Cakes became the most popular in all of Taiwan in just over a year's time. What's more, his company has opened shops in Tokyo and Shanghai that neighbor the likes of Prada. Thanks to the internet, this little Pineapple Cake is sold all over the world without the help of storefronts or television commercials.

生詞二 Vocabulary II 🎧 09-04

Vocabulary

1	鳳梨鳳梨	fènglí	ㄈㄥˋ ㄌㄧˊ	(N)	pineapple
2	農產品	nóngchǎnpǐn	ㄋㄨㄥˊ ㄔㄢˇ ㄆㄧㄣˇ	(N)	agricultural product
3	出口	chūkǒu	ㄔㄨ ㄎㄡˇ	(V)	to export
4	曾經	céngjīng	ㄘㄥˊ ㄐㄧㄥ	(Adv)	been the case before, once
5	占	zhàn	ㄓㄢˋ	(Vst)	to constitute, to account for
6	成本	chéngběn	ㄔㄥˊ ㄅㄣˇ	(N)	costs
7	價格	jiàgé	ㄐㄧㄚˋ ㄍㄜˊ	(N)	price
8	競爭競爭	jìngzhēng	ㄐㄧㄥˋ ㄓㄥ	(Vi)	to compete against
9	好運	hǎoyùn	ㄏㄠˇ ㄩㄣˋ	(N)	good luck
10	內餡	nèixiàn	ㄋㄟˋ ㄒㄧㄢˋ	(N)	filling (of pastries etc.)
11	當做	dāngzuò	ㄉㄤ ㄗㄨㄛˋ	(V)	to treat as, to serve as
12	喜餅	xǐbǐng	ㄒㄧˇ ㄅㄧㄥˇ	(N)	wedding-announcement pastries
13	喜愛	xǐ'ài	ㄒㄧˇ ㄞˋ	(Vst)	fond of
14	茶點	chádiǎn	ㄔㄚˊ ㄉㄧㄢˇ	(N)	snacks, dessert (served with tea)
15	商機	shāngjī	ㄕㄤ ㄐㄧ	(N)	business opportunity
16	代表	dàibiǎo	ㄉㄞˋ ㄅㄧㄠˇ	(V)	to represent
17	政府	zhèngfǔ	ㄓㄥˋ ㄈㄨˇ	(N)	government
18	舉辦	jǔbàn	ㄐㄩˇ ㄅㄢˋ	(V)	to organize, hold

19	產值	chǎnzhí	ㄔㄢˇ ㄓˊ	(N)	production value, output
20	提高	tígāo	ㄊㄧˊ ㄍㄠ	(V)	to increase, to elevate
21	知名	zhīmíng	ㄓ ㄇㄧㄥˊ	(Vs)	well known, renowned
22	出現	chūxiàn	ㄔㄨ ㄒㄧㄢˋ	(Vp)	to appear
23	科技	kējì	ㄎㄜ ㄐㄧˋ	(N)	technology
24	(台) 斤	(Tái) jīn	(ㄊㄞˊ) ㄐㄧㄣ	(M)	catty, a unit of measure in Taiwan, equivalent to 600 grams
25	叔叔	shúshu	ㄕㄨˊ ㄕㄨ	(N)	uncle (father's younger brother)
26	口味	kǒuwèi	ㄎㄡˇ ㄨㄟˋ	(N)	flavor
27	結果	jiéguǒ	ㄐㄧㄝˊ ㄍㄨㄛˇ	(Adv)	as a result
28	購買	gòumǎi	ㄍㄡˋ ㄇㄞˇ	(V)	to purchase
29	改善	gǎishàn	ㄍㄞˇ ㄕㄢˋ	(V)	to improve
30	並且	bìngqiě	ㄅㄧㄥˋ ㄑㄧㄝˇ	(Conj)	moreover
31	行銷	xíngxiāo	ㄒㄧㄥˊ ㄒㄧㄠ	(V)	to market
32	團購	tuángòu	ㄊㄨㄢˊ ㄍㄡˋ	(V)	to group buy (for cheaper prices)
33	店面	diànmiàn	ㄉㄧㄢˋ ㄇㄧㄢˋ	(N)	storefront
34	全	quán	ㄑㄩㄢˊ	(Det)	entire

Names

35	閩南語	Mǐnnányǔ	ㄇㄧㄣˇ ㄋㄢˊ ㄩˇ		Southern Min dialect, i.e., Taiwanese
36	旺來	wànglái	ㄨㄤˋ ㄌㄞˊ		Southern Min sound for pineapple, lit."abundance comes"
37	東京	Dōngjīng	ㄉㄨㄥ ㄐㄧㄥ		Tokyo

Phrases

38	鳳梨酥	fènglí sū	ㄈㄥˋ ㄌㄧˊ ㄙㄨ		pineapple shortcake
39	第二位	dì èr wèi	ㄉㄧˋ ㄦˋ ㄨㄟˋ		second (place)
40	鳳梨農	fènglí nóng	ㄈㄥˋ ㄌㄧˊ ㄋㄨㄥˊ		pineapple farmer

文法 Grammar

I. 靠 *to rely on, by means of* 🎧 09-05

英譯 p.223

Function: As a main verb, 靠 means 'to rely on', but when it is the first verb in a sentence with two verbs, its meaning is reduced to 'by means of' with 靠 acting more like a preposition.

(As a main verb)

❶ 有句話說,「在家靠父母,出外靠朋友」,說明了家人和朋友的重要。

(As a secondary verb)

❷ 他靠自己的努力賺錢買了這棟房子。

❸ 現在工作非常難找;我是靠朋友幫忙才找到的。

❹ 他靠打工賺的錢養家,生活過得並不輕鬆。

❺ 張太太的孩子在國外工作,她靠電子郵件跟網路電話了解孩子生活的情形。

練習 Exercise

Answer the following questions using 靠.

❶ A:你不是說工作多,壓力很大嗎?怎麼還在玩網路遊戲?

　B:＿＿＿＿＿＿＿＿＿＿＿＿＿＿＿＿＿＿＿(放鬆心情)。

❷ A:小農賣的有機蔬菜比較貴,你為什麼還願意買呢?(支持)

　B:小農看天吃飯,收入不穩定,得＿＿＿＿＿＿＿＿＿＿。

❸ A:你每天那麼晚才回家,你養的寵物怎麼辦?誰來照顧?

　B:＿＿＿＿＿＿＿＿＿＿＿＿＿＿＿＿＿＿＿。

❹ A:恭喜你畢業了。念研究所花了不少錢吧?(獎學金)

　B:＿＿＿＿＿＿＿＿＿＿＿＿＿＿＿＿＿＿＿。

❺ A:你會不會迷路?要不要我過去接你?(網路地圖)

　B:不用了,謝謝你。我的手機可以上網。＿＿＿＿＿＿。

II. 既…又… *not merely…, but…as well* 09-06

Function: This structure indicates that the subject has two qualities at the same time.

❶ 打工的好處很多。既可以賺錢，又可以交朋友。
❷ 單親爸爸既要賺錢養家，又要照顧孩子，非常辛苦。
❸ 廣告上這種最新型的手機，款式既新，功能又多，應該很快就會流行起來。
❹ 她人既長得漂亮，外語能力又強，難怪是學校裡的風雲人物。
❺ 張先生對吃特別講究，他吃的東西既要味道好，顏色又要美。

Usage:

1. 既 and 又 are both adverbs and sentences using this pattern usually only have one subject.

2. The use of 既…又… and 不但…也… and 又…又… are very similar, but when a speaker uses 既…又…, the addition is clearly incremental. Compare the following.

   (1) 學習外語不但要練習聽和說，也要認字寫字。
       （重要性相當的兩件事）(Items are of similar importance.)

   (2) 學習外語既要練習聽和說，又要認字寫字。
       （要做的事可真多）(Studying languages requires a lot of work.)

3. Verb groups being connected cannot have adverbs of degree. （*既很好看，又很漂亮）

4. 既…又… is more formal and literary than 又…又…; therefore, the number of syllables in the verbs (verb groups) following both 既 and 又 should either be the same or close, as symmetry is important in this pattern.

5. The meaning of the words that follow 既 and 又 should be both positive or both negative. You cannot say *農夫的社會地位既不高，收入又很穩定.

練習 Exercise

Please complete the following sentences, indicating two different qualities using 既…又….

....

❶ 這件外套_____，多花一點錢買也值得。

❷ 這個城市_____，難怪能吸引那麼多觀光客來玩。

❸ 使用天然堆肥_____，好處很多。

❹ 養寵物，_____，照顧起來並不輕鬆。

❺ 透過網路賣農產品，_____，對農夫來說，幫助很大。

III. …以內 *within…* 🎧 09-07　　　　　🔍 英譯 p.223

Function: This is a formal expression that indicates 'within a temporal, spatial or quantity range'.

❶ 他讓我在一個禮拜以內把這份報告寫完。這怎麼可能？

❷ 在台灣宅配很快，一般來說，下訂單以後，24 小時以內就能收到商品。

❸ 外套的價格，只要是在兩千塊以內，我都能接受。

❹ 他找的房子不但要在捷運站附近，而且離公司坐捷運一定要在十站以內。

❺ 我的體力還不錯，三千公尺以內，我想我都跑得完。

Usage: 以內 can be used for describing quantity (❸ above), spatial (❹ , ❺), and temporal (❶ , ❷).

練習 Exercise

Please re-write the following sentences using 以內.

....

❶ 這個星期結束以前，學校會讓學生知道錄取了沒有。

→ 學校會在_____。

---

❷ 房租一萬塊錢還可以；比一萬塊貴的房子我就租不起了。

→ 我只租得起_____。

❸ 民宿離車站不太遠，最多八百公尺吧，走路就到了。

→ _____。

❹ 我希望在 35 歲以前就買得起房子。（現在 30 歲）

→ _____。

❺ 演唱會的票一上網賣，兩個多鐘頭就賣完了。

→ _____。

IV. 占 *to constitute* 09-08

英譯 p.223

Function: The verb 占 defines percentage or ranking.

❶ 這次考試的成績，口試、筆試各占一半。

❷ 電子產品的產值占台灣出口商品第一位。

❸ 我並不是整天都在公司裡上班；我在公司裡的時間只占工作時間的一小部分。

❹ 我剛剛給你的資料還不完整；那些只占整份報告的一小部分。

❺ 成本包括很多部分。實際上材料成本只占不到一半。

練習 Exercise

Answer the following questions by giving a ranking or percentage using 占.

❶ A：在你的國家，產值占第一位的農產品是什麼？

B：_____。

❷ A：你的房租貴嗎？在生活費當中，房租占多少？

B：_____。

❸ A：聽說你去旅行的時候，大部分的時間都在參觀古蹟？

B：是啊，我對歷史很有興趣，所以_____。

④ A：在台北，24 小時營業的商店多嗎？（一小部分）

B：不太多，其實除了便利商店以外，＿＿＿＿＿＿＿＿＿＿。

⑤ A：聽說在台灣，賣得最好的汽車是 Benz，真的嗎？

B：是真的。＿＿＿＿＿＿＿＿＿＿＿＿＿＿＿＿。

V.（在）NP 上 *regarding NP* 09-09

英譯 p.224

Function: This pattern applies the validity of the main predicate to the NP in question.

① 有機蔬果在價格上雖然比較貴一點。但是一般來說，它的品質，顧客比較信任。

② 有機蔬果在市場上的價錢雖然很高，但是實際上農夫的利潤並不高。

③ 中國人習慣上都是先吃飯再喝湯。你們呢？

④ 我跟我最好的朋友在個性上很不一樣，她個性比我急。

⑤ 我來台灣快一年了，生活上都沒問題了，學習上也相當順利，中文進步了不少。

Usage:

1. In most cases, a noun comes between 在 and 上.

2. The 在 in this pattern can be omitted, but the 上 cannot.

練習 Exercise

Please re-write the following sentences using（在）…上.

① 這件事，你雖然沒有法律責任，可是有道德責任。

→ ＿＿＿＿＿＿＿＿＿＿＿＿＿＿＿＿＿＿＿。

② 夜市的東西雖然品質不是那麼好，不過價錢還可以接受。

→ ＿＿＿＿＿＿＿＿＿＿＿＿＿＿＿＿＿＿＿。

❸ 按照傳統，參加婚禮，見到新人的時候一定要說一些吉祥話。

→ ＿＿＿＿＿＿＿＿＿＿＿＿＿＿＿＿＿＿＿＿＿＿＿＿。

❹ 他從來沒念過企業管理，因此公司的經營管理需要靠別人。

→ ＿＿＿＿＿＿＿＿＿＿＿＿＿＿＿＿＿＿＿＿＿＿＿＿。

❺ 我認為一個人只有經濟獨立了才能算是真正的獨立。

→ ＿＿＿＿＿＿＿＿＿＿＿＿＿＿＿＿＿＿＿＿＿＿＿＿。

VI. 給⋯帶來 *to bring… to…* 🎧 09-10 英譯 p.224

Function: The preposition 給 introduces the beneficiary of the action.

❶ 好的生活習慣能給人帶來健康。

❷ 朋友的關心給他帶來溫馨的感覺。

❸ 在天燈上寫下願望給人帶來新的希望。

❹ 大部分的中國人都認為拜神、祭祖能給家人帶來平安和幸福。

❺ 科技發展給我們的生活帶來了很多的便利。

練習 Exercise

Please complete the following sentences using 給⋯帶來.

❶ 他努力提高自己的外語能力，希望好的語言能力能

＿＿＿＿＿＿＿＿＿＿＿＿＿＿＿＿＿＿＿＿。（更多的工作機會）

❷ 他非常喜歡水上活動；每次去海邊玩水，都能＿＿＿＿＿＿＿＿。
（很大的快樂）

❸ 考上公職＿＿＿＿＿＿＿＿＿＿＿＿＿＿＿。（穩定的生活）

❹ 使用農藥會＿＿＿＿＿＿＿＿＿＿＿＿＿＿。（嚴重的汙染）

❺ 鳳梨酥大受歡迎＿＿＿＿＿＿＿＿＿＿＿＿。（鳳梨農、商機）

VII. 結果 *consequently, in the end* 09-11 英譯 p.224

Function: The 結果 connects the second clause to the first. In most cases, the second clause consists of an undesirable consequence.

(A. consequently)

❶ 他每天熬夜打電玩,結果成績不理想,被當了。

❷ 店員沒把合約的內容解釋清楚,結果害他多花了好幾千塊錢。

❸ 他沒買除濕機,結果雨季的時候,衣服、鞋子都發霉了。

(B. in the end)

❹ 他們在媒體上做了不少廣告,結果生意還是不好。

❺ 他帶了發票,結果店員還是拒絕讓他退換。

Usage: Sentences with 結果 always relate to events in the past. Some, not all (not B sentences), such sentences can be paraphrased using 因為…所以….

練習 Exercise

Please complete the 結果 portions of the sentences by stating the undesirable consequence.

❶ 他出門沒帶手機,又看不懂中文,結果＿＿＿＿＿＿＿＿＿＿。

❷ 我們下山的時候,錯過了公車,結果＿＿＿＿＿＿＿＿＿＿。

❸ 我們原來打算去聽跨年演唱會,沒想到到處都擠滿了人,結果＿＿＿＿＿＿＿＿＿＿＿＿＿＿＿＿＿＿。

❹ 他發現撞衫,雖然天氣很冷,還是把新買的外套脫掉,結果＿＿＿＿＿＿＿＿＿＿＿＿＿＿＿＿。

❺ 他大學畢業以後,參加過不少次面試,結果＿＿＿＿＿＿＿＿。

語法例句英譯
▶▶ Grammar Examples in English •

I. 靠 *to rely on, by means of*

Function:

❶ There's a saying, "When at home, rely on your parents, when away from home, depend on friends." It underscores the importance of family and friends.

❷ He bought this house with his own hard-earned money.

❸ Jobs are hard to find now. I found mine through friends.

❹ He supports his family with money earned with a part-time job. His life is by no means easy.

❺ Mrs. Zhang's children work abroad. She keeps up to date with their lives by means of email and internet phone.

II. 既…又… *not merely…, but…as well*

Function:

❶ Working part time has a lot of advantages. Not only can you make money, but you can also make friends.

❷ Single dads not only have to make money to raise their families, they also have to take care of their kids. It's really tough.

❸ The latest cell phone being advertised not only comes in a new style, it also has a lot of functions. It's likely going to catch on fast.

❹ She's not only pretty, but her foreign language skills are also very good. It's no wonder she is so well known throughout the school.

❺ Mr. Zhang is especially particular about eating. The food he eats has to be both delicious and colorful.

Usage:

2. (1) When studying a foreign language, you not only have to practice listening and speaking, you also need to learn to read and write.

(2) When studying a foreign language, you not only have to practice listening and speaking, you also need to learn to read and write.

III. …以內 *within…*

Function:

❶ He's having me write this report within a week. How is that even possible?

❷ Home delivery in Taiwan is very fast. Generally, products are received within 24 hours of putting in the order.

❸ I can accept a price for the coat as long as it's within NT$2,000.

❹ He's looking for a house that's not only near an MRT station; it has to be within 10 stops to his company.

❺ I'm in pretty good shape. I think I could run any distance within 3,000 meters.

IV. 占 *to constitute*

Function:

❶ For this test, the oral and written tests will each account for one half of the grade.

❷ Electronics hold top position when it comes to production value of Taiwan's exports.

❸ I don't work all day at the office. My time in the office only accounts for a small percentage of my work day.

❹ I didn't give you the whole information just now. That's just a small part of the entire report.

❺ Many things contribute to operating costs. (In reality) materials don't even account for half.

V. （在）NP 上 *regarding NP*

Function:

1. As far as prices go, organic fruits and vegetables are a little more expensive, but generally speaking, customers trust the quality more.

2. As far as prices on the market go, organic fruits and vegetables are expensive, but farmers don't actually make very high profits.

3. In terms of custom, Chinese have soup after eating the main meal. What about you?

4. My best friend and I are different in terms of personality. She is more impatient.

5. I've been in Taiwan almost a year. In terms of my life, I have no problems. As far as my studies go, those are going smoothly, too. My Chinese has improved a lot.

VI. 給…帶來 *to bring… to…*

Function:

1. Good habits in life can bring health to the individual.

2. His friends' concern brought him a feeling of warmth.

3. Writing wishes on sky lanterns brings people new hope.

4. Most Chinese believe that honoring gods and ancestors brings peace and happiness to their families.

5. Technological developments have brought a lot of convenience to our lives.

VII. 結果 *consequently, in the end*

Function:

1. He stayed up every night playing video games. Consequently, his grades weren't ideal, and he failed.

2. The store employee didn't explain the content of the contract clearly. As a result, he overpaid by a few thousand NT dollars.

3. He didn't buy a dehumidifier. As a result, during the rainy season, his clothes and shoes all mildewed.

4. They put a lot of ads in the media, in the end; however, their business was still poor.

5. He brought the receipt. In the end, however, the store employee refused to let him exchange.

課室活動 Classroom Activities

I. How I Shop Online

Goal: Learning to explain the pros and cons of online shopping.

Task: Which online shopping services have you used/never used? Why? Pair up, discuss these questions, and then report the results to the class.

Try to use the following sentence patterns and vocabulary words:

網購	搜尋	宅配	退換	下訂單
比價	隨時	風險	信用	店面

II. Survey Reports

Goal: Learning to talk about ratios and rankings in Chinese.

Task: The following chart shows changes in sales volume and market ranking before and after Company A~E holds a marketing campaign. Please refer to the chart below and explain the changes resulting from the marketing campaign.

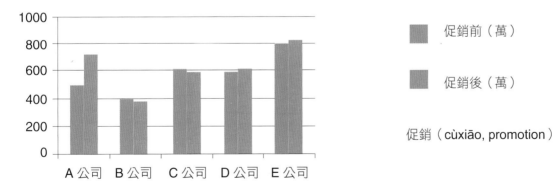

促銷前（萬）

促銷後（萬）

促銷（cùxiāo, promotion）

Try to use the following sentence patterns and vocabulary words:

靠	（在）…以內	既…又…	第 Nu 位
占	從…提高到…	給…帶來	結果

III. Marketing Proposals

Goal: Learning to explain the pros and cons of internet marketing.

Task: Think of a food or handicraft that can best represent the traditional culture of your country. Then, explain the marketing techniques you would use to make it a favorite of tourists to your country and tell your classmates how you expect the techniques would help.

Try to use the following sentence patterns and vocabulary words:

當做	提高	透過	全 N
占	從…提高到…	給…帶來	結果

文化 *Bits of Chinese Culture*

The Abacus

Have you ever thought about how Chinese engaged in trade and bought things before the introduction of cash registers? Perhaps in a movie or a play, you saw something along these lines: a shop clerk, head down, quickly flicking beads on an abacus. Most adept abacus-users can do the problem 76+68+39+54+27+16 within three seconds. A contest between an abacus and a calculator held in Changzhou, China in the 1990s proved that the abacus can be faster than an electronic calculator for addition and subtraction.

⚠ Students in elementary schools learn how to use the abacus to help them concentrate better.

There are many theories as to the origins of the abacus, but most believe that it was invented in the Yuan Dynasty, meaning that the abacus has existed in China for over 700 years. It was an indispensible skill for Chinese merchants for over seven centuries. The spread of cash registers and computers since the 1970s has resulted in decline in the use of the abacus among businesses, but prior to 1993, the abacus was a required part of mathematics courses in Taiwan's elementary schools, while China didn't remove it from their curriculum until 2000.

The abacus, however, hasn't been relegated to the trash bin of history. This is evident from the large numbers of cram schools that teach the abacus and mental calculation. They teach students mnemonic formulas for the abacus. Today, students range from pre-school age children to seniors in their 70s. Many parents believe that children who study the abacus and mental calculation starting from elementary school concentrate better and calculate faster. In addition, a medical study in 2013 indicates that seniors that take up the abacus and mental calculation see their θ waves strenghthen, slowing down the aging of the cerebrum. This sparked interest in the art among seniors.

Self-Assessment Checklist

I can talk about online shopping methods and processes.

20%   40%   60%   80%   100%

I can explain the pros and cons of different shopping methods.

20%   40%   60%   80%   100%

I can talk about traditional foods that best represent local cultures.

20%   40%   60%   80%   100%

I can discuss product manufacturing, market share, and market ranking.

20%   40%   60%   80%   100%

LESSON 10

第十課

我住院了

I'm Staying in the Hospital

學習目標 **Learning Objectives**

Topic: 醫療 Health Care

- Learning to describe what happened in an automobile accident.

- Learning to explain injuries and discuss treatment with doctors.

- Learning to discuss issues related to cosmetic surgery.

- Learning to provide data and real-life examples supporting your views.

我住院了

I'm Staying in the Hospital

對話 Dialogue 10-01

（李文彥走過來）

羅珊蒂：怎麼回事？你的手怎麼了？臉也受傷了。

李文彥：我出車禍了。我上個禮拜騎腳踏車來學校的路上被一輛車撞了。

羅珊蒂：你一定是為了趕時間，不遵守交通規則。

李文彥：哪裡是我的錯。我過馬路的時候，有一輛右轉車不讓我，把我撞倒了。我躺在地上，痛得起不來。

羅珊蒂：好可怕！當時有沒有人幫你？誰送你去醫院的？

李文彥：撞到我的人打電話報警。救護車馬上把我送到急診室去了。

陳 敏 萱：你的傷嚴重嗎？（看著李文彥的手）是不是骨折了？

李 文 彥：是啊，我一進急診室，醫生就讓我去照 X 光。

陳 敏 萱：後來呢？

李 文 彥：醫生看了片子，要我住院開刀。我住院住了五天呢。

陳 敏 萱：我聽說大醫院的急診室總是擠滿了病人。如果情況不是那麼緊急的話，有時候要等幾天才等得到病床，真的嗎？

李 文 彥：是啊，我那個時候痛得要命，醫生先給我打止痛針。可是他說還有更緊急的病人，讓我等一等。最快要到第二天才能動手術。

陳 敏 萱：出車禍的事，你家人知道嗎？

李 文 彥：警察幫我打電話給我阿姨。她一聽說要開刀，緊張得一直問醫生，有沒有危險，以後動作會不會受到影響。

羅 珊 蒂：醫生怎麼說？

李 文 彥：醫生說這不算大手術，可是開刀多少會有一些風險。至於動作會不會受到影響，得看受傷的部位。最好的情況大概可以恢復八成到九成。

羅 珊 蒂：你現在覺得怎麼樣了？

李 文 彥：我還好，不怎麼痛了。可是很不方便，連穿衣服都要別人幫忙。只好搬到阿姨家去住一段時間。

陳 敏 萱：你在阿姨家還習慣嗎？

李 文 彥：我跟阿姨很親，她像媽媽一樣地照顧我，每天都煮魚湯給我喝。你看我現在除了手不太方便以外，不是都很好嗎？

陳 敏 萱：喝魚湯？你阿姨為什麼讓你每天喝魚湯？

李 文 彥：阿姨說多喝魚湯，傷口會恢復得比較快。哎呀，我應該要走了。我得去看醫生。明天見。

課文簡體字版 Text in Simplified Characters

（李文彦走过来）

罗　珊　蒂 ：怎么回事？你的手怎么了？脸也受伤了。

李　文　彦 ：我出车祸了。我上个礼拜骑脚踏车来学校的路上被一辆车撞了。

罗　珊　蒂 ：你一定是为了赶时间，不遵守交通规则。

李　文　彦 ：哪里是我的错。我过马路的时候，有一辆右转车不让我，把我撞倒了。我躺在地上，痛得起不来。

罗　珊　蒂 ：好可怕！当时有没有人帮你？谁送你去医院的？

李　文　彦 ：撞到我的人打电话报警。救护车马上把我送到急诊室去了。

陈　敏　萱 ：你的伤严重吗？（看着李文彦的手）是不是骨折了？

李　文　彦 ：是啊，我一进急诊室，医生就让我去照 X 光。

陈　敏　萱 ：后来呢？

李　文　彦 ：医生看了片子，要我住院开刀。我住院住了五天呢。

罗　珊　蒂 ：我听说大医院的急诊室总是挤满了病人。如果情况不是那么紧急的话，有时候要等几天才等得到病床，真的吗？

李　文　彦 ：是啊，我那个时候痛得要命，医生先给我打止痛针。可是他说还有更紧急的病人，让我等一等。最快要到第二天才能动手术。

陈　敏　萱 ：出车祸的事，你家人知道吗？

李　文　彦 ：警察帮我打电话给我阿姨。她一听说要开刀，紧张得一直问医生，有没有危险，以后动作会不会受到影响。

罗　珊　蒂 ：医生怎么说？

李　文　彦 ：医生说这不算大手术，可是开刀多少会有一些风险。至于动作会不会受到影响，得看受伤的部位。最好的情况大概可以恢复八成到九成。

罗　珊　蒂 ：你现在觉得怎么样了？

李　文　彦 ：我还好，不怎么痛了。可是很不方便，连穿衣服都要别人帮忙。只好搬到阿姨家去住一段时间。

陈　敏　萱 ：你在阿姨家还习惯吗？

李　文　彦 ：我跟阿姨很亲，她像妈妈一样地照顾我，每天都煮鱼汤给我喝。你看我现在除了手不太方便以外，不是都很好吗？

陈　敏　萱 ：喝鱼汤？你阿姨为什么让你每天喝鱼汤？

李　文　彦 ：阿姨说多喝鱼汤，伤口会恢复得比较快。哎呀，我应该要走了。我得去看医生。明天见。

課文英譯 Text in English

(Li Wenyan walks over.)

Luo Shandi : What happened? What happened to your hand? Your face is also injured.

Li Wenyan : I was in an accident. Last week, when I was riding my bicycle on my way to school, I was hit by a car.

Luo Shandi : You must have been in a hurry and not following traffic regulations.

Li Wenyan : It wasn't my fault! When I was crossing the street, a car turning right didn't yield for me and knocked me down. I lay on the ground in so much pain that I couldn't get up.

Luo Shandi : That's terrible! Did anybody help you? Who took you to the hospital?

Li Wenyan : The person who hit me called the police. An ambulance took me to the emergency room right away.

Chen Minxuan : Were you hurt bad? (*looking at Li Wenyan's hand*) Is it broken?

Li Wenyan : Yes, the doctors sent me for X-Rays as soon as I got to the ER.

Chen Minxuan : And then?

Li Wenyan : After looking at the X-ray, the doctor wanted me to stay in the hospital for an operation. I was hospitalized for five days.

Chen Minxuan : I've heard that ERs at large hospitals are always packed with patients. If a patient's situation isn't all that urgent, sometimes you have to wait a few days for a hospital bed. Is that true?

Li Wenyan : Yes. I was in terrible pain at the time. The doctor gave me a shot for the pain, but he said that he had to tend to other more urgent patients for now and I had to wait. The earliest he could perform the surgery was the next day.

Chen Minxuan : Do your parents know about your accident?

Li Wenyan : The police called my aunt for me. As soon as she heard that I had to have surgery, she was so anxious that she kept asking the doctor, is it serious? Will my movement be affected?

Luo Shandi : What did the doctor say?

Li Wenyan : The doctor said that it wasn't considered a major operation, but that there is always some degree of risk with surgery. As to whether my movement would be affected, that would depend on where the injury is located. In the best case scenario I will recover 80 to 90 percent.

Luo Shandi : How do you feel now?

Li Wenyan   : I'm okay. It doesn't hurt so much, but it's very inconvenient. I even need other people's help to get dressed. I had no choice but to move into my aunt's house for a while.

Chen Minxuan: How is it going living in your aunt's home?

Li Wenyan   : I'm very close to my aunt. She takes care of me as if she were my mom. She cooks fish soup for me to drink every day. Look, except for my arm not being completely usable, everything else is fine, right?

Chen Minxuan: Drink fish soup? Why does your aunt have you drink fish soup every day?

Li Wenyan   : My aunt says having lots of fish soup will help the injury heal quicker. Yikes! I gotta go. I have to go see the doctor. See you tomorrow.

生詞一 Vocabulary I   🎧 10-02

Vocabulary

1	住院 zhùyuàn	ㄓㄨˋ ㄩㄢˋ	(V-sep)	to stay in a hospital, be hospitalized
2	臉 liǎn	ㄌㄧㄢˇ	(N)	face
3	受傷 shòushāng	ㄕㄡˋ ㄕㄤ	(Vp-sep)	to be injured
4	撞 zhuàng	ㄓㄨㄤˋ	(V)	to hit, collide
5	遵守 zūnshǒu	ㄗㄨㄣ ㄕㄡˇ	(V)	to obey, follow, comply with
6	規則 guīzé	ㄍㄨㄟ ㄗㄜˊ	(N)	rules, regulations
7	報警 bàojǐng	ㄅㄠˋ ㄐㄧㄥˇ	(V-sep)	to report to (or call) the police
8	急診室 jízhěnshì		(N)	emergency room
9	傷 shāng	ㄕㄤ	(N)	injury
10	骨折 gǔzhé	ㄍㄨˇ ㄓㄜˊ	(Vp)	to fracture, break a bone
11	片子 piànzi	ㄆㄧㄢˋ ㄗ	(N)	(X-ray) film
12	開刀 kāidāo	ㄎㄞ ㄉㄠ	(V-sep)	to have surgery
13	病人 bìngrén	ㄅㄧㄥˋ ㄖㄣˊ	(N)	patient
14	情況 qíngkuàng	ㄑㄧㄥˊ ㄎㄨㄤˋ	(N)	situation

15	緊急 jǐnjí	ㄐㄧㄣˇ ㄐㄧˊ	(Vs)	urgent
16	病床 bìngchuáng	ㄅㄧㄥˋ ㄔㄨㄤˊ	(N)	hospital bed
17	要命 yàomìng	ㄧㄠˋ ㄇㄧㄥˋ	(Vs)	murderous, horrible
18	打針 dǎzhēn	ㄉㄚˇ ㄓㄣ	(V-sep)	to inject, give a shot
19	止痛 zhǐtòng	ㄓˇ ㄊㄨㄥˋ	(Vi)	to kill pain (lit. stop pain)
20	手術 shǒushù	ㄕㄡˇ ㄕㄨˋ	(N)	operation, surgery
21	警察 jǐngchá	ㄐㄧㄥˇ ㄔㄚˊ	(N)	police
22	危險 wéixiǎn	ㄨㄟˊ ㄒㄧㄢˇ	(N)	danger
23	至於 zhìyú	ㄓˋ ㄩˊ	(Ptc)	as to, regarding
24	部位 bùwèi	ㄅㄨˋ ㄨㄟˋ	(N)	(body) part, location
25	恢復 huīfù	ㄏㄨㄟ ㄈㄨˋ	(Vp)	to recover
26	傷口 shāngkǒu	ㄕㄤ ㄎㄡˇ	(N)	wound
27	哎呀 āiya	ㄞ ㄧˇㄚ	(Ptc)	interjection for realization of something important, oh no, yikes

Phrases

28	出車禍 chū chēhuò	ㄔㄨ ㄔㄜ ㄏㄨㄛˋ		to have an automobile accident
29	趕時間 gǎn shíjiān	ㄍㄢˇ ㄕˊ ㄐㄧㄢ		to be in a hurry
30	撞倒 zhuàng dǎo	ㄓㄨㄤˋ ㄉㄠˇ		to knock down, knock over
31	救護車 jiùhù chē	ㄐㄧㄡˋ ㄏㄨˋ ㄔㄜ		ambulance
32	照 X 光 zhào X guāng	ㄓㄠˋ X ㄍㄨㄤ		to take an X-ray
33	動手術 dòng shǒushù	ㄉㄨㄥˋ ㄕㄡˇ ㄕㄨˋ		to have/undergo a surgery

短文 Reading ◯ 10-03

醫病還是醫美

何雅婷的香港朋友愛林聽說台灣的微整型技術在亞洲是數一數二的，而且價錢又合理，因此她趁休假到台灣來做微整型。有許多像愛林這樣的外國人利用假期來台灣做醫美手術。他們希望假期結束以後，能變得更迷人，在職場上更有競爭力。

根據調查，百分之六十一的人認為整型除了可以增加自信，還可以改善職場的人際關係。另外，研究也發現，外表好看的人收入比外表普通的人多百分之十到十五。因為這樣，這幾年醫美成為很大的商機，一年有好幾百億的產值，而且一直在增加。也因此，全台灣 44,000 多位醫生，其中有 12,000 多位從事醫美。

醫生的工作是醫治病人，社會地位一向很高，但是現在為什麼有這麼多的醫生選擇去做一般人認為不需要太多專業技術的微整型？主要原因有兩個：一個是在一般的醫院工作辛苦，待遇又不高，另外一個是社會環境改變了。

就拿公立醫院外科醫生來說，每星期工作時間超過一百個小時，但是薪水只有十萬塊。可是當微整型醫生，每星期只要工作四十五個小時，薪水卻是兩、三倍。另一方面是價值觀的問題。以前醫生受人尊敬，可是現在的病人動不動就告醫生；平均每天最少有一位醫生被告；醫療糾紛也給醫生帶來很大的壓力。

很多人擔心，我們的醫療品質會不會因為那麼多外科醫生去從事整型工作而受到影響？可是如果醫生的工作環境和待遇不能改善，我們怎麼能怪他們選擇醫美。再說，醫美也是幫助人找回自信，開始新生活的好方法，不是嗎？

医病还是医美

何雅婷的香港朋友爱林听说台湾的微整型技术在亚洲是数一数二的，而且价钱又合理，因此她趁休假到台湾来做微整型。有许多像爱林这样的外国人利用假期来台湾做医美手术。他们希望假期结束以后，能变得更迷人，在职场上更有竞争力。

根据调查，百分之六十一的人认为整型除了可以增加自信，还可以改善职场的人际关系。另外，研究也发现，外表好看的人收入比外表普通的人多百分之十到十五。因为这样，这几年医美成为很大的商机，一年有好几百亿的产值，而且一直在增加。也因此，全台湾 44,000 多位医生，其中有 12,000 多位从事医美。

医生的工作是医治病人，社会地位一向很高，但是现在为什么有这么多的医生选择去做一般人认为不需要太多专业技术的微整型？主要原因有两个：一个是在一般的医院工作辛苦，待遇又不高，另外一个是社会环境改变了。

就拿公立医院外科医生来说，每星期工作时间超过一百个小时，但是薪水只有十万块。可是当微整型医生，每星期只要工作四十五个小时，薪水却是两、三倍。另一方面是价值观的问题。以前医生受人尊敬，可是现在的病人动不动就告医生；平均每天最少有一位医生被告；医疗纠纷也给医生带来很大的压力。

很多人担心，我们的医疗品质会不会因为那么多外科医生去从事整型工作而受到影响？可是如果医生的工作环境和待遇不能改善，我们怎么能怪他们选择医美。再说，医美也是帮助人找回自信，开始新生活的好方法，不是吗？

課文英譯 Text in English

Heal the Sick or Go into Cosmetic Surgery

He Yating's friend from Hong Kong, Ailin, heard that cosmetic surgery skills in Taiwan are among the most advanced in Asia, and the price is reasonable too, so she took advantage of time off to come to Taiwan and have plastic surgery done. There are many foreigners like Ailin that use their vacations to come to Taiwan for cosmetic surgery. They hope that by the time their vacation is over, they will be more attractive and be more competitive in the workplace.

According to surveys, 61% of people believe that in addition to increasing self-confidence, cosmetic surgery can improve interpersonal relations in the workplace. Studies have also found that the salaries of attractive people are between 10% and 15% higher than people with average looks. Because of this, in recent years, cosmetic surgery has become a big business worth tens of billions of New Taiwan dollars each year, and it continues to grow. Consequently, over 12,000 of Taiwan's more than 44,000 doctors are engaged in cosmetic surgery.

The work of physicians, who have always enjoyed high social position, is to heal the sick, but why are so many doctors now choosing to go into cosmetic surgery, a field that is generally not considered to require much specialized skill? There are two primary reasons. First, the work is exhausting at a general hospital, and the pay isn't high. Second, the social landscape has changed.

Take surgeons at public hospitals for example. They work more than 100 hours a week, but their salaries are only NT$100,000 a month. But as a plastic surgeon, you work 45 hours a week and your salary can be two or three times that amount. Then, there's the issue of values. In the past, physicians were respected, but now, patients sue doctors at the drop of a hat. At least one doctor is sued on average each day. Medical disputes also give doctors a great deal of stress.

Many people are worried about whether or not the quality of our health care will be impacted by so many surgeons going into plastic surgery. But if the work environment and pay of doctors cannot be improved, how can we blame them for choosing cosmetic surgery? Furthermore, cosmetic surgery also helps people rediscover their self-confidence and is a good way for people to start a new life, isn't it?

生詞二 Vocabulary II 10-04

Vocabulary

1	醫美醫美醫美 yīměi	ㄧ ㄇㄟˇ	(N)	cosmetic surgery
2	合理合理合理 hélǐ	ㄏㄜˊ ㄌㄧˇ	(Vs)	reasonable
3	休假休假休假 xiūjià 休假	ㄒㄧㄡ ㄐㄧㄚˋ	(V-sep)	to take time off
4	迷人迷人迷人 mírén	ㄇㄧˊ ㄖㄣˊ	(Vs)	charming, attractive
5	職場職場職 zhíchǎng 場職場	ㄓˊ ㄔㄤˇ	(N)	workplace
6	競爭力競爭力 jìngzhēnglì 競爭力	ㄐㄧㄥˋ ㄓㄥ ㄌㄧˋ	(N)	competitive edge
7	調查調查調 diàochá 查	ㄉㄧㄠˋ ㄔㄚˊ	(N)	survey, investigation
8	整型整型整 zhěngxíng 型	ㄓㄥˇ ㄒㄧㄥˊ	(V-sep)	plastic surgery
9	增加增加 zēngjiā	ㄗㄥ ㄐㄧㄚ	(V)	to increase
10	自信自信 zìxìn	ㄗˋ ㄒㄧㄣˋ	(N)	self-confidence
11	外表外表外表 wàibiǎo	ㄨㄞˋ ㄅㄧㄠˇ	(N)	appearance, exterior
12	普通普通 pǔtōng	ㄆㄨˇ ㄊㄨㄥ	(Vs)	common, ordinary
13	從事從事從 cóngshì 事	ㄘㄨㄥˊ ㄕˋ	(V)	to be engaged in, work in (a field of work)
14	醫治治醫治 yīzhì	ㄧ ㄓˋ	(V)	to heal, cure
15	一向一向一向 yíxiàng	ㄧˊ ㄒㄧㄤˋ	(Adv)	have always
16	一般一般 yìbān	ㄧˋ ㄅㄢ	(Vs-attr)	general, most
17	主要主要主要 zhǔyào	ㄓㄨˇ ㄧㄠˋ	(Vs-attr)	primary, main
18	待遇待遇 dàiyù	ㄉㄞˋ ㄩˋ	(N)	pay
19	公立公立 gōnglì	ㄍㄨㄥ ㄌㄧˋ	(Vs-attr)	public; government-run
20	外科外科外科 wàikē	ㄨㄞˋ ㄎㄜ	(N)	department of surgery
21	超過超過 chāoguò	ㄔㄠ ㄍㄨㄛˋ	(Vpt)	to exceed
22	倍倍倍 bèi	ㄅㄟˋ	(M)	times, -fold
23	另另另 lìng	ㄌㄧㄥˋ	(Det)	another, additional
24	價值觀價值觀 jiàzhíguān	ㄐㄧㄚˋ ㄓˊ ㄍㄨㄢ	(N)	values
25	尊敬尊敬 zūnjìng	ㄗㄨㄣ ㄐㄧㄥˋ	(Vst)	to respect, respectful of

26	告告告	gào	ㄍㄠˋ	(V)	to sue, bring suit against
27	平均平均平均 píngjūn 平均		ㄆㄧㄥˊ ㄐㄩㄣ	(Adv)	average
28	醫療醫療療 yīliáo		ㄧ ㄌㄧㄠˊ	(N)	medical treatment, health care
29	怪怪怪怪	guài	ㄍㄨㄞˋ	(V)	to blame

Names

| 30 | 愛林 | Àilín | ㄞˋ ㄌㄧㄣˊ | | female person's name |

Phrases

31	微整型	wéi zhěngxíng	ㄨㄟˊ ㄓㄥˇ ㄒㄧㄥˊ		micro-cosmetic surgery, plastic surgery, face contouring
32	數一數二	shǔyī shǔ'èr	ㄕㄨˇ ㄧ ㄕㄨˇ ㄦˋ		one of the top or best in..., leading…
33	人際關係	rénjì guānxì	ㄖㄣˊ ㄐㄧˋ ㄍㄨㄢ ㄒㄧˋ		interpersonal relations
34	動不動就	dòng bú dòng jiù	ㄉㄨㄥˋ ㄅㄨˊ ㄉㄨㄥˋ ㄐㄧㄡˋ		to do something impetuously
35	找回	zhǎo huí	ㄓㄠˇ ㄏㄨㄟˊ		to rediscover, to retrieve

文法 Grammar

I. Introducing a New Topic with 至於 … *as to, as far as… is concerned*

🎧 10-05　🔍 英譯 p.248

Function: 至於 is a new-topic marker, introducing or shifting to a new topic that is related to a noun mentioned in a previous sentence.

❶ 聽說李文彥受傷了。至於傷得怎麼樣,我就不清楚了。

❷ 這件外套的大小、樣子都很合適。至於顏色,我覺得淺了一點。

❸ 我對醫學系完全沒興趣,我想當警察。至於我父母,他們當然反對。我也沒辦法,我要做自己。

④ 我吃東西只講究營養。至於味道好不好，沒關係。

⑤ 她喜歡個性好的人。至於外表，她覺得不重要。

練習 Exercise

Complete the following dialogues, shifting to a new topic with 至於.

❶ A：聽說美美生病住院了，嚴重不嚴重？要住多久？

　　B：好像不太嚴重。至於＿＿＿＿＿＿＿＿＿＿＿＿＿＿。

❷ A：我的女兒很怕打針，可不可以不打針？吃藥可以嗎？

　　B：打針好得比較快。至於＿＿＿＿＿＿＿＿＿＿＿＿。

❸ A：外表好看的人比較受歡迎，收入也真的比外表普通的人多嗎？

　　B：一般來說外表好看的人是比較受歡迎。

　　　至於＿＿＿＿＿＿＿＿＿＿＿＿＿＿＿＿＿。

❹ A：根據調查，醫學系學生選外科的人比以前少了，是真的嗎？你覺得會不會影響醫療品質？

　　B：媒體都這樣說。至於＿＿＿＿＿＿＿＿＿＿＿。

❺ A：你覺得為什麼會發生醫療糾紛？一定是醫生的錯嗎？

　　B：發生醫療糾紛的原因很多。至於＿＿＿＿＿＿＿＿。

❻ A：聽說有的國家規定 18 歲才可以做微整型，你同意嗎？

　　B：我不反對做微整型。至於＿＿＿＿＿＿＿＿＿＿。

II. 看 *depends on*　🎧 10-06　英譯 p.248

Function: The verb 看 has many meanings. In this lesson, it presents a factor, it's object, that determines an issue.

❶ 考不考得上公職，除了努力以外，還得看運氣。

❷ 傷口多久會好，得看是哪裡受傷。

③ 產品有沒有競爭力，要看價格。要是價格太高怎麼會有人想買？

④ 在網路上賣東西生意好不好，要看賣家的信用好不好。

⑤ 台灣的學費貴不貴，很難說，得看是私立的還是公立的學校。

Usage: All the sentences above have a 'whether... or not' segment, but this is not a requirement. Sentences below do not.

① 微整型沒有傷口，什麼時候都可以做，不必看什麼時候放假。

② 這是一件小事，不必看老闆的意見吧。

練習 Exercise

Complete the dialogues below using 看 to present the determining factor.

① A：醫生，我馬上就能住院開刀嗎？

B：最近病人很多，＿＿＿＿＿＿＿＿＿＿＿＿＿＿＿。

② A：我的女兒腿被撞傷了，以後走路會不會不方便？

B：＿＿＿＿＿＿＿＿，不過最好的情況只能恢復八成到九成。

③ A：微整型的價錢都一樣嗎？

B：不一樣吧。＿＿＿＿＿＿＿＿＿＿＿＿＿＿＿。

④ A：整過型的人在結婚以前應該告訴要跟他／她結婚的人嗎？

B：＿＿＿＿＿＿＿＿＿＿＿＿＿＿＿＿＿。

⑤ A：你覺得發生醫療糾紛的時候，一定是醫生的錯嗎？

B：＿＿＿＿＿＿＿＿＿＿＿＿＿＿＿＿＿。

III. 一向 *all along, has always...* 10-07　　　　　 英譯 p.249

Function: The adverb 一向 means 'it has always been the case that', referring to habits or aptitudes.

① 他一向很熱心，總是喜歡幫助人。

❷ 他對自己的能力一向有自信；他不會放棄的。

❸ 這家公司一向重視品質。你可以放心買他們的產品。

❹ 他一向喜歡開玩笑。他說的話，都要打個折扣。

❺ 他一向很照顧學生。不管學生碰到什麼問題，他都盡量幫忙。

Usage:

1. Both 一向 and 一直 indicate the continuation of an action or a state from the past to the present. 一向, however, stresses something being habitual, while 一直 emphasizes continuation. They are thus not always interchangeable. E.g.,

   (1) （從昨天到今天，）他一直不相信我說的話。

   (2) 他一向不相信我說的話。

   (3) 她一向不聽別人的建議，你別再說了。（*一直）

   (4) 他旅行以前，一向先計畫好。（*一直）

2. Although 一向 indicates habit, the habit can change. E.g.,

   (1) 這裡的冬天一向很潮濕，今年卻變了。

   (2) 他一向不喜歡吃海鮮，昨天卻點了一道檸檬魚。

3. 一向 can only be used to describe something in the past, while 一直 can be used to express something in the future. E.g.,

   他會一直陪著你走到學校。（*一向）

練習 Exercise

Complete the following sentences with 一直 or 一向 .

❶ 我_____不喜歡打擾朋友。旅行的時候從來不住朋友家。

❷ 他頭痛了好久，可是醫生_____找不出原因。只好吃止痛藥。

❸ 大醫院的急診室裡＿＿＿＿＿＿擠滿了病人，好不容易才能等到一張病床。

❹ 外表迷人，在職場上＿＿＿＿＿＿比較有競爭力。難怪做微整型的人越來越多。

❺ 他＿＿＿＿＿＿怪父母，小時候不讓他學音樂；要不然現在可以靠音樂賺錢。

❻ 醫生的待遇＿＿＿＿＿＿比別的工作好，因此醫學系也是最難考上的科系。

❼ 他＿＿＿＿＿＿＿愛著王小姐，可是不敢說出來。

IV. 拿…來說 *take…as an example* 10-08　　　🔍英譯 p.249

Function: With this pattern, the speaker presents a statement from a given perspective.

❶ 我們公司的產品最有競爭力。拿價錢來說，我們的產品是市場上最便宜的。

❷ 我最怕參加比賽了。拿上次演講比賽來說，我緊張得把要說的話全忘了。

❸ 車禍的原因常常都是速度太快。拿王大明上次出車禍來說，他的速度幾乎超過規定的一倍。

❹ 這家公司的待遇真不錯。拿休假來說，只要工作兩年就能休十天的假。

❺ 麗麗對穿很講究。拿外套來說，黑色的就有十件不同的款式。

練習 Exercise

Complete the following sentences by giving an example with 拿…來說.

❶ 這次考試全班成績都進步了。拿＿＿＿＿＿＿＿＿＿＿＿＿＿＿＿＿。

❷ 最近連老人的購物習慣都改變了。拿＿＿＿＿＿＿＿＿＿＿＿＿＿＿＿。

❸ 網路真的給我們生活帶來很大的方便。拿＿＿＿＿＿＿＿＿＿＿＿＿。

❹ 她做過好幾次微整型。拿＿＿＿＿＿＿＿＿＿＿＿＿＿＿＿。

❺ 人際關係有的時候比能力還重要。拿＿＿＿＿＿＿＿＿＿＿＿。

❻ 從事醫美的醫生外表都不錯。拿＿＿＿＿＿＿＿＿＿＿＿＿＿。

V. Passive Sentences with 受 10-09

Function: Sentences with the transitive verb 受 indicate a passive meaning, 'to be..., to get...'.

❶ 在台灣，教授是個受人尊敬的工作。

❷ 五月天的歌很受大學生喜愛，他們演唱會的票很快就賣完了。

❸ 他的能力很強，老闆很喜歡他，所以他在公司裡越來越受重視。

❹ 那位醫生常上電視，她不但經驗多，而且口才好，非常受歡迎。

❺ 他一向按照規定辦事情，今天不遵守規定，應該是受了很大的壓力。

Usage:

A. Two structures are possible with 受. It either takes an object or it is followed by the subject of yet another verb.

1. 受＋O

   (1) 她受過很好的教育 (jiàoyù, education)。

   (2) 他選擇放棄，應該是受了很大的壓力。

2. 受＋S＋V

   (1) 他教書很活潑，很受學生（的）歡迎。

   (2) 她寫的歌很受大家（的）喜愛。

   (3) 他提出的想法很受店長（的）重視。

B. Comparing the passive with 受 and the passive with 被.

1. 被 is a passive particle, and 受 is a verb. Words like 很, 非常, and 大 can be placed in front of 受 as adverbials. These cannot be placed in front of 被.

E.g.,

(1) 比賽的時候天氣不好，他的成績大受影響。

(2) 聽了吳寶春的故事，他很受感動。

(3) 他把學生當做孩子，非常受學生尊敬。

2. 被 - passives relate to events that are often unfortunate for the subject or the speaker of the sentence, whereas 受 - passives are free from this tendency.

E.g.,

(1) 她的手機被朋友弄壞了。

(2) 這件事情被她發現就麻煩了。

(3) 他偷東西的時候被人看見了。

(4) 她很喜歡這個電影，看了以後很受感動。

(5) 我喜歡接近自然，是受她影響。

(6) 她念書很專心，不受別人打擾。

3. 受 is in most cases used with transitive state verbs. 被, on the other hand, is in most cases used with action verbs.

E.g.,

(1) 他把賣菜賺的錢都給了窮人，很受人尊敬。

(2) 他說話很有意思，很受朋友歡迎。

(3) 這種遊戲很有意思，很受高中學生喜愛。

(4) 他沒把事情做好，被老闆罵了一頓。

(5) 我的車上個週末停在路邊，結果被撞壞了。倒楣死了！

(6) 他安靜地走進辦公室，不想被發現。

練習 **Exercice**

Complete the following sentences using 受 plus a verb as given below.

受 歡迎 / 照顧 / 鼓勵 / 尊敬 / 支持 / 影響 / 重視 / 喜愛 / 感動

❶ 他昨天演講的時候說到他從小＿＿＿＿＿＿。要是沒有他們，他不可能成功。

❷ 他告訴老闆要用有機食材做麵包，沒想到會＿＿＿＿＿＿。

❸ 他很努力地教書卻不＿＿＿＿＿＿＿＿，讓他很難過。

❹ 老師說他的中文進步很多，說得越來越流利，他＿＿＿＿＿＿就更用功了。

❺ 這個電影談的是狗跟人的關係。那隻狗好可愛，牠那麼愛主人，看的人都＿＿＿＿＿＿＿＿＿＿＿。

VI. 動不動就⋯ *to do something impetuously* 10-10   英譯 p.250

Function: The idiom 動不動就 refers to doing something or getting into some state quite often and without good reason. This pattern is used as a criticism.

❶ 現在年輕人動不動就換工作，怎麼能成功？

❷ 這是你自己的問題，不要動不動就怪別人。

❸ 你別動不動就打擾別人工作，等他們有空的時候再去請教他們。

❹ 你很健康，不要動不動就去醫院檢查身體。

❺ 最近高鐵動不動就出問題，讓搭高鐵的人很不放心。

練習 **Exercise**

Re-write the following sentences using 動不動就⋯.

❶ 她的身體不好，常常生病。

→ ＿＿＿＿＿＿＿＿＿＿＿＿＿＿＿＿＿＿＿。

2 他跟女朋友有問題的時候，他女朋友總是說「我們分手吧」，讓他很痛苦。

→ _____ 。

3 李大明不喜歡跟別人競爭，碰到有人跟他競爭的時候，總是說「我放棄」。

→ _____ 。

4 最近我的電腦常常壞，送去修理，也找不出原因。

→ _____ 。

5 他總是罵人，大家才不喜歡他的。

→ _____ 。

6 她一有錢就去整型，這次是她第十次去整型了。

→ _____ 。

語法例句英譯
Grammar Examples in English

I. Introducing a New Topic with 至於… *as to, as far as… is concerned*
Function:

1 I hear that Li Wenyan was injured. As to how serious the injury is, I don't know.
2 The size and style of this coat are both suitable. As for the color, I think it's a bit light.
3 I have no interest in medical school, I want to be a policeman. As for my parents, they obviously oppose the idea strongly. But I can't help that, I want to be true to myself.
4 I am only fastidious about nutritious food. As to whether the taste is good or not, that's irrelevant.
5 She likes people with good personalities. As to looks, she thinks that's unimportant.

II. 看 *depends on*
Function:

1 Whether or not you can pass the exam for the public service, in addition to studying hard, it also depends on luck.
2 How long it takes for an injury to heal depends on where the injury is.
3 Whether or not a product is competitive depends on the price. If the price is too high, how is anyone going to want to buy it?
4 Whether or not an online sales business will do well depends on the trustworthiness of the seller.
5 It's hard to say if tuition in Taiwan is high. It depends on whether the school is private or public.

Usage:

❶ There are no abrasions with micro-cosmetic surgery, so it can be done anytime. You don't need to take into consideration when you have time off.

❷ This is a small matter. No need to take the boss' views into consideration.

III. 一向 *all along, has always…*

Function:

❶ He has always been passionate and has always liked helping others.

❷ He has always been confident in his abilities. He won't give up.

❸ This company has always attached a great deal of importance to quality. You can set your mind at ease when you buy their products.

❹ He has always loved to joke around. You need to take what he says with a grain of salt.

❺ He has always looked after his students. No matter what problems they face, he does everything he can to help.

Usage:

1. (1) (From yesterday to today,) He hasn't believed what I said.
   (2) He has never believed what I say.
   (3) She never accepts other people's suggestions. Don't waste your breath.
   (4) He always plans ahead before traveling.
2. (1) It has always been humid here in the winter. This year, however, that has changed.
   (2) He has never liked eating seafood, but yesterday, he ordered lemon fish.
3. He will walk with you all the way to school.

IV. 拿…來說 *take…as an example*

Function:

❶ Our company's products are highly competitive. Take prices as an example; our products are the cheapest on the market.

❷ I hate taking part in competitions. Take the last speech contest for example; I was so nervous that I completely forgot everything I was going to say.

❸ Speeding is often the reason for car accidents. Take Wang Daming's accident earlier as an example. He was going almost twice the stipulated speed.

❹ This company's terms of employment are really good. Take paid vacation for example. You only need to work here two years to get ten days of vacation.

❺ Lili is very fussy about clothes. Take coats for example; she has ten different styles of coat that are all black.

V. Passive Sentences with 受

Function:

❶ In Taiwan, teaching in university is a respected line of work.

❷ Mayday's songs are loved by the college crowd. Their concert tickets sell out quickly.

❸ He is very capable and the boss likes him. He is valued more and more in the company.

❹ The doctor frequently appears on television. She is not only highly experienced, she is also eloquent. She is very well received.

❺ He has always done things by the book. He didn't follow the rules today probably because he's under a lot of pressure.

Usage:

A.
1. (1) She received a good education.
   (2) He decided to give up. He was probably under too much pressure.

2. (1) He teaches with a lot of energy and is very popular with students.

(2) The songs she writes are very well liked by everyone.

(3) The ideas he proposes carry a great deal of weight with the store manager.

B.

1. (1) The weather was bad during the competition and his score was greatly impacted.

(2) Having heard Wu Baochun's story, he was deeply moved.

(3) He views students as his own children and is very much respected by them.

2. (1) Her phone was broken by a friend.

(2) If she finds out about this, there'll be a lot of trouble.

(3) Someone saw him stealing.

(4) She likes this movie; she was really moved after watching it.

(5) My affinity for nature is due to her influence.

(6) She is very focused when she studies. Other people can't disturb her.

3. (1) He is highly respected, because he gives all the money he makes from selling vegetables to the poor.

(2) He is a very interesting speaker. He is very popular with his friends.

(3) This is a fun game and is very popular with high school students.

(4) He didn't do a good job and was reamed out by the boss.

(5) I parked my car on the side of the road last weekend, and it got smashed into. What rotten luck!

(6) He walked quietly into the office. He didn't want to be noticed.

VI. 動不動就… *to do something impetuously*

Function:

❶ Young people today change jobs at the drop of a hat. How are they going to succeed?

❷ This is your problem. Don't go blaming others at the drop of a hat.

❸ Don't interrupt others when they're working whenever you feel like it. Wait until they have time, and then ask them your questions.

❹ You're very healthy. Don't go to the hospital for checkups at the drop of a hat.

❺ The HSR has been having all kinds of problems lately, causing anxiety among people who take it.

課室活動 Classroom Activities

I. What Should You Do When There's a Car Accident?

Goal: Learning to describe car accidents and assistance provided.

Task: Discuss automobile accidents and the steps involved in providing assistance. Please list them in the order that they should occur.

- ☐ ❶ 打 119 叫救護車
- ☐ ❷ 不可以移動（yídòng, to move）受傷的人或是車
- ☐ ❸ 照相
- ☐ ❹ 打 110 報警

II. I've Been Injured

Goal: Learning to talk about injuries and experience with staying in the hospital in Chinese.

Task: Xiaogao is leaving the hospital and he runs into a classmate at the entrance. Xiaogao tells the classmate about his accident and the medical care he received from the medical staff at the hospital after he arrived. Class, divide into two groups and perform a skit entitled "I broke my arm" or "I'm staying in the hospital".

Try to use the following sentence patterns and vocabulary words:

照 X 光	骨折	等病床	打止痛針
醫生說開刀的風險	會不會完全恢復	傷口	住院

III. I'm 18-years Old And I Want Cosmetic Surgery

Goal: Learning to provide data and real-life examples supporting your views.
Task: Please refer to the information below, then split the class into two teams to debate the issue "Should 18-year olds be permitted to undergo cosmetic surgery?"

Try to use the following sentence patterns and vocabulary words:

倍	～成	X 分之 Y	競爭力
風險	自信	得看	拿…來說

參考資料

Information for your reference

對微整型的看法：**Views on micro-cosmetic surgery**

❶ 七成二的人認為微整型也是一種整型
(72% of people believe that micro-cosmetic surgery is a kind of cosmetic surgery.)

❷ 四成五的人認為微整型可以恢復，所以想試試看
(45% of people believe that the results of micro-

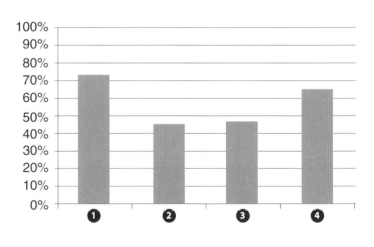

cosmetic surgery eventually fade, so they would like to try it out.)

❸ 四成七的人為了讓自己看起來更美，而做微整型
(47% of people receive micro-cosmetic surgery to look more attractive.)

❹ 六成二的人擔心會有副作用，不敢做微整型
(62% of people are concerned about side affects, so they are afraid to undergo cosmetic surgery.)

不考慮微整型的原因：**Reasons for not considering cosmetic surgery**

❶ 六成八的人擔心副作用 (68% of people are concerned about side effects.)

❷ 六成八的人認為太貴 (68% of people think it's too expensive.)

❸ 五成的人認為自然就是美 (50% of people think natural beauty is best.)

❹ 三成二的人怕痛 (32% of people are afraid of the pain.)

❺ 二成四的人找不到可靠的醫生 (24% of people can't find a doctor they can trust.)

❻ 二成三的人認為現在沒有需要 (23% of people don't think they need cosmetic surgery at present.)

❼ 5% 怕別人的眼光 (5% of people are afraid of what other people might think.)

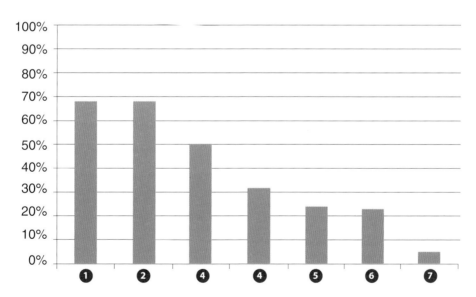

沒整過型的原因：**Reasons for not receiving cosmetic surgery**

沒有必要 44%	Not necessary 44%
自然就是美 42%	Natural beauty is best 42%
錢不夠 9%	Can't afford sugery 9%
怕被看不起 2%	Afraid of what others will think 2%
其他 3%	Other 3%

整型的原因：**Reasons for undergoing cosmetic surgery**

不滿意自己的外表 46%	Not satisfied with appearance 46%
想改運 23%	To change luck 23%
因為流行 12%	Because it is a trend 12%
好奇 12%	Curious 12%
朋友都整型 4%	Because friends are doing it 4%
其他 3%	Other 3%

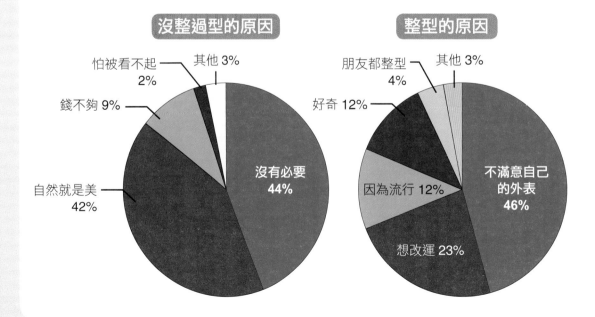

文化 *Bits of Chinese Culture*

Cold, Balanced, and Hot Food

The study of nutrition uses concepts like proteins, calories, carbohydrates, vitamins, and minerals when assessing the nutrional value of foods. Chinese medicine, however, attaches importance to food "properties". It divides them into five types—cold（寒 hán）, cool（涼 liáng）, balanced（平 píng）, warm（溫 wēn）, and hot（熱 rè）, but most generally three types: cold（寒涼）, balanced（平性）, and hot（溫熱）.

寒涼

▲ Watermelons, balsam pears, bananas, and mung bean soup are considered cool and cold foods.

Being hot in terms of temperature doesn't mean that a food is necessarily hot according to the Chinese medicine definition of the word, nor does being cold in terms of temperature mean that a food is cold to a practitioner of Chinese medicine. Whether a food is hot or cold depends on the body's response to it when it is consumed. For example, a person feels warm after eating mutton pot in the winter. And a person can sweat after eating spicy hot food. From the way the body feels after eating lamb, hot peppers, and garlic, we can know that these foods are hot. If you eat a slice of watermelon or a bowl mung bean soup in the summer, you immediately feel cool and refreshed. As a result, the ancients categorized watermelon and mung bean soup as cold foods.

溫熱

▲ Hotpot, lamb, garlic, hot peppers, walnuts, and pine nuts are considered warm and hot foods.

People, too, can be divided into hot and cold, depending on their health. People who have cold hands and feet, who like to drink hot liquids, who have pale complexions, and who lack energy often have chronic illnesses. They are considered to have cold constitutions and should eat plenty of warm and hot foods. These foods have such functions as making the spleen healthier, improving appetite, and strengthening the kidneys. In contrast, individuals who radiate heat, don't like hot weather, are often thirsty, like to drink cold beverages, have a red complexion, and are easily agitated frequently experience acute sicknesses or have virus or germ infections. They have hot constitutions and should consume plenty of cool and cold foods. Cool and cold foods have such functions as clearing internal heat, relieving inflammation and fever, as well as detoxifying.

When deciding what to eat, you not only have to take into account your constitution type, you also have to choose foods based on the season. In the summer, you should eat colder foods, like bitter melon, watermelon, and bananas to reduce internal heat. Eating too many warm and hot foods, like lamb, walnuts, and pine nuts, will make you thirsty and give you a sore throat. In the winter, you should eat plenty of hot foods in hot pots and stews. Cold foods, like watermelon, not only can make you feel cool and refreshed, if eaten in excess, they can cause diarrhea. Are you eating right?

Self-Assessment Checklist

I can describe what happened in an automobile accident.

20%　　40%　　60%　　80%　　100%

I can explain injuries and discuss treatment with doctors.

20%　　40%　　60%　　80%　　100%

I can discuss issues related to cosmetic surgery.

20%　　40%　　60%　　80%　　100%

I can provide data and real-life examples supporting my views.

20%　　40%　　60%　　80%　　100%

LESSON 11

第十一課

台灣故事
The Story of Taiwan

學習目標 **Learning Objectives**

Topic: 歷史 History

- Learning to understand stories on the history of Taiwan.
- Learning to give a rough introduction of your own country's history.
- Learning to discuss the relationship between food and culture.
- Learning to explain the origins and narrate the details of an event.

對話 Dialogue 11-01

（在活動中心）

安德思：何雅婷，妳現在有空嗎？能不能幫我看一下這份作業？

何雅婷：什麼作業？紅毛城的故事？你們現在學台灣歷史嗎？

安德思：是啊。下個星期一輪到我報告紅毛城的歷史。可是我的中文不夠好，有些資料看不懂，想請妳幫忙。

何雅婷：好啊，有什麼問題？

安德思：網路上說，紅毛城最早是西班牙人建的，後來荷蘭人又重建。到底是怎麼回事？

何雅婷：十六世紀，歐洲許多國家到東方從事貿易活動。十七世紀初，荷蘭人先在台灣南部建立城市。過了兩年，西班牙人也到了台灣北部，在淡水建了紅毛城。1642年，為了商業利益，荷蘭派軍隊打敗了西班牙。西班牙人離開台灣以前，把城燒了。所以現在的紅毛城是荷蘭人重建的。

安德思：為什麼叫紅毛城？因為城牆是紅色的嗎？

何雅婷：不是，不是，是因為西方人頭髮顏色的關係。當時的台灣人叫西方人「紅毛」。

安德思：那時候台灣沒有政府嗎？為什麼歐洲人可以自由地來來去去，甚至在台灣打仗？

何雅婷：那時候台灣不是一個國家，沒有政府。除了少數來開墾跟做生意的漢人以外，都是原住民。

安德思：這麼說，台灣應該有很多原住民才對。可是為什麼我的朋友當中一個原住民都沒有？

何雅婷：這就要從鄭成功說起了。鄭成功是明朝的一位將軍，他在1662年帶著兩萬五千個軍人打敗荷蘭，建立台灣歷史上第一個漢人政府。

安德思：鄭成功到台灣就跟西班牙人到中南美洲的情形一樣嗎？

何雅婷：嗯。從那以後，移民到台灣來的漢人越來越多。慢慢地，本來住在平原的原住民有的搬到山上去，更多的人跟漢人結婚了。現在台灣人口當中原住民只占百分之二，差不多有五十幾萬人。

安德思：妳的意思是，台灣有很多人都有原住民的血統嘍？

何雅婷：是的。十七世紀末，清朝政府打敗了鄭成功的孫子，台灣正式成為大清帝國的領土。但是清朝政府只讓男性來台灣開墾，禁止他們帶家人來。所以漢人男性想結婚只能娶原住民。

安德思：謝謝妳告訴我這麼多跟台灣有關的故事。我相信下個星期我的報告會非常精彩。

課文簡體字版 Text in Simplified Characters

（在活动中心）

安 德 思：何雅婷，妳现在有空吗？能不能帮我看一下这份作业？

何 雅 婷：什么作业？红毛城的故事？你们现在学台湾历史吗？

安 德 思：是啊。下个星期一轮到我报告红毛城的历史。可是我的中文不够好，有些资料看不懂，想请妳帮忙。

何 雅 婷：好啊，有什么问题？

安 德 思：网路上说，红毛城最早是西班牙人建的，后来荷兰人又重建。到底是怎么回事？

何 雅 婷：十六世纪，欧洲许多国家到东方从事贸易活动。十七世纪初，荷兰人先在台湾南部建立城市。过了两年，西班牙人也到了台湾北部，在淡水建了红毛城。1642 年，为了商业利益，荷兰派军队打败了西班牙。西班牙人离开台湾以前，把城烧了。所以现在的红毛城是荷兰人重建的。

安 德 思：为什么叫红毛城？因为城墙是红色的吗？

何 雅 婷：不是，不是，是因为西方人头发颜色的关系。当时的台湾人叫西方人「红毛」。

安 德 思：那时候台湾没有政府吗？为什么欧洲人可以自由地来来去去，甚至在台湾打仗？

何 雅 婷：那时候台湾不是一个国家，没有政府。除了少数来开垦跟做生意的汉人以外，都是原住民。

安 德 思：这么说，台湾应该有很多原住民才对。可是为什么我的朋友当中一个原住民都没有？

何 雅 婷：这就要从郑成功说起了。郑成功是明朝的一位将军，他在1662 年带着两万五千个军人打败荷兰，建立台湾历史上第一个汉人政府。

安 德 思：郑成功到台湾就跟西班牙人到中南美洲的情形一样吗？

何 雅 婷：嗯。从那以后，移民到台湾来的汉人越来越多。慢慢地，本来住在平原的原住民有的搬到山上去，更多的人跟汉人结婚了。现在台湾人口当中原住民只占百分之二，差不多有五十几万人。

安 德 思：妳的意思是，台湾有很多人都有原住民的血统喽？

何 雅 婷：是的。十七世纪末，清朝政府打败了郑成功的孙子，台湾正式成为大清帝国的领土。但是清朝政府只让男性来台湾开垦，禁止他们带家人来。所以汉人男性想结婚只能娶原住民。

安 德 思：谢谢妳告诉我这么多跟台湾有关的故事。我相信下个星期我的报告会非常精彩。

課文英譯 Text in English

(In the activity center)

An Desi : He Yating, are you free? Can you look at this assignment for me?

He Yating : What assignment? The story of Fort Santo Domingo? Are you studying Taiwanese history?

An Desi : Yes. Next Monday, it's my turn to give a report on Fort Santo Domingo's history. But my Chinese is not good enough. There is some information I can't understand and I'd like to ask you to help.

He Yating : Sure, how can I help?

An Desi : On the internet, it says that Fort Santo Domingo was originally built by the Spanish, and then the Dutch rebuilt it. What on earth is that all about?

He Yating : In the 16th century, many European countries came to the East to engage in trade activities. In the early 17th century, the Dutch first arrived in southern Taiwan where they established a settlement. Two years later, the Spanish arrived in northern Taiwan and built Fort Santo Domingo in Tamsui. In 1642, the Netherlands sent an army which fought and beat the Spanish over business interests. Before the Spanish left Taiwan, they burnt the fort, so the current Fort Santo Domingo was rebuilt by the Dutch.

An Desi : Why is it called "Hongmaocheng"? Because the defensive walls are red?

He Yating : No, no. It has to do with the hair color of westerners. At the time, Taiwanese called westerners "red hair".

An Desi : Did Taiwan not have a government at that time? Why could the Europeans come and go freely and even fight battles in Taiwan?

He Yating : At the time, Taiwan wasn't a country, there was no government. With the exception of a few Han Chinese who came to develop the land for farming and do business, they were all aborigines.

An Desi : Then, Taiwan should have a lot of aborigines. But why is it that not even one of my friends is an aborigine?

He Yating : For this, we need to start our story with Zheng Chenggong (a.k.a. Koxinga). Zheng Chenggong was a Ming Dynasty general. In 1662, he led 25,000 soldiers to fight and beat the Dutch and established the first Han Chinese government in Taiwan.

An Desi : When Zheng Chenggong arrived in Taiwan, was the situation like that when the Spanish arrived in Central and South America?

He Yating : Uh-huh. From then on, more and more Han Chinese immigrated to Taiwan. Gradually, of the aborigines who originally lived in the flatlands, some moved to the mountains and even more married Han Chinese. Only 2% of Taiwan's current population is aborigine—around 500,000 people.

An Desi : You mean to say many people in Taiwan have aboriginal blood?

He Yating : That's right. At the end of the 17th century, the Qing Dynasty government conquered Zheng Chenggong's grandson and Taiwan formally became a territory of the Qing Empire. But the Qing government only allowed males to come to Taiwan to open up the land and didn't allow them to bring their families. So if Han males wanted to marry, they could only marry aborigines.

An Desi : Thank you for telling me so many stories about Taiwan. I'm sure my report next week will be brilliant.

生詞一 Vocabulary I 🎧 11-02

Vocabulary

1	建	jiàn	ㄐㄧㄢˋ	(V)	to build (Classical Chinese)
2	重建重建	chóngjiàn	ㄔㄨㄥˊ ㄐㄧㄢˋ	(V)	to rebuild
3	到底到底到底	dàodǐ	ㄉㄠˋ ㄉㄧˇ	(Adv)	in the end, after all
4	世紀世紀世紀shìjì世紀世紀	shìjì	ㄕˋ ㄐㄧˋ	(N)	century
5	貿易貿易	màoyì	ㄇㄠˋ ㄧˋ	(N)	trade
6	商業	shāngyè	ㄕㄤ ㄧㄝˋ	(N)	commerce, business
7	利益	lìyì	ㄌㄧˋ ㄧˋ	(N)	gains, benefit
8	派	pài	ㄆㄞˋ	(V)	to send, dispatch
9	軍隊	jūnduì	ㄐㄩㄣ ㄉㄨㄟˋ	(N)	army, military
10	燒	shāo	ㄕㄠ	(V)	to burn
11	城牆	chéngqiáng	ㄔㄥˊ ㄑㄧㄤˊ	(N)	city walls, defensive walls
12	頭髮	tóufǎ	ㄊㄡˊ ㄈㄚˇ	(N)	hair
13	甚至	shènzhì	ㄕㄣˋ ㄓˋ	(Adv)	even, even to the point of
14	打仗	dǎzhàng	ㄉㄚˇ ㄓㄤˋ	(V-sep)	to engage in warfare

15	少數	shǎoshù	ㄕㄠˇ ㄕㄨˋ	(N)	minority, a few
16	開墾	kāikěn	ㄎㄞ ㄎㄣˇ	(V)	to open up land for farming
17	將軍	jiāngjūn	ㄐㄧㄤ ㄐㄩㄣ	(N)	general
18	軍人	jūnrén	ㄐㄩㄣ ㄖㄣˊ	(N)	military service member
19	平原	píngyuán	ㄆㄧㄥˊ ㄩㄢˊ	(N)	flatland, plains
20	人口	rénkǒu	ㄖㄣˊ ㄎㄡˇ	(N)	population
21	血統	xiětǒng	ㄒㄧㄝˇ ㄊㄨㄥˇ	(N)	blood, bloodline
22	嘍	lou	ㄌㄡ	(Ptc)	a sentence-final particle meaning 'in that case'
23	孫子	sūnzi	ㄙㄨㄣ ㄗ	(N)	grandson
24	領土	lǐngtǔ	ㄌㄧㄥˇ ㄊㄨˇ	(N)	territory (of a nation)
25	男性	nánxìng	ㄋㄢˊ ㄒㄧㄥˋ	(N)	male
26	禁止	jìnzhǐ	ㄐㄧㄣˋ ㄓˇ	(V)	to forbid
27	娶	qǔ	ㄑㄩˇ	(V)	to take a woman in marriage
28	相信	xiāngxìn	ㄒㄧㄤ ㄒㄧㄣˋ	(Vst)	to believe
29	精彩	jīngcǎi	ㄐㄧㄥ ㄘㄞˇ	(Vs)	splendid, brilliant as (of a performance)

Names

30	紅毛城	Hóngmáo chéng	ㄏㄨㄥˊ ㄇㄠˊ ㄔㄥˊ		Fort Santo Domingo, lit. red-hair city
31	東方	Dōngfāng	ㄉㄨㄥ ㄈㄤ		the East, the Orient
32	淡水	Dànshuǐ	ㄉㄢˋ ㄕㄨㄟˇ		Tamsui
33	漢人	Hàn rén	ㄏㄢˋ ㄖㄣˊ		Han-ethnic Chinese
34	鄭成功	Zhèng Chénggōng	ㄓㄥˋ ㄔㄥˊ ㄍㄨㄥ		Koxinga, 國姓爺, 1624-1662, who ruled Taiwan against the Manchu sovereignty
35	明朝	Míng cháo	ㄇㄧㄥˊ ㄔㄠˊ		Ming Dynasty, 1368-1644

36	中南美洲	Zhōngnán Měizhōu	ㄓㄨㄥ ㄋㄢˊ ㄇㄟˇ ㄓㄡ	Central and South America
37	清朝	Qīng cháo	ㄑㄧㄥ ㄔㄠˊ	Qing Dynasty, 1644-1911
38	大清帝國	Dàqīng dìguó	ㄉㄚˋ ㄑㄧㄥ ㄉㄧˋ ㄍㄨㄛˊ	the Qing Empire

Phrases

39	輪到	lúndào	ㄌㄨㄣˊ ㄉㄠˋ	one's turn, it's up to
40	十七世紀初	shíqī shìjì chū	ㄕˊ ㄑㄧ ㄕˋ ㄐㄧˋ ㄔㄨ	early 17th century
41	打敗	dǎ bài	ㄉㄚˇ ㄅㄞˋ	to defeat
42	十七世紀末	shíqī shìjì mò	ㄕˊ ㄑㄧ ㄕˋ ㄐㄧˋ ㄇㄛˋ	late 17th century

短文 Reading 🎧 11-03

餐桌上的歷史

星期六早上何雅婷帶安德思到一家很有名的中式早餐店去吃早餐。何雅婷點了一套燒餅油條、一份蛋餅、一個飯糰，還有一碗甜豆漿跟一碗鹹豆漿。何雅婷告訴他，這家早餐店的老闆是 1949 年的時候跟著蔣介石一起到台灣來的。國共內戰，蔣介石打輸了，就帶著一百多萬的軍隊跟人民到了台灣。

那時候有些人為了生活，不得不擺個攤子，賣起家鄉的美食。這家店就是這麼開始的。

但是安德思看到早餐店的菜單上也有蘿蔔糕。他想起上烹飪課的時候，老師說過蘿蔔糕是客家人過年時一定要吃的。何雅婷告訴他，因為蘿蔔長得快，而且不太需要照顧，秋天收成以後種下的蘿蔔就成了客家人冬天重要的蔬菜。何雅婷接著又說，在中國歷史上，客家人因為戰爭不斷而往南方遷移，現在台灣客家人的祖先多半是清朝的時候移民來的。因為來的時間比閩南人晚，只好住在山邊，生活比較困難。節儉的客家主婦就利用曬乾以後的蘿蔔煎蛋、煮湯，做出各種各樣的菜色，以及美味的點心。

安德思還發現，這家早餐店賣的飯糰跟他在便利商店買的不一樣。何雅婷覺得安德思買的應該是日式飯糰。日本曾經殖民統治台灣五十年，所以台灣人的飲食習慣受到很深的影響，像壽司、味噌湯都很普遍，到處都吃得到。不過台灣的味噌湯裡有時候會加一小段油條，飯糰裡也常能見到客家蘿蔔乾。安德思從來沒想到從餐桌上可以看出一個地方的歷史。這頓早餐讓他對台灣有了更進一步的了解。

課文簡體字版 Text in Simplified Characters

餐桌上的历史

星期六早上何雅婷带安德思到一家很有名的中式早餐店去吃早餐。何雅婷点了一套烧饼油条、一份蛋饼、一个饭团，还有一碗甜豆浆跟一碗咸豆浆。何雅婷告诉他，这家早餐店的老板是 1949 年的时候跟着蒋介石一起到台湾来的。国共内战，蒋介石打输了，就带着一百多万的军队跟人民到了台湾。那时候有些人为了生活，不得不摆个摊子，卖起家乡的美食。这家店就是这么开始的。

但是安德思看到早餐店的菜单上也有萝卜糕。他想起上烹饪课的时候，老师说过萝卜糕是客家人过年时一定要吃的。何雅婷告诉他，因为萝卜长得快，而且不太需要照顾，秋天收成以后种下的萝卜就成了客家人冬天重要的蔬菜。何雅婷接着又说，在中国历史上，客家人因为战争不断而往南方迁移，现在台湾客家人的祖先多半是清朝的时候移民来的。因为来的时间比闽南人晚，只好住在山边，生活比较困难。节俭的客家主妇就利用晒干以后的萝卜煎蛋、煮汤，做出各种各样的菜色，以及美味的点心。

安德思还发现，这家早餐店卖的饭团跟他在便利商店买的不一样。何雅婷觉得安德思买的应该是日式饭团。日本曾经殖民统治台湾五十年，所以台湾人的饮食习惯受到很深的影响，像寿司、味噌汤都很普遍，到处都吃得到。不过台湾的味噌汤里有时候会加一小段油条，饭团里也常能见到客家萝卜干。安德思从来没想到从餐桌上可以看出一个地方的历史。这顿早餐让他对台湾有了更进一步的了解。

課文英譯 Text in English

The History on the Dining Table

On Saturday morning, He Yating brought An Desi to a well known Chinese-style breakfast restaurant to eat breakfast. He Yating ordered a shaobing and youtiao combo, a danbing, a fantuan, as well as a bowl of sweet soy milk and a bowl of savory soy milk. He Yating told him that the owner of this breakfast shop came with Chiang Kai-Shek to Taiwan in 1949. In the Chinese Civil War, Chiang Kai-Shek lost and brought over one million troops and civilians to Taiwan. At the time, some people had no choice but to set up vending stands and sell foods from their hometowns to make a living. This shop started that way.

But An Desi saw that the breakfast shop also had fried daikon cakes. He remembered that in cuisine class, the teacher said that fried daikon cakes are a must for the Hakka people during the lunar new year. He Yating told him that because they grow very quickly and don't need a lot of care, daikon radishes, which are planted after the autumn harvest, became an important vegetable for the Hakka in winter. He Yating then went on to say that over the course of Chinese history, the Hakka people kept relocating southward, because of continual war. Most of the Hakka in Taiwan immigrated to Taiwan during the Qing Dynasty. Because they arrived later than the Minnan people, they had no choice but to live next to mountains where their lives were more difficult. Frugal Hakka housewives fried eggs, made soup, and made a variety of dishes and delicious desserts with sundried daikon.

An Desi also discovered that the fantuan sold in the breakfast shop are different from those that he had purchased in convenience stores. He Yating thinks that An Desi probably bought Japanese-style fantuan. Japan once ruled Taiwan as a colony for 50 years, so the dietary habits of the Taiwanese have been deeply influenced by the Japanese. Foods like sushi and miso soup are commonly available. But in Taiwan, the miso soup sometimes has a little section of youtiao added to it and the fantuan often has dried Hakka daikon in it. An Desi never imagined that food on a dining table could tell the history of a place. That breakfast gave him a better understanding of Taiwan.

生詞二 Vocabulary II 🎧 11-04

Vocabulary

1	餐桌	cānzhuō	ㄘㄢ ㄓㄨㄛ	(N)	dining table
2	中式	Zhōngshì	ㄓㄨㄥ ㄕˋ	(N)	Chinese-style

3	套	tào	ㄊㄠˋ	(M)	set of (books, clothes, equipment etc.)
4	燒餅	shāobǐng	ㄕㄠ ㄅㄧㄥˇ	(N)	clay oven sesame seed biscuits, like Indian 'nan'
5	油條	yóutiáo	ㄧㄡˊ ㄊㄧㄠˊ	(N)	deep-fried dough sticks
6	飯糰	fàntuán	ㄈㄢˋ ㄊㄨㄢˊ	(N)	rice rolls with various fillings
7	豆漿	dòujiāng	ㄉㄡˋ ㄐㄧㄤ	(N)	soy milk
8	內戰	nèizhàn	ㄋㄟˋ ㄓㄢˋ	(N)	civil war
9	人民	rénmín	ㄖㄣˊ ㄇㄧㄣˊ	(N)	the people
10	攤子	tānzi	ㄊㄢ ㄗ˙	(N)	roadside stand, vendor's stall
11	菜單	càidān	ㄘㄞˋ ㄉㄢ	(N)	menu
12	蘿蔔	luóbo	ㄌㄨㄛˊ ㄅㄛ˙	(N)	daikon radish
13	接著	jiēzhe	ㄐㄧㄝ ㄓㄜ˙	(Adv)	to continue, to pick up where something left off
14	戰爭	zhànzhēng	ㄓㄢˋ ㄓㄥ	(N)	war
15	不斷	búduàn	ㄅㄨˊ ㄉㄨㄢˋ	(Vs)	continual, incessant
16	遷移	qiānyí	ㄑㄧㄢ ㄧˊ	(Vi)	to migrate
17	多半	duōbàn	ㄉㄨㄛ ㄅㄢˋ	(Adv)	mostly, in the majority of cases
18	困難	kùnnán	ㄎㄨㄣˋ ㄋㄢˊ	(Vs)	difficult
19	節儉	jiéjiǎn	ㄐㄧㄝˊ ㄐㄧㄢˇ	(Vs)	frugal
20	主婦	zhǔfù	ㄓㄨˇ ㄈㄨˋ	(N)	housewife
21	煎	jiān	ㄐㄧㄢ	(V)	to pan fry
22	菜色	càisè	ㄘㄞˋ ㄙㄜˋ	(N)	variety of dishes
23	以及	yǐjí	ㄧˇ ㄐㄧˊ	(Conj)	and, as well as
24	美味	měiwèi	ㄇㄟˇ ㄨㄟˋ	(Vs)	delicious
25	點心	diǎnxīn	ㄉㄧㄢˇ ㄒㄧㄣ	(N)	desserts
26	日式	Rìshì	ㄖˋ ㄕˋ	(N)	Japanese-style
27	飲食	yǐnshí	ㄧㄣˇ ㄕˊ	(N)	food, diet
28	深	shēn	ㄕㄣ	(Vs)	deep

Names

29	蔣介石	Jiǎng Jièshí	ㄐㄧㄤˇ ㄐㄧㄝˋ ㄕˊ	Chiang Kai-Shek, 1887-1975
30	國共內戰	Guó Gòng nèizhàn	ㄍㄨㄛˊ ㄍㄨㄥˋ ㄋㄟˋ ㄓㄢˋ	the Chinese Civil War (i.e., between the Kuomintang and the Communists), 1927-1937, 1945-1950
31	客家人	Kèjiā rén	ㄎㄜˋ ㄐㄧㄚ ㄖㄣˊ	the Hakka people, a branch of Han
32	閩南人	Mǐnnán rén	ㄇㄧㄣˇ ㄋㄢˊ ㄖㄣˊ	the Southern Min people, also called Hokkien

Phrases

33	蛋餅	dàn bǐng	ㄉㄢˋ ㄅㄧㄥˇ	an egg wrap
34	打輸	dǎ shū	ㄉㄚˇ ㄕㄨ	to be defeated
35	擺攤子	bǎi tānzi	ㄅㄞˇ ㄊㄢ ㄗ	to set up a vendor's stall
36	蘿蔔糕	luóbo gāo	ㄌㄨㄛˊ ㄅㄛ ㄍㄠ	daikon cakes
37	烹飪課	pēngrèn kè	ㄆㄥ ㄖㄣˋ ㄎㄜˋ	cooking class
38	曬乾	shài gān	ㄕㄞˋ ㄍㄢ	to sun dry
39	各種各樣	gèzhǒng gèyàng	ㄍㄜˋ ㄓㄨㄥˇ ㄍㄜˋ ㄧㄤˋ	various types
40	殖民統治	zhímín tǒngzhì	ㄓˊ ㄇㄧㄣˊ ㄊㄨㄥˇ ㄓˋ	to colonise and rule
41	味噌湯	wèizēng tāng	ㄨㄟˋ ㄗㄥ ㄊㄤ	miso soup (Japanese food)
42	蘿蔔乾	luóbo gān	ㄌㄨㄛˊ ㄅㄛ ㄍㄢ	dried daikon
43	進一步	jìn yí bù	ㄐㄧㄣˋ ㄧˊ ㄅㄨˋ	further

文法 Grammar

I. 到底 *after all? how on earth…?* 🎧 11-05

Function: The adverb 到底 is used when the speaker is perplexed about something and is eager to find out about the truth. The sentence carries a strong tone of inquisitiveness and impatience.

❶ 小陳幾天以前說想去麵包店當學徒，今天說想去鄉下種水果，他到底想做什麼？

❷ 你不要看到新型的電子產品就買，「貨比三家不吃虧」這句話的意思，你到底懂不懂？

❸ 那家商店賣的鳳梨酥特別受歡迎，他們到底用的是什麼行銷方式？

❹ 我昨天介紹給你的那位先生，到底你對他的印象怎麼樣？

❺ 真羨慕你有這麼多好朋友。你到底是怎麼跟別人建立關係的？

Usage: 到底 is only used in non 嗎 questions. It can appear either before or after the subject, but when the subject is a question-word, 到底 can only occur sentence-initially.

❶ a. 你到底去不去？ b. 到底你去不去？

❷ a. 他到底哪裡不舒服？ b. 到底他哪裡不舒服？

❸ a. 你到底買菜了沒有？ b. 到底你買菜了沒有？

But you cannot say：

*誰到底要去？ *哪裡到底好玩？ *什麼人到底才能參加？

Prior to saying a 到底 question like '臭豆腐到底臭不臭？', one of the statements below must be true.

1. Some say it is, while others say it is not.

2. Someone keeps saying it is or it is not.

269

In the following situations, it cannot be used.

1. Nobody is talking about 臭豆腐.

2. Someone says it is or it is not, only once.

練習 Exercise

Please complete the following 到底 sentences.

❶ 好久沒有小王的消息了，他在美國到底＿＿＿＿＿＿＿＿＿＿？

❷ 你說上網訂購月餅，很快就能收到。到底＿＿＿＿＿＿＿＿？

❸ 我從來沒在網路上買過東西。你可不可以告訴我在網路上買東西，到底＿＿＿＿＿＿＿＿＿＿？

❹ 這棟建築外表看起來很舊，到底＿＿＿＿＿＿＿＿？

❺ 我做的事情，他總是不滿意。我到底＿＿＿＿＿＿＿＿？

II. 甚至 *even* 🎧 11-06　　　🔍 英譯 p.276

Function: 甚至 'even' is an adverb which marks something in the sentence as extraordinary.

❶ 這種款式的包包非常受歡迎，甚至連續劇的女主角都拿過。我非買不可。

❷ 很多小農為了友善對待土地，最近甚至連農藥都不用了。

❸ 鳳梨對臺灣經濟發展一直有很大的幫助，臺灣出口的鳳梨甚至曾經占世界第二位。

❹ 十六世紀時，歐洲人不但到中南美洲做生意，甚至到東方來從事貿易活動。

❺ 臺灣的微整型做得非常好，價錢又合理，甚至連外國人都利用假期來臺灣做微整型。

Usage:

1. 甚至 is often followed by 連, which marks exceptional circumstances. (Please see Vol. 2, Lesson 14.)

2. 甚至 is not related to 至於. (Lesson 10)

練習 Exercise

Please complete the following sentences, indicating exceptionality using 甚至.

❶ 小王是一個很節省的人，＿＿＿＿＿＿＿＿＿＿＿＿都不開冷氣。

❷ 他現在住的地方，不但手機收不到訊號，＿＿＿＿＿＿＿＿＿。

❸ 他對吃真講究，＿＿＿＿＿＿＿＿＿＿＿＿＿跑一趟臺南。

❹ 他小時候家裡很窮，不但買不起新衣服，＿＿＿＿＿＿＿＿。

❺ 百貨公司週年慶的時候，大部分的商品都會有不錯的折扣，
有的東西＿＿＿＿＿＿＿＿＿＿＿＿＿＿＿＿。

III. 這麼說 *that being the case, in that case* 11-07   英譯 p.276

Function: The pattern 這麼說 presents a statement as a natural consequence of the previous statement.

❶ A：現在上網購物越來越普遍，這幾年大家的購物習慣真的改變了很多。

　B：這麼說，將來我就不能開服裝店了，是不是？

❷ A：醫生看了片子，說小王是骨折。

　B：這麼說，他得住院開刀嘍。

❸ A：我叔叔打算用穩定的價格跟當地小農購買芒果，做成芒果蛋糕來賣。

　B：這麼說，那些小農就不需要擔心芒果賣不出去了。

❹ A：小陳從九月起，要到美國念 EMBA 研究所。

　B：這麼說，他將來想成為企業家嘍。

❺ A：我父母說大學念什麼系不重要，最重要的是要有興趣。

　B：這麼說，你念服裝設計系，你父母應該不會反對。

練習 **Exercise**

Please complete the following dialogues using 這麼說.

1 A：小張的姐姐上個月去法國學烹飪了。

　　B：這麼說，＿＿＿＿＿＿＿＿＿＿＿＿＿＿＿＿＿。

2 A：我覺得他說話很誇張。他說的話，都要打個折扣。

　　B：這麼說，＿＿＿＿＿＿＿＿＿＿＿＿＿＿＿＿＿。

3 A：大明說小王不但愛抱怨，還喜歡亂罵人。

　　B：這麼說，＿＿＿＿＿＿＿＿＿＿＿＿＿＿，對不對？

4 A：小美說一個人生活很自由，想做什麼就做什麼。

　　B：這麼說，＿＿＿＿＿＿＿＿＿＿＿＿＿＿＿＿＿。

5 先生：下個月起，我的薪水會增加 5,000 塊。

　　太太：這麼說，＿＿＿＿＿＿＿＿＿＿＿＿＿＿＿＿。

IV. 跟 B 有關的 A　*A is related to B*　🎧 11-08　🔍 英譯 p.276

Function: In this pattern, the preposition 跟 introduces an item (B) that is related to A. A in this pattern is the main topic.

1 上網買東西雖然方便，但是最近電視上有不少跟網購糾紛有關的新聞。你還是小心一點。

2 我剛剛放在你桌上的是跟演講比賽有關的資料，請你收好。

3 他大學念的是歷史，而且輔系是經濟，所以跟臺灣經濟發展有關的歷史，你應該去請教他。

4 想要了解跟原住民有關的風俗文化，你最好去一趟花蓮。

5 我建議跟這一次校外教學有關的活動，都讓小王一個人安排。

練習 Exercise

Please complete the following sentences with 跟 B 有關的 A. The items given in brackets play the role of B.

❶ 他昨天跟我談了很多_____，
真是可怕。（環境汙染）

❷ _____很多，也很有趣，
你想不想聽？（中秋節）

❸ 小王的夢想是當一位烘焙師傅，所以決定到日本學習
_____。（做麵包、蛋糕）

❹ 整型可以增加自信，還可以改善人際關係，因此醫美成為很
大的商機，越來越多人從事_____。（醫美）

❺ 他拍的這部 (M, for movies)_____，
許多人看了都很感動。（國共內戰）

V. 不得不 *have no choice but to* 11-09　　　　　🔍 英譯 p.277

Function: The pattern 不得不 is used when one is engaged in doing something reluctantly, as a last resort. There are no other options.

❶ 我不喜歡吃魚，但是為了讓傷口恢復得比較快，不得不喝點
魚湯。

❷ 因為小明去參加畢業旅行，媽媽不得不幫他照顧寵物。

❸ 現代人的飲食習慣改變了，很多傳統小吃店不得不改賣年輕
人喜歡的食物。

❹ 他的腿受傷了，不得不放棄這場 (M, for games) 比賽。

❺ 陳如美的父親生病住院，所以她不得不休學去工作，改善家
裡的生活。

練習 Exercise

Please complete the following sentences, indicating an obligation using 不得不 .

❶ 台灣因為平原小，人口多，因此＿＿＿＿＿＿＿＿＿＿＿＿＿＿＿。

❷ 雖然我不太敢吃辣的，但是這碗酸辣湯是老師做的，

　　我＿＿＿＿＿＿＿＿＿＿＿＿＿＿＿＿＿＿＿＿＿＿＿。

❸ 小王的國家內戰不斷，所以他＿＿＿＿＿＿＿＿＿＿＿＿＿。

❹ 為了提高職場上的競爭力，他＿＿＿＿＿＿＿＿，充實自己。

❺ 她的錢包掉了，又沒帶車票，＿＿＿＿＿＿＿＿＿＿＿＿＿。

VI. 以及 *as well as* 11-10   英譯 p.277

Function: 以及 is a literary conjunction, which connects nouns or sentences.

❶ 我表哥念高中的時候，最喜歡的課有英文、歷史以及藝術。

❷ 台北、台中以及高雄都是人口兩百萬以上的大城市。

❸ 這個城市的交通很亂，怎麼改善交通問題以及減少車禍的發生，是這個城市的人民最關心的事情。

❹ 這次颱風，台灣東部以及南部都會受到影響。

❺ 明天要去旅行，請你把外套、鞋子以及日用品放在背包裡。

Usage: Conjunctions in Chinese can be of three types: those which connect nouns, those which connect sentences, and those which can connect either. 以及 belongs to the last category.

Type 1: connects noun, e.g., 和、跟

(1) 那家商店賣青菜、水果和一些日用品。

(2) 他剛去超市買了牛肉、魚跟麵包。

Type 2: connects sentences, e.g., 不過、但是

(1) 這裡白天的溫度很高,不過剛剛下過雨,我覺得涼快多了。

(2) 她想去國外旅行,但是想到一個人旅行有點麻煩,就下不了決心。

Type 3: connects nouns & sentences

(1) 去國外念書,當地的生活費以及學費,是學生最關心的事。

(2) 你要不要跟王先生見面,以及見面以後,要談什麼,你最好想清楚。

練習 Exercise

Please complete the following sentences, connecting nouns or sentences using the conjunction 以及.

❶ 房租貴不貴,離捷運站近不近,＿＿＿＿＿＿＿＿＿＿＿＿＿,
都是我租房子的時候必須考慮的。

❷ 羅珊蒂說她回國以後,一定忘不了臺灣的美食＿＿＿＿＿＿＿＿
＿＿＿＿＿＿＿＿＿＿＿＿＿＿＿＿＿＿＿＿＿＿。

❸ 吳寶春是怎麼努力學習,怎麼努力工作,＿＿＿＿＿＿＿＿＿
＿＿＿＿＿＿＿＿＿＿＿＿＿＿,大家是清楚的。

❹ 小王把這件事情的經過情形,＿＿＿＿＿＿＿＿＿＿＿＿＿＿,
都清清楚楚地跟老闆報告了。

❺ 新郎、新娘敬酒的時候,包括「百年好合」、「新婚快樂」,
＿＿＿＿＿＿＿＿＿＿＿＿＿＿,都是客人常用來祝福新人的話。

語法例句英譯
Grammar Examples in English •

I. 到底 *after all? how on earth…?*

Function:

1. The other day, Xiao Chen said he wanted to apprentice at a bakery. Today, he said he wants to go to the countryside and grow fruit. What does he really want to do?
2. Stop buying the latest electronic product whenever you see one. You understand the saying "shop around and you won't get ripped off", don't you?
3. The pineapple cakes sold at that store are especially popular. What is their marketing scheme?
4. What is your impression of the gentleman I introduced to you yesterday?
5. You have so many friends. I really envy you. How in the world do you make friends like that?

Usage:

1. Are you or are you not going?
2. Where, exactly, is he feeling pain?
3. Did you buy vegetables after all?

II. 甚至 *even*

Function:.

1. This style of bag is quite popular. Even the leading lady in a TV series had one. I have to buy one.
2. For the sake of a healthy soil, recently, many small farmers are even going so far as to not use pesticides.
3. Pineapples have always been a big help to Taiwan's economic development. Taiwan's pineapple exports were even once number two in the world.
4. During the 16th century, Europeans not only went to Central and South America to do business, they even came to the East to engage in trade activities.
5. Taiwan's micro-cosmetic surgery is very advanced and the prices are reasonable. Foreigners even use their holidays to come to Taiwan and undergo micro-cosmetic surgery.

III. 這麼說 *that being the case, in that case*

Function:

1. A: It is becoming increasingly common to shop online. In recent years, everyone's shopping habits have really changed a lot.
   B: That being the case, I won't be able to open a clothing store in the future, right?
2. A: After looking at the X-ray, the doctor told Xiao Wang that he had a broken bone.
   B: In that case, he'll have to be hospitalized and undergo surgery.
3. A: My uncle plans to buy mangoes at stable prices from small farmers in the area, and use them to make mango cakes which he will then sell.
   B: That being the case, those small farmers won't have to worry that they can't sell their mangoes.
4. A: Xiao Chen is going to the US where he'll study in an EMBA graduate school program starting in September.
   B: That being the case, I assume he wants to become an entrepreneur.
5. A: My parents say that it doesn't matter what major you study in. What matters most is that you find it interesting.
   B: In that case, your parents shouldn't oppose you studying fashion design.

IV. 跟 B 有關的 A *A is related to B*

Function:

1. Going online to buy things is convenient, but there have been a lot of TV news about disputes related to online shopping lately. You still need to be careful.

276

2 I just put some information about the speech contest on your desk. Please put it somewhere where you won't lose it.

3 He studied history in university and minored in economics, so any history questions related to Taiwan's economic development, you should direct to him.

4 If you want to better understand the customs and culture of aborigines, your best bet is to take a trip to Hualian.

5 I suggest that we let Xiao Wang make all arrangements for activities related to the class excursion by himself.

V. 不得不 *have no choice but to*

Function:

1 I don't like fish, but if I want to heal my wound quicker I have no choice but to drink some fish soup.

2 Because Xiaoming went on a graduation trip, his mom has no choice but to take care of his pet for him.

3 The dietary habits of people today have changed. Many traditional eateries have had to change and sell foods that young people like.

4 He has an injured leg, so he has no choice but to sit out this match.

5 Chen Rumei's father is sick and staying in the hospital, so she had no choice but to take a break from school and go to work to help improve her family's life.

VI. 以及 *as well as*

Function:

1 My cousin's favorite courses in high school were English, history, and art.

2 Taipei, Taichung and Kaohsiung are all cities with a population of more than 2 million people.

3 The traffic in this city is chaotic. The people of this city are most concerned with how to improve the traffic situation and reduce the number of accidents.

4 The eastern and southern parts of Taiwan will both be affected by this typhoon.

5 We're going on a trip tomorrow. Please put your coat, shoes, and daily necessities in your backpack.

Usage:

Type 1:

(1) That shop sells vegetables, fruit, and some daily necessities.

(2) He just went to the supermarket where he bought beef, fish, and bread.

Type 2:

(1) The temperature here during the day is high, but it just rained, (so) I feel a lot cooler.

(2) She wants to travel abroad, but when she thought about how traveling alone is a bit of a pain, she couldn't make up her mind.

Type 3:

(1) When studying abroad, students are most concerned with the local cost of living and tuition fees.

(2) It would be in your best interest to think clearly about meeting Mr. Wang or not and what you are going to talk to him.

課室活動 Classroom Activities

I. Recommending Historical Sites

Goal: Learning to describe historical sites, explain why they are worth visiting, and recommend them to others.

Task: Introduce the origins of an historical site and recommend it to somebody. Students pair up and share your experience in this area with each other.

Try to use the following sentence patterns and vocabulary words:

跟 B 有關的 A	拿…來說	給…帶來	既…又…

II. My Country's History and Geographical Location

Goal: Learning to talk about my country's history and geographical location.

Task: Students pair up and tell each other about the history and geographical location of your country.

Try to use the following sentence patterns and vocabulary words:

到底	不得不	甚至	占

III. Food and Culture

Goal: Learning to explain in detail the origins of foods as well as talk about the relationship between food and culture.

Task: Talk about a food that your country originally did not have, but having been influenced by another country, became popular. Examples: 拉麵 lāmiàn (ramen) in Taiwan and 咖哩 kālǐ (curry) in Japan.

Try to use the following sentence patterns and vocabulary words:

受到（…的）影響	各種各樣	以及	結果

文化 *Bits of Chinese Culture*

Origins of Geographical Names in Taiwan

For historical reasons, a variety of ways have been used to name geographical locations in Taiwan. For example, some names find their origins in homophones, some in characteristics of the terrain, and some in anecdotes.

▲ 三貂角 , Taiwan's easternmost cape, is a transliteration of the name Santiago.
《聯合報》邱奕寧／攝影

▲ 基隆 was named after the Katagalan people and the name was shortened to Keelung.

Take, for example, the Taiwan's easternmost cape 三貂角 （Sāndiāojiǎo） . Some people might think that maybe it got its name when somebody saw three martens （三隻貂） there. But that's not the case. It is called 三貂角 because in 1626, Spaniards arrived in ships in the waters off northeastern Taiwan where they made plans to occupy Taiwan. They called the place Santiago （聖地牙哥） . The Taiwanese pronunciation of the word evolved into 三貂角 .

There is also an anecdote for 花蓮 in eastern Taiwan. The old area of Hualian used to be at the mouth of the Hualian River. The ocean off of this area has a well known warm-water current known as "Kuroshio"

▲ 花蓮 used to be called Huelan Harbor, because of the warm water current 洄瀾 .
達志影像／提供

that flows from south to north. The coast juts out here and the current comes in contact with the land, causing eddies, which in Chinese are 洄瀾（huílán） , so the locals named the area 洄瀾港（Taiwanese pronunciation: Huelan kang, Huelan Harbor） . In the Taiwanese dialect, the pronunciation of 洄瀾 and 花蓮 are very similar, so during the Qing Dynasty, the place name was changed from 洄瀾港 to the more pleasant sounding 花蓮港 . When Taiwan was a Japanese colony, the name was shortened to 花蓮 .

Some place names in Taiwan are related in some way to the aborigines. 基隆（Jīlóng, Keelung） , for example, was named after the Ketagalan people who lived in the area. The people who named it, extracted the "taga" from the Ketagalan, leaving Kalan, which in Taiwanese, sounds like "Gelong" （chicken coop） , a name which was later transformed to a more palatable 基隆 .

If you ever take it upon yourself to research Taiwan place names, you'll find yourself learning a great deal about the history of Taiwan.

Self-Assessment Checklist

I can understand stories on the history of Taiwan.

20%   40%   60%   80%   100%

I can give a rough introduction of my own country's history.

20%   40%   60%   80%   100%

I can discuss the relationship between food and culture.

20%   40%   60%   80%   100%

I can explain the origins and narrate the details of an event.

20%   40%   60%   80%   100%

LESSON 12

第十二課
我要去投票
I'm Going to Cast My Vote

....

學習目標 Learning Objectives

Topic: 政治 Politics

- Learning to discuss issues related to elections for elected representatives.
- Learning to analyze logic and offer various possibilities.
- Learning to express your views and reasons for opposing something.
- Learning to introduce candidates and their experience in politics.

我要去投票

I'm Going to Cast My Vote

何 雅 婷：真抱歉，今天晚上我不能跟你們去聽演唱會了。

高橋健太：不是說好了嗎？怎麼不去了？

何 雅 婷：我表妹從香港回來了。我阿姨叫我過去吃晚飯。

陳 敏 萱：妳表妹不是在香港念書嗎？現在不是假期，
她怎麼回來了？

何 雅 婷：她要參加這個週末的反核遊行。我阿姨擔心
她對政治太熱衷，會影響她的前途，讓我過
去勸勸她。

陳 敏 萱：只不過參加遊行而已，妳阿姨想太多了吧。
在民主社會，人民參加遊行，直接表達意見
是很普遍的。妳表妹關心公共議題是件很好
的事啊。

高橋健太 ： 妳的話雖然有道理，可是要不要核能電廠是一個專業的問題，應該由專家來討論、決定。再說，一般人對這個問題沒有辦法全面了解。既然我們選了民意代表，就應該由他們代表人民處理這些問題，不是嗎？

何 雅 婷 ： 政治是很複雜的。我覺得民意代表關心的常常不是人民的利益，而是他們自己或是政黨的利益。我怎麼能相信他們呢？

陳 敏 萱 ： 難道妳從來不去投票嗎？

何 雅 婷 ： 我今年滿二十歲。按照憲法的規定，有投票權了。不過年底的選舉我不會去投票的。

高橋健太 ： 我覺得妳應該去投票。如果妳不去，不就放棄了表達意見的權利嗎？

何 雅 婷 ： 不去投票也是表達意見的一種方式。這樣做表示我對所有的候選人都不滿意。

高橋健太 ： 可是如果大家都像妳一樣，不去投票，投票的結果就不能反映真正的民意，不是嗎？

陳 敏 萱 ： 對啊。再說，還是有一些有理想的候選人，願意出來為人民服務。妳應該支持這些又熱心、又有能力的人，讓他們有機會為大家做事。

高橋健太 ： 民主政治有一個好處，就是每一個職位都有任期。如果選民不滿意當選的人，下次別再選他就好了。

陳 敏 萱 ： 雖然民主制度並不完美，但是選民還是應該積極地表達自己的意見，這樣社會才會更好。如果我是妳，我一定會去投票的。

何 雅 婷 ： 好吧，我會好好考慮考慮的。謝謝。你們真是民主政治的最佳推銷員。

課文簡體字版 Text in Simplified Characters

何 雅 婷 ： 真抱歉，今天晚上我不能跟你们去听演唱会了。

高桥健太 ： 不是说好了吗？怎么不去了？

何 雅 婷 ： 我表妹从香港回来了。我阿姨叫我过去吃晚饭。

陈 敏 萱 ： 妳表妹不是在香港念书吗？现在不是假期，她怎么回来了？

何 雅 婷 ： 她要参加这个周末的反核游行。我阿姨担心她对政治太热衷，会影响她的前途，让我过去劝劝她。

陈 敏 萱 ： 只不过参加游行而已，妳阿姨想太多了吧。在民主社会，人民参加游行，直接表达意见是很普遍的。妳表妹关心公共议题是件很好的事啊。

高桥健太 ： 妳的话虽然有道理，可是要不要核能电厂是一个专业的问题，应该由专家来讨论、决定。再说，一般人对这个问题没有办法全面了解。既然我们选了民意代表，就应该由他们代表人民处理这些问题，不是吗？

何 雅 婷 ： 政治是很复杂的。我觉得民意代表关心的常常不是人民的利益，而是他们自己或是政党的利益。我怎么能相信他们呢？

陈 敏 萱 ： 难道妳从来不去投票吗？

何 雅 婷 ： 我今年满二十岁。按照宪法的规定，有投票权了。不过年底的选举我不会去投票的。

高桥健太 ： 我觉得妳应该去投票。如果妳不去，不就放弃了表达意见的权利吗？

何 雅 婷 ： 不去投票也是表达意见的一种方式。这样做表示我对所有的候选人都不满意。

高桥健太 ： 可是如果大家都像妳一样，不去投票，投票的结果就不能反映真正的民意，不是吗？

陈 敏 萱 ： 对啊。再说，还是有一些有理想的候选人，愿意出来为人民服务。妳应该支持这些又热心、又有能力的人，让他们有机会为大家做事。

高桥健太 ： 民主政治有一个好处，就是每一个职位都有任期。如果选民不满意当选的人，下次别再选他就好了。

陈 敏 萱 ： 虽然民主制度并不完美，但是选民还是应该积极地表达自己的意见，这样社会才会更好。如果我是妳，我一定会去投票的。

何 雅 婷 ： 好吧，我会好好考虑考虑的。谢谢。你们真是民主政治的最佳推销员。

He Yating	: I'm very sorry. I can no longer go with you to the concert tonight.
Gaoqiao Jiantai	: Didn't we agree? Why you are not going now?
He Yating	: My cousin is back from Hong Kong. My aunt asked me to go over and have dinner.
Chen Minxuan	: Isn't your cousin studying in Hong Kong? It's not a holiday now. How come she's back?
He Yating	: She wants to take part in the anti-nuclear power demonstration this weekend. My aunt is concerned that she is too zealous about politics and that it will affect her career, so she's having me go over to have a talk with her.
Chen Minxuan	: She's just taking part in a demonstration. Your aunt is over-analyzing the situation. In democratic societies, it's very common for the people to participate in marches to directly express their views. Your cousin's concern about public issues is a good thing.
Gaoqiao Jiantai	: What you say makes sense, but whether or not we have nuclear power plants is a specialized problem and should be discussed and decided by experts. What's more, most people are unable to understand the big picture in regards to this issue. Since we elected public representatives, they should represent the people and deal with these problems, right?
He Yating	: Politics is complicated. I believe that what concerns public representatives often is not the interests of the people; rather, it's their own or their party's interests. How can I trust them?
Chen Minxuan	: Don't you ever vote?
He Yating	: I turned 20 this year. According to provisions in the constitution, I have the right to vote. But I won't go vote in the year-end elections.
Gaoqiao Jiantai	: I think you should go vote. If you don't go, aren't you forfeiting your right to express your opinion?
He Yating	: Not going to vote is another way of expressing your views. Doing so means that I am unhappy with all of the candidates.
Gaoqiao Jiantai	: But if everybody is like you, not going to vote, then the ballot results don't really reflect the will of the people, right?
Chen Minxuan	: That's right. In addition, there are still some candidates with ideals who are willing to come forward and serve the people. You should support enthusiastic and capable individuals like these, allowing them to have the opportunity to serve everybody.

Gaoqiao Jiantai : Democracy has one advantage—every position has a term limit. If the voters are unhappy with an elected individual, then next time, simply don't re-elect him.

Chen Minxuan : The democratic system isn't perfect, but voters should still take it upon themselves to express their own opinions. Only in that way will society improve. If I were you, I would definitely go vote.

He Yating : Oh, all right. I will really think about it. Thanks. You two really are a great salesperson for democracy.

生詞一 Vocabulary I 🎧 12-02

Vocabulary

1	投票投票投 tóupiào 票		ㄊㄡˊ ㄆㄧㄠˋ	(V-sep)	to vote
2	抱歉抱歉	bàoqiàn	ㄅㄠˋ ㄑㄧㄢˋ	(Vs)	sorry, apologetic
3	表妹表妹	biǎomèi	ㄅㄧㄠˇ ㄇㄟˋ	(N)	younger female cousin
4	反核反核	fǎn hé	ㄈㄢˇ ㄏㄜˊ	(Vs-attr)	anti-nuclear
5	遊行遊行	yóuxíng	ㄧㄡˊ ㄒㄧㄥˊ	(N)	demonstration, rally
6	政治政治政 zhèngzhì 治		ㄓㄥˋ ㄓˋ	(N)	politics
7	熱衷	rèzhōng	ㄖㄜˋ ㄓㄨㄥ	(Vst)	enthusiastic about, passionate about
8	前途	qiántú	ㄑㄧㄢˊ ㄊㄨˊ	(N)	future, prospects
9	勸	quàn	ㄑㄩㄢˋ	(V)	to persuade, to urge
10	而已	éryǐ	ㄦˊ ㄧˇ	(Ptc)	only, merely
11	民主	mínzhǔ	ㄇㄧㄣˊ ㄓㄨˇ	(Vs)	democratic
12	表達	biǎodá	ㄅㄧㄠˇ ㄉㄚˊ	(V)	to express
13	公共	gōnggòng	ㄍㄨㄥ ㄍㄨㄥˋ	(Vs-attr)	public
14	議題	yìtí	ㄧˋ ㄊㄧˊ	(N)	issue
15	核能	hénéng	ㄏㄜˊ ㄋㄥˊ	(N)	nuclear power
16	電廠	diànchǎng	ㄉㄧㄢˋ ㄔㄤˇ	(N)	power plant
17	由	yóu	ㄧㄡˊ	(Prep)	up to, by (a doer)

18	專家	zhuānjiā	ㄓㄨㄢ ㄐㄧㄚ	(N)	expert, specialist
19	全面	quánmiàn	ㄑㄩㄢ ㄇㄧㄢ	(Adv)	comprehensively
20	民意	mínyì	ㄇㄧㄣ ㄧ	(N)	public will, popular opinion
21	代表	dàibiǎo	ㄉㄞ ㄅㄧㄠ	(N)	representative
22	處理	chǔlǐ	ㄔㄨ ㄌㄧ	(V)	to deal with, handle, tackle
23	政黨政黨	zhèngdǎng	ㄓㄥ ㄉㄤ	(N)	political party
24	難道難道	nándào	ㄋㄢ ㄉㄠ	(Adv)	Could it be that...?, Is it that...?
25	滿滿	mǎn	ㄇㄢ	(Vpt)	to become
26	憲法憲法憲法	xiànfǎ	ㄒㄧㄢ ㄈㄚ	(N)	constitution
27	投票權投票權	tóupiàoquán	ㄊㄡ ㄆㄧㄠ ㄑㄩㄢ	(N)	right to vote, suffrage
28	選舉選舉選舉	xuǎnjǔ	ㄒㄩㄢ ㄐㄩ	(N)	election
29	權利權利權	quánlì	ㄑㄩㄢ ㄌㄧ	(N)	right
30	表示表示表示表示	biǎoshì	ㄅㄧㄠ ㄕ	(V)	to mean, indicate
31	反映反映反映映反映	fǎnyìng	ㄈㄢ ㄧㄥ	(Vpt)	to reflect
32	為為為	wèi	ㄨㄟ	(Prep)	for
33	服務服務	fúwù	ㄈㄨ ㄨ	(V)	to serve
34	職位職位職位	zhíwèi	ㄓ ㄨㄟ	(N)	position, job
35	任期任期任期	rènqí	ㄖㄣ ㄑㄧ	(N)	term of office
36	選民選民選民	xuǎnmín	ㄒㄩㄢ ㄇㄧㄣ	(N)	voters, electorate
37	完美完美完美	wánměi	ㄨㄢ ㄇㄟ	(Vs)	perfect
38	積極積極積極	jījí	ㄐㄧ ㄐㄧ	(Vs)	actively, to take it upon oneself to, take the initiative to
39	最佳最佳最最佳最佳	zuìjiā	ㄗㄨㄟ ㄐㄧㄚ	(Vs-attr)	the very best, the best possible
40	推銷員推銷員推銷員	tuīxiāoyuán	ㄊㄨㄟ ㄒㄧㄠ ㄩㄢ	(N)	salesperson

Phrases

41	有道理	yǒu dàolǐ	ㄧㄡ ㄉㄠ ㄌㄧ		there's some truth (to what you are saying)
42	候選人	hòuxuǎn rén	ㄏㄡ ㄒㄩㄢ ㄖㄣ		candidate

為人民服務的路

李文彥的叔叔原來是一位知名的大學教授，在學術界有很高的地位。可是他一直想從政。他認為只有好的政策才能為人民帶來幸福、安定的生活。為了理想，他辭掉了工作，參加民意代表選舉。因為頭腦清楚、口才好，再加上常上電視對許多政治改革的議題提出看法，因此很受選民的歡迎。尤其是他在教育改革跟國民年金方面的努力，讓他得到選民普遍的支持，順利地連任了四屆。

不過，上一屆的選舉，雖然他的民意支持度在所有的候選人當中一直是最高的，結果卻落選了。他覺得很失望。他本來以為，中間選民會把票投給他，沒想到得票率不如預期。太太看他這麼難過，建議暫時先回鄉下老家休息一陣子，再考慮下一步怎麼走。

回到老家以後，因為以前從政形象好，家鄉的人大大小小的事都來找叔叔商量，他也盡可能利用自己的人脈和資源幫助了不少弱勢家庭。沒過多久，有一家出版社老闆要退休，可是孩子不願意接他的事業。老闆找到了李文彥的叔叔。經過考慮，叔叔答應買下出版社，並且在鄉下開了一家書店。他到處請認識的人捐出二手書、捐錢，甚至請大學生下課以後過來義務教孩子英文。另外，他還在書店裡幫小農賣有機農產品，把賺來的錢當做英文班的經費。

日子雖然過得很充實，叔叔也很滿意現在的生活，但是隨著選舉越來越接近，叔叔也開始考慮要不要再出來競選民意代表。也許回到政治界，有了權力，他能為更多人服務。但是也許離開政治、離開城市，他為大家服務的理想更容易實現。誰知道呢？

課文簡體字版 Text in Simplified Characters

为人民服务的路

　　李文彦的叔叔原来是一位知名的大学教授，在学术界有很高的地位。可是他一直想从政。他认为只有好的政策才能为人民带来幸福、安定的生活。为了理想，他辞掉了工作，参加民意代表选举。因为头脑清楚、口才好，再加上常上电视对许多政治改革的议题提出看法，因此很受选民的欢迎。尤其是他在教育改革跟国民年金方面的努力，让他得到选民普遍的支持，顺利地连任了四届。

　　不过，上一届的选举，虽然他的民意支持度在所有的候选人当中一直是最高的，结果却落选了。他觉得很失望。他本来以为，中间选民会把票投给他，没想到得票率不如预期。太太看他这么难过，建议暂时先回乡下老家休息一阵子，再考虑下一步怎么走。

　　回到老家以后，因为以前从政形象好，家乡的人大大小小的事都来找叔叔商量，他也尽可能利用自己的人脉和资源帮助了不少弱势家庭。没过多久，有一家出版社老板要退休，可是孩子不愿意接他的事业。老板找到了李文彦的叔叔。经过考虑，叔叔答应买下出版社，并且在乡下开了一家书店。他到处请认识的人捐出二手书、捐钱，甚至请大学生下课以后过来义务教孩子英文。另外，他还在书店里帮小农卖有机农产品，把赚来的钱当做英文班的经费。

　　日子虽然过得很充实，叔叔也很满意现在的生活，但是随着选举越来越接近，叔叔也开始考虑要不要再出来竞选民意代表。也许回到政治界，有了权力，他能为更多人服务。但是也许离开政治、离开城市，他为大家服务的理想更容易实现。谁知道呢？

課文英譯 Text in English

The Road for Serving the People

　　Li Wenyan's uncle was a well known university professor with a high status in academic circles. But he had always wanted to go into politics. He believed that only good policies could give the people happy and stable lives. For the sake of his ideals, he quit his work and took part in an election for public representative. Because he has a clear mind, is eloquent, and often went on TV to offer his views on many political reform issues, he was very well received by the voters. His hard work in the areas of educational reform and the national pension, in particular, won him widespread support among voters and he successfully served four consecutive terms.

But in the last election, although his approval rating remained highest among all the candidates, in the end, he still lost the election. He felt disappointed. He originally thought that swing voters would vote for him. Unexpectedly, the percentage of votes he received was less than anticipated. Seeing him this upset, his wife suggested that he temporarily return to his hometown and take a break for a while, and then decide his next step.

After he returned to his hometown, because his image in politics was good, the people of his hometown would seek "Uncle" out to discuss all kinds of matters, both large and small. And to the best of his ability, he employed his contacts and resources to assist many disadvantaged families. Soon afterward, the owner of a publishing company was going to retire, but his children weren't willing to take over his business. The owner sought out Li Wenyan's uncle and after consideration, his uncle agreed to buy the publishing company and opened up a bookstore in the countryside. He went around asking people he knew to donate secondhand books, donate money, and even asked college students to come over after classes and teach children English voluntarily. In addition, he even sold organic agricultural products for small farmers in his bookstore and used the profits as funds for the English classes.

Although his days were productive and Uncle was very satisfied with his current life, as the elections got closer and closer, he also began to think about whether or not to come out again and run for public representative. Perhaps, by returning to the world of politics, he would have power and would be able to serve more people. But perhaps, by leaving politics and by leaving the city, he would more easily be able to realize his dream of serving others. Who knows?

生詞二 Vocabulary II 12-04

Vocabulary

1	學術界	xuéshùjiè	ㄒㄩㄝˊ ㄕㄨˋ ㄐㄧㄝˋ	(N)	academia, the academic fields or circles
2	從政	cóngzhèng	ㄘㄨㄥˊ ㄓㄥˋ	(Vi)	to engage in politics
3	政策	zhèngcè	ㄓㄥˋ ㄘㄜˋ	(N)	policy
4	安定	āndìng	ㄢ ㄉㄧㄥˋ	(Vs)	stable
5	辭	cí	ㄘˊ	(Vp)	to quit, resign
6	頭腦	tóunǎo	ㄊㄡˊ ㄋㄠˇ	(N)	brain, mind
7	改革	gǎigé	ㄍㄞˇ ㄍㄜˊ	(N)	reforms
8	看法	kànfǎ	ㄎㄢˋ ㄈㄚˇ	(N)	view, opinion

9	教育	jiàoyù	ㄐㄧㄠˋ ㄩˋ	(N)	education
10	方面	fāngmiàn	ㄈㄤ ㄇㄧㄢˋ	(N)	in the areas of (an issue)
11	得到	dédào	ㄉㄜˊ ㄉㄠˋ	(V)	to obtain
12	連任	liánrèn	ㄌㄧㄢˊ ㄖㄣˋ	(V)	to serve a successive term
13	屆	jiè	ㄐㄧㄝˋ	(M)	term, tenure of elected office
14	支持度	zhīchídù	ㄓ ㄔˊ ㄉㄨˋ	(N)	approval rating
15	落選	luòxuǎn	ㄌㄨㄛˋ ㄒㄩㄢˇ	(Vp)	to lose an election
16	得票率	dépiàolǜ	ㄉㄜˊ ㄆㄧㄠˋ ㄌㄩˋ	(N)	percentage of votes received
17	預期	yùqí	ㄩˋ ㄑㄧˊ	(N)	expectation
18	暫時	zhànshí	ㄓㄢˋ ㄕˊ	(Adv)	temporarily, for the time being
19	老家	lǎojiā	ㄌㄠˇ ㄐㄧㄚ	(N)	hometown
20	形象	xíngxiàng	ㄒㄧㄥˊ ㄒㄧㄤˋ	(N)	image
21	商量	shāngliáng	ㄕㄤ ㄌㄧㄤˊ	(V)	to confer, consult with
22	人脈	rénmài	ㄖㄣˊ ㄇㄞˋ	(N)	network of people, contacts
23	弱勢	ruòshì	ㄖㄨㄛˋ ㄕˋ	(N)	disadvantaged (lit. weak power)
24	退休	tuìxiū	ㄊㄨㄟˋ ㄒㄧㄡ	(Vp)	to retire
25	事業	shìyè	ㄕˋ ㄧㄝˋ	(N)	business, career
26	捐	juān	ㄐㄩㄢ	(V)	to donate
27	義務	yìwù	ㄧˋ ㄨˋ	(Adv)	to volunteer, on a voluntary basis, to do something gratis
28	經費	jīngfèi	ㄐㄧㄥ ㄈㄟˋ	(N)	funds
29	競選	jìngxuǎn	ㄐㄧㄥˋ ㄒㄩㄢˇ	(V)	run for (an office)
30	也許	yěxǔ	ㄧㄝˇ ㄒㄩˇ	(Adv)	perhaps
31	政治界	zhèngzhìjiè	ㄓㄥˋ ㄓˋ ㄐㄧㄝˋ	(N)	the world of politics
32	權力	quánlì	ㄑㄩㄢˊ ㄌㄧˋ	(N)	power

Phrases

| 33 | 辭掉 | cídiào | ㄘˊ ㄉㄧㄠˋ | | to quit, resign |
| 34 | 提出 | tíchū | ㄊㄧˊ ㄔㄨ | | to propose |

35	國民年金	guómín niánjīn	ㄍㄨㄛˊ ㄇㄧㄣˊ ㄋㄧㄢˊ ㄐㄧㄣ	national pension (scheme)
36	中間選民	zhōngjiān xuǎnmín	ㄓㄨㄥ ㄐㄧㄢ ㄒㄩㄢˇ ㄇㄧㄣˊ	swing voters
37	一陣子	yí zhèn zi	ㄧˊ ㄓㄣˋ ˙ㄗ	a while, a short duration of time
38	下一步	xià yí bù	ㄒㄧㄚˋ ㄧˊ ㄅㄨˋ	the next step (in doing things)
39	盡可能	jìn kěnéng	ㄐㄧㄣˋ ㄎㄜˇ ㄋㄥˊ	as far as possible, do one's best
40	出版社	chūbǎn shè	ㄔㄨ ㄅㄢˇ ㄕㄜˋ	publishing company
41	捐出	juānchū	ㄐㄩㄢ ㄔㄨ	to donate
42	二手書	èrshǒu shū	ㄦˋ ㄕㄡˇ ㄕㄨ	secondhand book

文法 Grammar

I. 只不過…（而已） *merely…; nothing more than…* 🎧 12-05

Function: This pattern consists of three elements: the adverb 只, the adverb 不過, and the sentence particle 而已. They are near synonyms, meaning 'only, merely.' Thus, this pattern is an instance of 3-way reinforcement and means 'merely, just'. 而已 can be omitted.

❶ 有些人認為，吳寶春只不過國中畢業而已，怎麼有能力念企管研究所呢？

❷ 他只不過上烹飪課的時候做過一次蘿蔔糕而已，就到處告訴別人他做得多美味。

❸ 他只不過說說而已，你難道認為他真的會辭掉工作？

❹ 只不過下了幾天的雨，衣服就全都發霉了。

❺ 這個學期你只不過選了三門課而已，怎麼就忙得連參加社團活動的時間都沒有了？

Usage:

1. Omission in multiple reinforcement is always possible in Chinese. In this pattern, the omission goes like this: ending with 而已 alone, 不過…而已 , and finally 只不過…而已 . The first two options are illustrated below.

(1) …而已
    a. 他隨便說說而已。哪裡是真的想養狗？
    b. 一個晚上沒睡好而已，就沒有精神上課了。
(2) 不過…而已
    a. 不過 18 度而已，你怎麼就穿起羊毛外套來了？
    b. 三號候選人不過是形象好而已，從政經驗其實並不多。

2. 只不過 vs. 才 (Vol. 2, Lesson 3, Grammar point 3):

(1) If a sentence contains a number in the object position, either 只不過 or 才 can be used.

E.g.,

    a. 雖然是百貨公司週年慶，可是商品只不過打八折而已。
    b. 雖然是百貨公司週年慶，可是商品才打八折而已。

There is, however, a difference in attitude on the part of the speaker. Although 只不過 also stresses that the amount mentioned is small, it is more factual, while 才 further indicates that the quantity falls short of expectation. E.g., in example (1)a. above, although the speaker also thinks 20% off isn't quite enough and is a little dissatisfied, the speaker's attitude in (1)b. that the discount falls short of common expectation is very clear.

(2) Therefore, when you want to stress something has fallen short of common expectation, you can only really use 才. See examples a, b, c, and d below.

    a. *你擺了一個早上的攤子，怎麼只不過賺了幾百塊錢？
    b. 你擺了一個早上的攤子，怎麼才賺了幾百塊錢？

Most people feel that when you have had a stall up for hours, you should have made much more than a few hundred NT dollars, therefore, you can only use 才. You can't use 只不過.

    c. *念醫學系只不過三年就畢業了？怎麼可能？
    d. 念醫學系才三年就畢業了？怎麼可能？

(3) If, however, 只不過 is followed by something other than an amount, then 只不過 cannot be substituted with 才. E.g.,

a. 我只不過開開玩笑而已，你怎麼就生氣了？

b. *我才開開玩笑而已，你怎麼就生氣了？

練習 Exercise

Use 只不過…而已 in your response to the following statements.

1 足球比賽打輸了，小張居然哭了起來。你對他說：

_____ 。

2 沒想到一間小小的早餐店，賣的東西種類那麼多。你說：

_____ 。

3 他又給寵物買推車，又送牠上美容院，你覺得很誇張。你說：

_____ 。

4 你幫朋友買了一杯 15 塊錢的豆漿，他要給你錢。你不收。
你說：

_____ 。

5 室友連去倒垃圾都要化妝。你很受不了。你說：

_____ 。

II. Introducing an Agent with 由 🎧 12-06 🔍 英譯 p.304

Function: 由 is a literary preposition 'by', which marks an agent, or doer of an action.

1 今天晚上的演講，我們請到張主任，由他來介紹語言學最新的發展。

2 今天我們來包餃子。餃子餡兒，你準備，至於包呢，由我來吧。

3 外交方面的問題，當然還是由專業的外交人員處理比較合適。

4 張先生嗎？今天由我為您檢查身體。現在請您躺下。

5 李先生退休以後，他的公司就由兩個女兒經營。

Usage:

1. The order is generally thus: 由 + agent + 來. The 來 introduces the verb. E.g., 由他來照顧這片土地。(He is responsible for taking care of this piece of land.) But if the verb consists of two syllables, the 來 can be omitted. If it consists of just one syllable, then the 來 is required to form the four character combination 由 S 來 V. E.g., 由我來做。(I'll do it.) More examples follow:

   (1) 既然是選民的意見，還是由民意代表來反映吧。

   (2) 在傳統的華人社會，孩子念什麼科系多半不是由孩子自己決定，而是由父母決定。

   (3) 車禍受傷後的整型，一般來說，不是由外科醫生來做，而是請整型醫生處理。

   (4) 下一屆的電腦展應該由誰來舉辦？

   (5) 這些公共議題是不是由當地人來投票決定比較合適？

   (6) 等一下是不是能由您代表說明大家的意見？

2. 由 and 被 are both agent markers. They are easily confused, but they have two major differences. First, in terms of sentence structure, 由 and 被 both precede syntactic subjects, but only action verbs can follow 由. 被, on the other hand, not only appears together with action verbs, it can also appear with other types of verbs. E.g., 他被人發現了 (He was found out by someone.) vs. *他由人發現了. Second, in terms of semantic meaning, 被 suggests something unfortunate or bad happened. 由 doesn't.

練習 Exercise 1

Complete the following sentences, introducing an agent using 由.

❶ 這件事情李主任最清楚。現在就_____。（說明）

❷ 這麼多人一起去恐怕會打擾教授休息。還是_____去看教授吧。（代表）

❸ 狗雖然是我去領養回來的，不過平常都_____。（照顧）

❹ 今天 Meyer 教授的演講內容，等一下會_____。（翻譯）

❺ 他不是一個人去看醫生的，是_____。（陪著）

練習 Exercise 2

Fill in blanks with 由 or 被.

❶ 我的手機不知道＿＿＿＿＿誰撿走了。我找來找去，都找不到。

❷ 這麼重要的合約還是＿＿＿＿＿您自己看過再簽名比較好吧。

❸ 等一下我得陪著主任，另外這幾位重要的客人就＿＿＿＿＿你招待吧。

❹ 他騎腳踏車經過公園的時候，＿＿＿＿＿狗咬了，幸虧傷口不大。

❺ 客服中心讓他到門市去，＿＿＿＿＿店長退錢給他。

III. 難道… *how could it possibly be true*   12-07   英譯 p.304

Function: By using the interrogative adverb 難道, the speaker expresses his doubt that something he considers unlikely could ever take place. It is basically a rhetorical question.

❶ 動了微整型手術以後，難道就真能變得更有自信？
❷ 難道他是因為趕時間才出車禍的？
❸ 因為父母反對就放棄念理想的科系，難道你不覺得遺憾？
❹ 這麼有名的鳳梨酥，難道你不想嚐嚐看？
❺ 今天是星期一，你怎麼有空來看我？難道你真的辭掉工作了？

Usage:

1. 難道 makes a sentence a question, but a 難道 sentence can also co-occur with 嗎. For example,

   (1) 他寧可跟女朋友分手也不願意結婚。難道結婚真的那麼可怕嗎？

   (2) 阿姨讓李文彥每天喝魚湯。難道魚湯可以讓傷口好得快一點嗎？

(3) 十七世紀歐洲人在台灣打仗。難道那時候台灣沒有政府嗎？

2. 難道 belongs to the same category of adverbs as 到底. This type of adverb can either precede or follow the subject. E.g., 你難道還下不了決心嗎？ or 難道你還下不了決心嗎？ 'Are you telling me you still can't make a decision?' In the former, the subject is prominently made the topic of the whole sentence. In the latter, 你 is a subject, but is not made a topic.

3. In dialogues, using 難道 can be rather curt, confrontational, or even rude, where the speaker challenges the other party by enlisting an extreme case, a least probable situation. E.g.,

   (1) 難道你要我把所有的錢都給你？
   (2) 難道你窮得連一杯豆漿都買不起？
   (3) 難道你預期他的得票率會超過百分之八十？

練習 Exercise 1

Please re-write the following sentences, inserting 難道 in the appropriate place.

❶ 你吃一頓飯就花掉了三千塊錢。非這麼講究不可嗎？

→ _____ ?

❷ 他今天晚上不去看足球比賽了。是因為天氣的關係嗎？

→ _____ ?

❸ 小張不打算成家，他父母也同意嗎？

→ _____ ?

❹ 你常騙人，不怕被發現嗎？

→ _____ ?

❺ 他對公職一點興趣也沒有，還要聽父母的話去考試嗎？

→ _____ ?

練習 Exercise 2

Complete the following dialogues using 難道 to form rhetorical questions.

❶ A：電信公司剛打過電話來，說你上個月的電話費還沒繳。

B：我讓小張替我去繳，＿＿＿＿＿＿＿＿＿＿＿＿＿＿？

❷ A：小張經濟壓力很大。為了養家，照顧父母，他一個人做三份工作。

B：他不是有好幾個兄弟姐妹嗎？＿＿＿＿＿＿＿＿＿？

❸ A：你說這個網站賣的冰箱比商店的便宜兩成。你不會是騙我的吧？

B：當然是真的。＿＿＿＿＿＿＿＿＿＿＿＿＿＿＿。

❹ A：上個月小張不是才給我們介紹他女朋友的嗎？怎麼今天卻說他現在單身？

B：＿＿＿＿＿＿＿＿＿＿＿＿＿＿＿＿＿？

❺ A：他去面談，回來以後一句話也不說。怎麼回事？

B：＿＿＿＿＿＿＿＿＿＿＿＿＿＿＿＿＿？

IV. To Reach a Ceiling with 滿　🎧 12-08　🔍 英譯 p.304

Function: Here, 滿 is a transitive process verb, suggesting 'to satisfy a required amount'. Some of the concepts in question may be puzzling or at least rather foreign to learners. This has to do with culture. When a baby is 滿月, it is exactly one month old. 30 full days are required for the 滿 reference to 'a month'.

❶ 台灣的法律規定，滿 18 歲才可以接受醫美手術。在你的國家呢？

❷ 按照我們公司的規定，服務滿一年可以休七天假。

❸ 最近百貨公司週年慶，不但最高打五折，消費滿三千塊錢，還另外再送禮物。

❹ 時間過得真快。再一個月，我來台灣就滿兩年了。

❺ 外國人在台灣住滿六個月就可以申請參加健康保險了。

Usage:

1. In most of the examples above, 滿 is a primary verb of the whole sentence. It can also be a complement to an action verb. For example:

(1) 服務生，麻煩你幫我把杯子加滿水。謝謝。

(2) 要是每天能睡滿八小時，身體一定會很健康。

(3) 媽媽在屋子前面種滿了花。

2. 滿 as used in this lesson is different from 滿 introduced in Lesson 5, where 滿 is consistently used as a verb complement in existential sentences.

練習 Exercise

Re-write the following sentences, inserting 滿 in the appropriate place.

❶ 醫生建議，小孩每天最少應該睡八個鐘頭。

→ _____ 。

❷ 到明年三月，李教授就教了 30 年的書了。

→ _____ 。

❸ 在台灣，20 歲生日以後有投票權。在你的國家呢？

→ _____ ？

❹ 買 1,000 塊錢的商品打九折。這種行銷方法有用嗎？

→ _____ ？

❺ 路口的那家餐廳，因為菜色不吸引人，只營業了幾個月就關門了。

→ _____ 。

V. Beneficiary marker 為

Function: The literary preposition 為 introduces a beneficiary noun into the sentence, a noun which benefits from the context of the following verb phrase. The term 'beneficiary' can have many meanings.

1. Recipient of the action. In this usage, the object of 為 seems to be the real object of the verb, e.g., (1) 為人民服務 (Serve on behalf of the people) (2) 為大家加油 (Root for everybody) (3) 為農夫帶來許多好處 (Bring many advantages to farmers).

2.On behalf of. In this usage, the verbs are mostly state verbs, e.g., (1) 為孩子擔心 (worry for/about the children) (2) 為家人難過 (feel bad for my family) (3) 為朋友高興 (happy for my friend).

3. For the sake of. In this usage, something has been done for the benefit of someone, e.g., (1) 為他們買健康保險 (buy health insurance for their sake) (2) 為他翻譯 (translate for his sake) (3) 為誰辛苦 (work hard for whose sake?).

練習 Exercise

Introduce the beneficiaries for each section below, answering questions using 為.

Recipient of action

❶ A：天氣這麼熱，你為什麼還是非要到現場看比賽不可？

B：當然要去現場。這樣才能＿＿＿＿＿＿＿＿＿＿。（加油）

❷ A：現代年輕人的生活已經夠忙了，為什麼還要想辦法找時間玩電玩呢？

B：雖然很忙，可是還得找時間輕鬆一下。

＿＿＿＿＿＿＿＿＿＿＿＿＿＿＿＿。（帶來／快樂）

❸ A：農夫透過網路行銷有什麼好處？

B：透過網路行銷，不必經過中間商，可以

＿＿＿＿＿＿＿＿＿＿＿＿＿＿＿＿。（帶來／利潤）

On behalf of

❶ A：他開刀以後恢復的情形怎麼樣？

B：不太理想。現在家人朋友全都＿＿＿＿＿＿＿。（擔心）

❷ A：小林跟女朋友分手，痛苦得不得了。我真不知道對他說什麼才好。

B：他女朋友總是騙人。分手就算了，哪裡需要

＿＿＿＿＿＿＿＿＿＿＿＿＿＿＿＿？（痛苦）

❸ A：聽說小張差一點就拿到獎學金了。

B：是啊，朋友們都＿＿＿＿＿＿＿＿＿＿。（可惜）

For the sake of

❶ A：上個週末你們都到哪裡去了？怎麼都找不到人？

B：上個週末是我室友的生日，我們去 KTV＿＿＿＿＿＿。（慶祝）

❷ A：先生，這上面寫的是什麼意思？我不太明白。

B：別擔心，讓我來＿＿＿＿＿＿＿＿＿＿。你一聽就懂了。（說明）

❸ A：聽說你成立了一個網站，幫農夫賣水果。

B：是啊，我想利用網路＿＿＿＿＿＿＿＿。（增加收入）

VI.（在）…方面 *with respect to; regarding* 12-09

Function: A sentence with the pattern（在）…方面 means that the sentence is true as far as '…' is concerned.

❶ 經過五十年的殖民統治，台灣人在飲食、生活習慣各方面都受到日本文化很深的影響。

❷ 最近幾年，中國在經濟方面發展得很快，吸引了許多外國人到那裡工作。

❸ 這棟大樓的環境，一般來說，還不錯。不過在衛生方面，還應該再改善。

❹ 明天李教授的演講談的是流行音樂。他在這方面相當有研究，應該很值得去聽。

❺ 他在門市服務快滿十年了，在處理消費糾紛方面很有經驗。你可以放心。

Usage:

1. There are similarities between（在）…方面 and（在）…上, but（在）…上 has more usages than（在）…方面.

2. （在）…上 can be used to indicate the foundation, standard, or principle upon which a statement, e.g.,

(1) 她跟男朋友只是同居，在法律上，還算是單身。

(2) 對中國人來說，中秋節是全家團聚的日子。習慣上，每個人都要回家。

(3) 雖然出車禍不是他的錯，可是他認為自己在道德上多少有一些責任。

When used this way, only abstract nouns can be inserted into the pattern and it is not interchangeable with（在）…方面. E.g.,

(4) *他家在吃上很講究。

(5) *她跟男朋友只是同居，在法律方面，還算是單身。

3. When, however,（在）…方面 and（在）…上 are used to explain different aspects of the same topic, the two patterns are interchangeable. E.g.,

(1) a. 我們是好朋友，在興趣上完全一樣，可是在個性上，他比我活潑得多。

b. 我們是好朋友，在興趣方面完全一樣，可是在個性方面，他比我活潑得多。

(2) a. 有牌子的包包在價格上當然比沒有牌子的高一點，但是在品質上，比較能得到顧客的信任。

b. 有牌子的包包在價格方面當然比沒有牌子的高一點，但是在品質方面，比較能得到顧客的信任。

(3) a. 我來台灣快一年了。生活上差不多都習慣了，學習上也相當順利，中文進步了不少。

b. 我來台灣快一年了。生活方面差不多都習慣了，學習方面也相當順利，中文進步了不少。

練習 Exercise

Complete the following（在）…方面 sentences.

❶ 台灣的微整型技術在亞洲是數一數二的，尤其是在_____ 方面，_____。

❷ 網購的好處很多，尤其是_____方面，_____。

❸ 我們的生活，在_____、_____、_____各個 方面，幾乎都離不開電腦。

❹ 他對穿很講究，不過在_____方面，_____。

❺ 他開始每天運動以後，不但精神變好了，_____方面， 也_____。

語法例句英譯
Grammar Examples in English •

I. 只不過…（而已） *merely…; nothing more than…*

Function:

❶ Wu Baochun only graduated from junior high school. Some people think, "How is he capable of studying in an MBA program?"

❷ He merely made some daikon cakes once in a cooking class. Now, he goes around telling people how well he cooks.

❸ He's was just talking (he didn't mean it). Did you actually think he really wants to quit his job?

❹ It merely rained a few days and the clothes are all mildewed.

❺ You're only taking three classes this semester. How come you're so busy that you don't even have the time to take part in any school club activities?

Usage:

1. (1) a. He was just talking. He doesn't actually want to have a dog.
   b. You only had one bad night of sleep and you have no energy to go to class.

   (2) a. It's only 18 degrees. How come you're wearing a wool coat?
   b. Candidate number three merely has a good image. He doesn't actually have much political experience.

2. (1) a. It's the department store's anniversary, but products are only 20% off.
   b. It's the department store's anniversary, but products are only 20% off.

   (2) b. You've had your stall set up all morning; how come you've only made a few hundred dollars?

303

d. (He) graduated from medical school in just three years? How is that possible?

(3) a. I was just joking. How come you're angry.

II. Introducing an Agent with 由

Function:

1. We've asked Director Zhang to speak tonight. He will be telling us about the latest developments in linguistics.

2. Let's make dumplings tonight. You prepare the stuffing. As to the wrapping, I'll be responsible for that.

3. It is obviously more appropriate for professional diplomats to handle foreign affairs issues.

4. Mr. Zhang? I'll be giving you a health checkup today. Could you lie down please?

5. After Mr. Li retired, his two daughters took over running his company.

Usage:

1. (1) Since it's the view of the voters, let it be voiced by our elected representative.

(2) In traditional Chinese society, what department children studied generally wasn't decided by the children; rather, it was decided by the parents.

(3) Reconstructive surgery after car accidents isn't generally performed by general surgeons; rather, a plastic surgeon is called upon to handle it.

(4) Who should organize the next computer exhibition?

(5) Wouldn't it be more appropriate to have locals decide by vote on these public issues?

(6) Can you act as a representative and explain everybody's view in just a minute?

III. 難道… *how could it possibly be true*

Function:

1. After undergoing micro-cosmetic surgery, are you telling me that a person really can gain self-confidence?

2. Could it be that he only had the accident because he was in a hurry?

3. Don't you think it a shame if one had to give up studying in the department he wanted just because his parents opposed it?

4. Pineapple cakes as famous as this, are you telling me that you don't even want to try one?

5. Today's Monday. How do you have time to come see me? Are you telling me that you really quit your job?

Usage:

1. (1) He would rather break up with his girlfriend than get married. Could it be that marriage is really that scary?

(2) Li Wenyan's aunt had him drink fish soup every day. Are you telling me that fish soup can heal your wound faster?

(3) In the 17th century, Europeans fought in Taiwan. Are you telling me that Taiwan didn't have a government at that time?

3. (1) Are you telling me that you want me to give you all the money?

(2) Are you telling me that you are so poor that you can't even afford a cup of soy milk?

(3) Are you telling me that you anticipate he will receive a percentage of votes that exceeds 80%?

IV. To Reach a Ceiling with 滿

Function:

1. Taiwan law stipulates that a person can only undergo cosmetic surgery after he or she is 18-years old. What about in your country?

❷ According to our company's rules, after serving in the company for one year, you can get seven days of vacation.

❸ The department store has been having its anniversary sale recently. Not only are they offering up to 50% off, if you spend NT$3,000, they will even give you a gift.

❹ Time passes really quickly. In another month, I'll have been in Taiwan two years.

❺ After living in Taiwan for six months, foreigners can apply for health insurance.

Usage:

1. **(1)** Waiter, please fill my glass up with water. Thank you.

   (2) If one can sleep a full eight hours a day, one is sure to be healthy.

   (3) Mom planted tons of flowers in front of the house.

VI. （在）⋯方面 *with respect to; regarding*

Function:

❶ After 50 years of colonial rule, Taiwanese were deeply influenced by Japanese culture in the areas of dietary and living habits.

❷ In recent years, China has developed very quickly with respect to its economy, attracting many foreigners there to work.

❸ This building's overall condition is, for the most part, pretty good. In terms of sanitation, however, it still needs some improvement.

❹ Professor Li's speech tomorrow will be on pop music. He has researched this area quite a lot. It should worth listening to.

❺ He has been working in the sales office for almost 10 years and has a lot of experience in the area of handling consumer disputes. You don't need to worry.

Usage:

2. **(1)** She is only living with her boyfriend. In terms of the law, she is still single.

   (2) For the Chinese people, the Mid-autumn Moon Festival is a day when families get together. Customarily, everyone returns home.

   (3) Although the accident wasn't his fault, he feels that, morally speaking, he needs to take some responsibility.

3. **(1)** We are good friends and share the same interests, but in terms of personality, we are completely different. He is much more lively than me.

   (2) Of course a designer bag is higher priced than a non-designer brand, but in terms of quality, consumers are more likely to trust brands.

   (3) I have been in Taiwan almost a year. In terms of day-to-day living, I'm just about used to it. In terms of study, things have been quite smooth; my Chinese has improved a lot.

Classroom Activities

I. I Oppose Your Running for Office

Goal: 1. Learning to express opposing views.

2. Learning to explain my ideals.

Task: After returning to his hometown for three years, Li Wenyan's uncle began thinking about once again running for office as a means to realizing his ideals. He discusses it with his wife, but his wife is very much against the idea. What do you think are his wife's considerations? Write down what they said during their conversation.

Try to use the following sentence patterns and vocabulary words:

為	由…來 V	（在）…方面	不過…而已	如果…不就…嗎？
難道	盡可能	提出	不是…而是	不是說好了嗎？

II. Public Issues That You Consider Important

Goal: 1. Learning to interview others about public issues they consider important and talk about those issues.

2. Learning to analyze and compare public issues that people in different countries are concerned about.

Task 1: Please interview two friends to find out which public issues they care about (e.g., nuclear power plants, educational reforms) and how they show their concern (e.g., taking part in marches, helping spread the message). Compare the issues you and your friends consider important and the ways they show their concern for those issues. In addition, ask the people you interview the primary reasons they are so concerned about the issues they raised.

	我	同學	原因	表達支持或反對的方式
❶ 核能電廠				
❷ 滿 18 歲有投票權				
❸ 教育改革				
❹ 國民年金				
❺ 弱勢家庭資源				
❻ 有機農產品				
❼				
❽				

Task 2: Select three issues that are similar or very different and write them down in the form of a formal report and give your own conclusion.

III. Should You Go Cast Your Vote?

Goal: Learning to express the reasons for my opinions and opposition.
Task 1: Class, separate into two groups. State opinions for and against voting or not voting. Carry out a debate accordingly.

Try to use the following sentence patterns and vocabulary words:

直接	表達	民意	代表	政黨
權利	利益	表示	反映	積極
權力	義務	改革	議題	政策

307

Elections and Numbers

In Chinese culture, homophones (characters with similar sounds) play a very important role. Employed well, homophones can bring good luck. Their use is not only a must for everything from weddings and other joyous occasions to funerals, they are also used in elections, where in white-hot contests, candidates fight over every vote. Despite the fact that some snort in contempt at the use of homophones and say that it's all just a bunch of hooey, candidates continue to use them on the off chance that the one they use might bring them luck and have some effect on the outcome of the election.

▲ Candidates who draw the number 1 use a "thumbs up" sign.

Many people say that elections in Taiwan are like festivals in that they are incredibly lively affairs. During dazzling election campaigns, characterized by tricks galore as well as slogans and placards designed to leave a deep impression on the hearts and minds of the electorate, thinking of some way to make voters remember your number on the ballot is also an essential part of running for office. As a consequence, the day that candidates draw lots to see who gets what number is a big deal and how they can use homophones of the numbers to their advantage is a good way to manufacture newsworthy discussion. For example, a candidate who draws the number 3 might make an "OK" sign with his thumb and index finger with the other three fingers fanned out to the side to suggest that "If I'm elected, everything will be OK." Regardless of what number a candidate draws, he has to be able to immediately make some similar lucky gesture or shout out some auspicious homophone. It's just part of the game of politics in Taiwan.

▲ Candidates who draw the number 2 use the victory sign.

▲ Candidates who draw the number 3 use the OK sign.

A candidate who draws the number 6, which represents 福祿（fúlù）will shout 六六大順（liùliù dàshùn） to indicate that he is confident that everything will go smoothly. The one who draws 7 will shout 旗開得勝（qíkāi déshèng, open the flag and win victory, i.e., win a speedy victory）to give himself momentum. Even the candidate that draws 4, the least favorite number, says, 事事如意、勢在必得（shìshì rúyì, shìzài bìdé, everything will go smoothly, the election is in the bag）to turn the tables in his favor. After all, having voters remember who you are and leaving them with an impression that you are confident is the first step to victory.

▲ Homophones are employed a great deal in elections. Candidates make number gestures to help voters remember their number.
《聯合報》曾增勳、林昭彰、張裕珍、游明煌／攝影

Self-Assessment Checklist

I can discuss issues related to elections for elected representatives.

20%   40%   60%   80%   100%

I can analyze logic and offer various possibilities.

20%   40%   60%   80%   100%

I can express my views and reasons for opposing something.

20%   40%   60%   80%   100%

I can introduce candidates and their experience in politics.

20%   40%   60%   80%   100%

中 - 英 Vocabulary Index (Chinese-English)

Pinyin	Traditional Characters	Simplified Characters	Lesson-Dialogue-Number
A			
āi	唉	唉	5-1-2
ài	愛	爱	4-1-1
Àilín	愛林	爱林	10-2-30
āiya	哎呀	哎呀	10-1-27
āmà	阿嬤	阿嬤	9-1-8
Ān Désī	安德思	安德思	1-1-1
āndìng	安定	安定	12-2-4
ānjìng	安靜	安静	6-2-31
ānpái	安排	安排	7-2-16
áoyè	熬夜	熬夜	1-1-27
āyí	阿姨	阿姨	7-2-2
B			
bài	拜	拜	3-2-10
bǎi tānzi	擺攤子	摆摊子	11-2-35
bàibài	拜拜	拜拜	3-2-12
bàifǎng	拜訪	拜访	6-2-20
bān	班	班	1-1-5
bàn	辦	办	1-2-16
bàn	伴	伴	7-2-19
bànfǎ	辦法	办法	2-2-15
bāngzhù	幫助	帮助	6-2-19
bāobāo	包包	包包	5-2-18
bàogào	報告	报告	1-1-12
bàojǐng	報警	报警	10-1-7
bāokuò	包括	包括	2-2-9
bàoqiàn	抱歉	抱歉	12-1-2
bèi	倍	倍	10-2-22
biànchéng	變成	变成	6-2-26
biànhuà	變化	变化	3-1-19
biǎo	表	表	1-2-15
biǎodá	表達	表达	12-1-12
biǎogē	表哥	表哥	6-1-2
biǎomèi	表妹	表妹	12-1-3

Pinyin	Traditional Characters	Simplified Characters	Lesson-Dialogue-Number
biǎoshì	表示	表示	12-1-30
bǐjià	比價	比价	9-1-18
bìmiǎn	避免	避免	5-2-17
bìng	並	并	2-2-8
bìngchuáng	病床	病床	10-1-16
bìngqiě	並且	并且	9-2-30
bìngrén	病人	病人	10-1-13
bīngxiāng	冰箱	冰箱	9-1-16
bǐshì	筆試	笔试	1-1-9
bìxū	必須	必须	9-1-21
bìyè zhǎn	畢業展	毕业展	8-1-33
búduàn	不斷	不断	11-2-15
bùguǎn	不管	不管	1-2-8
bùrú	不如	不如	5-1-14
bùwèi	部位	部位	10-1-24
C			
càidān	菜單	菜单	11-2-11
càisè	菜色	菜色	11-2-22
cānzhuō	餐桌	餐桌	11-2-1
céngjīng	曾經	曾经	9-2-4
chā	差	差	3-1-21
chà yì diǎn	差一點	差一点	1-1-33
chádiǎn	茶點	茶点	9-2-14
chǎndì	產地	产地	6-2-4
chàng	唱	唱	5-1-9
chǎnpǐn	產品	产品	5-2-20
chǎnzhí	產值	产值	9-2-19
chāoguò	超過	超过	10-2-21
cháoshī	潮濕	潮湿	3-1-28
Chén Mǐnxuān	陳敏萱	陈敏萱	3-1-1
chéngběn	成本	成本	9-2-6
chénggōng	成功	成功	5-1-6
chénggōng	成功	成功	8-2-40
chéngjī dān	成績單	成绩单	1-2-19
chéngjiā	成家	成家	7-2-21

Pinyin	Traditional Characters	Simplified Characters	Lesson-Dialogue-Number
chénglì	成立	成立	9-1-5
chéngqiáng	城牆	城墙	11-1-11
chéngwéi	成為	成为	8-2-35
chī dào bǎo	吃到飽	吃到饱	2-2-22
chídào	遲到	迟到	1-1-32
Chìkǎn Lóu	赤崁樓	赤崁楼	4-2-26
chīkǔ	吃苦	吃苦	8-2-23
chīkuī	吃虧	吃亏	9-1-17
chóngjiàn	重建	重建	11-1-2
chǒngwù	寵物	宠物	7-1-29
chū chēhuò	出車禍	出车祸	10-1-28
chū dà tàiyáng	出大太陽	出大太阳	3-1-32
chū wèntí	出問題	出问题	6-2-33
chūbǎn shè	出版社	出版社	12-2-40
chūchǎn	出產	出产	6-2-21
chūkǒu	出口	出口	9-2-3
chǔlǐ	處理	处理	12-1-22
chūshēng	出生	出生	8-2-18
chúshījī	除濕機	除湿机	3-1-25
chūxiàn	出現	出现	9-2-22
cí	辭	辞	12-2-5
cídiào	辭掉	辞掉	12-2-33
cóngshì	從事	从事	10-2-13
cóngzhèng	從政	从政	12-2-2
cuòguò	錯過	错过	4-2-5

D

Pinyin	Traditional Characters	Simplified Characters	Lesson-Dialogue-Number
dǎ	打	打	7-1-19
dǎ bài	打敗	打败	11-1-41
dǎ shū	打輸	打输	11-2-34
dǎ wán zhé	打完折	打完折	2-1-31
dàhǎn dàjiào	大喊大叫	大喊大叫	8-1-30
dài	戴	戴	3-2-14
dāi	待	待	4-2-22
dàibiǎo	代表	代表	9-2-16
dàibiǎo	代表	代表	12-1-21

Pinyin	Traditional Characters	Simplified Characters	Lesson-Dialogue-Number
dàiyù	待遇	待遇	10-2-18
dàkāi yǎnjiè	大開眼界	大开眼界	8-2-48
dàn bǐng	蛋餅	蛋饼	11-2-33
dàng	當	当	1-1-28
dāng chéng	當成	当成	7-1-39
dāngbīng	當兵	当兵	8-2-25
dāngdì	當地	当地	4-1-13
dāngjì	當季	当季	5-2-4
dāngzhōng	當中	当中	3-2-3
dāngzuò	當做	当做	9-2-11
dānqīn	單親	单亲	7-2-9
dānshēn	單身	单身	7-1-30
Dànshuǐ	淡水	淡水	11-1-32
dānxīn	擔心	担心	1-2-13
dànzǎimiàn	擔仔麵	担仔面	4-1-11
dàodé	道德	道德	7-2-29
dàodì	道地	道地	4-2-14
dàodǐ	到底	到底	11-1-3
dǎoméi	倒楣	倒楣	5-1-7
Dàqīng dìguó	大清帝國	大清帝国	11-1-38
dàsài	大賽	大赛	8-2-2
dǎzhàng	打仗	打仗	11-1-14
dǎzhé	打折	打折	2-1-16
dǎzhēn	打針	打针	10-1-18
dédào	得到	得到	12-2-11
dēng	燈	灯	8-1-3
dépiàolǜ	得票率	得票率	12-2-16
dì èr wèi	第二位	第二位	9-2-39
diànchǎng	電廠	电厂	12-1-16
diànmiàn	店面	店面	9-2-33
diànwán	電玩	电玩	8-1-4
diànxìn	電信	电信	2-2-3
diǎnxīn	點心	点心	11-2-25
diànyuán	店員	店员	2-1-12
diànzhǎng	店長	店长	2-1-27
diànzǐ	電子	电子	5-2-21

Pinyin	Traditional Characters	Simplified Characters	Lesson-Dialogue-Number
diàochá	調查	调查	10-2-7
dié dǎo	跌倒	跌倒	7-1-38
dìngdān	訂單	订单	9-1-1
dìnggòu	訂購	订购	9-1-4
dìwèi	地位	地位	6-1-12
Dōngfāng	東方	东方	11-1-31
Dōngjīng	東京	东京	9-2-37
dōngqū	東區	东区	4-1-21
dòng bú dòng jiù	動不動就	动不动就	10-2-34
dòng shǒushù	動手術	动手术	10-1-33
dòujiāng	豆漿	豆浆	11-2-7
dù	度	度	3-1-8
duǎn	短	短	2-1-13
Duānwǔ jié	端午節	端午节	3-2-32
duìdài	對待	对待	6-2-7
duīféi	堆肥	堆肥	6-1-10
dúlì	獨立	独立	7-2-15
dùn	頓	顿	2-2-14
dùn	頓	顿	4-2-17
duǒ	躲	躲	3-1-7
duōbàn	多半	多半	11-2-17
duōshǎo	多少	多少	3-2-19
duōyuán	多元	多元	7-2-1
dúshēngnǚ	獨生女	独生女	1-2-1
dúshū	讀書	读书	8-1-15

E

Pinyin	Traditional Characters	Simplified Characters	Lesson-Dialogue-Number
EMBA(gāojí guǎnlǐ rényuán gōngshāng guǎnlǐ shuòshì)	EMBA（高級管理人員工商管理碩士）	EMBA（高级管理人员工商管理硕士）	8-2-46
è sǐle	餓死了	饿死了	3-1-36
en	嗯	嗯	7-1-6
ér	而	而	4-1-15
èrshǒu shū	二手書	二手书	12-2-42
éryǐ	而已	而已	12-1-10
érzi	兒子	儿子	8-1-25

F

Pinyin	Traditional Characters	Simplified Characters	Lesson-Dialogue-Number
fāméi	發霉	发霉	3-1-24
fán	煩	烦	8-1-11
fǎn hé	反核	反核	12-1-4

Pinyin	Traditional Characters	Simplified Characters	Lesson-Dialogue-Number
fǎnduì	反對	反对	1-2-9
fàng	放	放	4-1-3
fāngbiàn	方便	方便	9-1-3
fāngmiàn	方面	方面	12-2-10
fàngqì	放棄	放弃	1-2-7
fāngshì	方式	方式	5-2-15
fàngsōng	放鬆	放松	5-1-22
fànmài	販賣	贩卖	9-1-7
fānqié	番茄	番茄	6-1-16
fàntuán	飯糰	饭团	11-2-6
fǎnyìng	反映	反映	12-1-31
fāpiào	發票	发票	2-1-23
fēiqù bùkě	非去不可	非去不可	4-2-29
fēn	分	分	1-1-18
X fēn zhī Y	X 分之 Y	X 分之 Y	8-2-49
fēndiàn	分店	分店	8-2-37
fēng	瘋	疯	8-1-21
fènglí	鳳梨	凤梨	9-2-1
fènglí nóng	鳳梨農	凤梨农	9-2-40
fènglí sū	鳳梨酥	凤梨酥	9-2-38
fēngsú	風俗	风俗	4-2-12
fēngxiǎn	風險	风险	9-1-19
fēngyún rénwù	風雲人物	风云人物	7-2-34
fēnshǒu	分手	分手	7-1-20
fùdān	負擔	负担	7-2-22
fùqīn	父親	父亲	8-2-20
fúwù	服務	服务	12-1-33
fǔxì	輔系	辅系	8-1-20
fúzhuāng	服裝	服装	5-2-13
fúzhuāng shèjì	服裝設計	服装设计	8-1-34

G

Pinyin	Traditional Characters	Simplified Characters	Lesson-Dialogue-Number
gǎi	改	改	7-2-5
gài	蓋	盖	4-2-21
gǎibiàn	改變	改变	8-2-13
gǎigé	改革	改革	12-2-7
gǎishàn	改善	改善	9-2-29
gǎitiān	改天	改天	4-1-19
gǎn	敢	敢	6-1-24
gān	乾	干	3-1-23
gǎn shíjiān	趕時間	赶时间	10-1-29

Pinyin	Traditional Characters	Simplified Characters	Lesson-Dialogue-Number
gǎndòng	感動	感动	4-1-10
gānggāng	剛剛	刚刚	4-1-18
gǎnjué	感覺	感觉	3-1-11
gǎnjué	感覺	感觉	4-1-26
gǎnzǒu	趕走	赶走	3-2-36
gào	告	告	10-2-26
gāojí	高級	高级	8-2-4
Gāoqiáo Jiàntài	高橋健太	高桥健太	3-1-2
gēcí	歌詞	歌词	5-1-12
gēnjù	根據	根据	3-2-4
gèxìng	個性	个性	1-2-10
gèzhǒng gèyàng	各種各樣	各种各样	11-2-39
gōnggòng	公共	公共	12-1-13
gōnggōng	公公	公公	7-2-6
gōnglì	公立	公立	10-2-19
gōngpíng	公平	公平	8-2-17
gōngwùyuán	公務員	公务员	8-1-10
gōngzhí	公職	公职	8-1-8
gǒu	狗	狗	7-1-4
gòumǎi	購買	购买	9-2-28
gòuwù	購物	购物	2-2-1
gǔ shíhòu	古時候	古时候	3-2-35
guà	掛	挂	3-2-16
guā fēng	颱風	刮风	3-1-33
guài	怪	怪	10-2-29
guānguāng	觀光	观光	6-2-29
guānjī	關機	关机	2-2-17
guànjūn	冠軍	冠军	8-2-1
gūdān	孤單	孤单	7-1-12
guīzé	規則	规则	10-1-6
guìzú	貴族	贵族	7-2-10
gǔjī	古蹟	古迹	4-2-9
gùkè	顧客	顾客	2-2-11
gǔlǎo	古老	古老	4-2-8
gǔlì	鼓勵	鼓励	8-2-41
Guó Gòng nèizhàn	國共內戰	国共内战	11-2-30
guò jié	過節	过节	3-2-37
guómín niánjīn	國民年金	国民年金	12-2-35
guòshì	過世	过世	7-1-8

Pinyin	Traditional Characters	Simplified Characters	Lesson-Dialogue-Number
guózhōng	國中	国中	8-2-8
gùshì	故事	故事	3-2-30
gǔzhé	骨折	骨折	10-1-10
H			
hài	害	害	5-2-11
hǎixiān	海鮮	海鲜	3-1-16
hǎn	喊	喊	8-1-7
Hàn rén	漢人	汉人	11-1-33
hángháng chū zhuàngyuán	行行出狀元	行行出状元	8-1-36
hǎoyùn	好運	好运	9-2-9
hé	合	合	1-2-4
Hé Yǎtíng	何雅婷	何雅婷	1-1-3
hēi	黑	黑	6-1-26
Hélán	荷蘭	荷兰	3-1-31
hélǐ	合理	合理	10-2-2
hénéng	核能	核能	12-1-15
hōngbèi	烘焙	烘焙	8-2-27
hóngchá	紅茶	红茶	4-1-29
Hóngmáo chéng	紅毛城	红毛城	11-1-30
hòumǔ liǎn	後母臉	后母脸	3-1-37
hòuxuǎn rén	候選人	候选人	12-1-42
huàn	換	换	2-1-26
huàn chéng	換成	换成	2-2-21
huàzhuāng	化妝	化妆	5-2-30
huīfù	恢復	恢复	10-1-25
huǒguō	火鍋	火锅	3-1-15
huópō	活潑	活泼	1-2-11
huò bǐ sān jiā bù chīkuī	貨比三家不吃虧	货比三家不吃亏	9-1-29
J			
jì	寄	寄	5-2-9
jì	既	既	9-1-13
jiàgé	價格	价格	9-2-7
Jiāhuá	家華	家华	7-2-33
jiàn	建	建	11-1-1
jiān	煎	煎	11-2-21
Jiǎng Jièshí	蔣介石	蒋介石	11-2-29
jiǎngjiù	講究	讲究	4-2-16
jiāngjūn	將軍	将军	11-1-17

Pinyin	Traditional Characters	Simplified Characters	Lesson-Dialogue-Number
jiànlì	建立	建立	7-1-33
jiǎnqīng	減輕	减轻	7-1-22
jiǎnshǎo	減少	减少	6-1-7
jiào	叫	叫	7-1-5
jiāo	交	交	4-1-16
jiǎofèi	繳費	缴费	2-2-19
jiàoyǎng	教養	教养	7-2-26
jiàoyù	教育	教育	12-2-9
jiàqián	價錢	价钱	4-1-25
jiàrì	假日	假日	9-1-6
jiātíng	家庭	家庭	7-1-35
jiàzhíguān	價值觀	价值观	10-2-24
jīchǔ	基礎	基础	8-2-15
jīdòng	激動	激动	8-1-6
jiè	屆	届	12-2-13
jiēdào	街道	街道	4-2-20
jiéguǒ	結果	结果	9-2-27
jiéjiǎn	節儉	节俭	11-2-19
jiējìn	接近	接近	6-2-24
jiěshì	解釋	解释	2-2-10
jiēshòu	接受	接受	7-2-27
jiēzhe	接著	接着	11-2-13
jīhū	幾乎	几乎	3-1-22
jījí	積極	积极	12-1-38
jìjié	季節	季节	3-1-14
jǐmǎn	擠滿	挤满	5-1-27
jìn kěnéng	盡可能	尽可能	12-2-39
jìn yí bù	進一步	进一步	11-2-43
jīngcǎi	精彩	精彩	11-1-29
jǐngchá	警察	警察	10-1-21
jīngfèi	經費	经费	12-2-28
jīngguò	經過	经过	8-2-31
jìngxuǎn	競選	竞选	12-2-29
jīngyíng	經營	经营	9-1-10
jìngzhēng	競爭	竞争	9-2-8
jìngzhēnglì	競爭力	竞争力	10-2-6
jǐnjí	緊急	紧急	10-1-15
jìnliàng	盡量	尽量	6-2-5
jǐnzhāng	緊張	紧张	7-1-21
jìnzhǐ	禁止	禁止	11-1-26
jīpái	雞排	鸡排	4-1-27

Pinyin	Traditional Characters	Simplified Characters	Lesson-Dialogue-Number
jìrán	既然	既然	5-2-12
jìshù	技術	技术	8-2-29
jiūfēn	糾紛	纠纷	2-2-2
jiùhù chē	救護車	救护车	10-1-31
jīyīn gǎizào	基因改造	基因改造	6-1-29
jízhěnshì	急診室	急诊室	10-1-8
jìzǔ	祭祖	祭祖	3-2-9
juān	捐	捐	12-2-26
juānchū	捐出	捐出	12-2-41
jǔbàn	舉辦	举办	9-2-18
jùjué	拒絕	拒绝	8-2-10
jūliúzhèng	居留證	居留证	2-2-5
jūnduì	軍隊	军队	11-1-9
jūnrén	軍人	军人	11-1-18
jūrán	居然	居然	5-2-10
jǔxíng	舉行	举行	8-1-23

K

Pinyin	Traditional Characters	Simplified Characters	Lesson-Dialogue-Number
kāi	開	开	8-1-2
kāi wánxiào	開玩笑	开玩笑	6-1-31
kāidāo	開刀	开刀	10-1-12
kāikěn	開墾	开垦	11-1-16
kāixué	開學	开学	1-1-4
kànfǎ	看法	看法	12-2-8
kàntiān chīfàn	看天吃飯	看天吃饭	6-1-32
kào	靠	靠	7-2-8
kǎoshàng	考上	考上	1-2-20
kě'ài	可愛	可爱	7-1-11
kèfú zhōngxīn	客服中心	客服中心	2-2-24
kèhù	客戶	客户	9-1-2
kējì	科技	科技	9-2-23
Kèjiā rén	客家人	客家人	11-2-31
kēxì	科系	科系	1-2-6
Kǒngmiào	孔廟	孔庙	4-1-32
kǒngpà	恐怕	恐怕	1-1-29
kōngqì	空氣	空气	3-1-3
kǒu	口	口	4-1-28
kǒucái	口才	口才	1-1-30
kǒushì	口試	口试	1-1-8
kǒutóu	口頭	口头	1-1-11
kǒuwèi	口味	口味	9-2-26

Pinyin	Traditional Characters	Simplified Characters	Lesson-Dialogue-Number
kuàijì	會計	会计	1-1-25
kuànián	跨年	跨年	4-1-23
kuǎnshì	款式	款式	5-2-5
kuāzhāng	誇張	夸张	8-1-22
kùnnán	困難	困难	11-2-18

L

Pinyin	Traditional Characters	Simplified Characters	Lesson-Dialogue-Number
lǎbākù	喇叭褲	喇叭裤	5-2-27
lái bù jí	來不及	来不及	5-1-33
lǎojiā	老家	老家	12-2-19
lěngqì	冷氣	冷气	3-1-30
Lǐ Wényàn	李文彥	李文彦	6-1-1
liǎn	臉	脸	10-1-2
liǎng chéng	兩成	两成	9-1-30
liángkuài	涼快	凉快	3-1-27
liánrèn	連任	连任	12-2-12
liánxùjù	連續劇	连续剧	5-2-6
lìng	另	另	10-2-23
Língmù	鈴木	铃木	4-2-25
lǐngtǔ	領土	领土	11-1-24
língxià	零下	零下	3-1-10
lǐngyǎng	領養	领养	7-1-9
línjū	鄰居	邻居	7-1-3
lìrùn	利潤	利润	6-1-14
lìshǐ	歷史	历史	4-2-11
liú xià lái	留下來	留下来	4-2-27
liúxíng	流行	流行	5-1-1
lǐxiǎng	理想	理想	4-1-17
lǐxiǎng	理想	理想	1-2-3
lìyì	利益	利益	11-1-7
lou	嘍	喽	11-1-22
luàn	亂	乱	7-1-17
luàn	亂	乱	7-2-25
lúndào	輪到	轮到	11-1-39
Luó Shāndì	羅珊蒂	罗珊蒂	1-1-2
luóbo	蘿蔔	萝卜	11-2-12
luóbo gān	蘿蔔乾	萝卜干	11-2-42
luóbo gāo	蘿蔔糕	萝卜糕	11-2-36
luòwǔ	落伍	落伍	5-2-24
luòxuǎn	落選	落选	12-2-15

Pinyin	Traditional Characters	Simplified Characters	Lesson-Dialogue-Number
lùqǔ	錄取	录取	8-2-39

M

Pinyin	Traditional Characters	Simplified Characters	Lesson-Dialogue-Number
máfán	麻煩	麻烦	2-1-20
màijiā	賣家	卖家	9-1-20
mǎn	滿	满	12-1-25
máng de guòlái	忙得過來	忙得过来	6-1-30
mànhuà	漫畫	漫画	5-1-19
mànhuà zhǎn	漫畫展	漫画展	5-1-32
mǎnyì	滿意	满意	9-1-24
màoyì	貿易	贸易	11-1-5
méi bànfǎ	沒辦法	没办法	1-1-35
měilì	美麗	美丽	4-2-24
měiróngyuàn	美容院	美容院	7-1-24
měishí	美食	美食	4-2-2
méitǐ	媒體	媒体	5-2-14
měiwèi	美味	美味	11-2-24
Měizhēn	美真	美真	7-2-32
mén	門	门	8-1-14
mēn	悶	闷	3-1-29
mèngxiǎng	夢想	梦想	8-2-34
ménshì	門市	门市	2-2-4
mí	迷	迷	5-1-11
miànshì	面試	面试	8-2-6
mìjí bān	密集班	密集班	8-1-32
Míng cháo	明朝	明朝	11-1-35
míngbái	明白	明白	8-2-24
Mǐnnán rén	閩南人	闽南人	11-2-32
Mǐnnányǔ	閩南語	闽南语	9-2-35
mínyì	民意	民意	12-1-20
mínzhǔ	民主	民主	12-1-11
mínzú	民族	民族	3-2-23
mírén	迷人	迷人	10-2-4
míxìn	迷信	迷信	3-2-21
mō	摸	摸	2-1-11
mù zào	木造	木造	4-2-28
mǔqīn	母親	母亲	8-2-21

N

Pinyin	Traditional Characters	Simplified Characters	Lesson-Dialogue-Number
nǎinai	奶奶	奶奶	7-1-7
nàixīn	耐心	耐心	4-1-9

Pinyin	Traditional Characters	Simplified Characters	Lesson-Dialogue-Number
nándào	難道	难道	12-1-24
nándé	難得	难得	3-2-8
nánguài	難怪	难怪	3-1-13
nánguò	難過	难过	5-1-13
nánxìng	男性	男性	11-1-25
nèiróng	內容	内容	5-1-20
nèixiàn	內餡	内馅	9-2-10
nèizhàn	內戰	内战	11-2-8
níngkě	寧可	宁可	6-2-10
nòng	弄	弄	2-1-24
nòng diū	弄丟	弄丢	2-1-32
nóngchǎnpǐn	農產品	农产品	9-2-2
nóngcūn	農村	农村	6-2-17
nóngfū	農夫	农夫	6-1-6
nónglì	農曆	农历	3-2-5
nóngrén	農人	农人	3-2-7
nóngyào	農藥	农药	6-1-8
nóngyè	農業	农业	3-2-6
nuǎnhuo	暖和	暖和	2-1-15
nǔlì	努力	努力	8-1-28

P

Pinyin	Traditional Characters	Simplified Characters	Lesson-Dialogue-Number
pài	派	派	11-1-8
páizi	牌子	牌子	2-1-7
pángtīng	旁聽	旁听	1-1-17
pào	泡	泡	4-2-4
pǎo	跑	跑	6-2-11
pèngdào	碰到	碰到	4-1-34
pēngrèn kè	烹飪課	烹饪课	11-2-37
piàn	片	片	6-1-21
piàn	騙	骗	2-2-13
piànzi	片子	片子	10-1-11
píngbǎn diànnǎo	平板電腦	平板电脑	5-1-29
píngjūn	平均	平均	10-2-27
Píngxī	平溪	平溪	4-1-30
píngyuán	平原	平原	11-1-19
pǐnzhí	品質	品质	2-1-8
pǐnzhǒng	品種	品种	6-1-17
pòdòng	破洞	破洞	2-1-22
pǔbiàn	普遍	普遍	9-1-26
pǔtōng	普通	普通	10-2-12

Q

Pinyin	Traditional Characters	Simplified Characters	Lesson-Dialogue-Number
qǐ	起	起	2-1-1
qiǎn lánsè	淺藍色	浅蓝色	5-2-32
qiáng	牆	墙	4-1-8
qiáng	強	强	7-2-12
qiānmíng	簽名	签名	2-1-21
qiántú	前途	前途	12-1-8
qiānyí	遷移	迁移	11-2-16
qìhòu	氣候	气候	6-1-18
qīn	親	亲	7-1-1
Qīng cháo	清朝	清朝	11-1-37
qīngchǔ	清楚	清楚	1-1-15
qíngkuàng	情況	情况	10-1-14
qióng	窮	穷	8-2-19
qíshí	其實	其实	8-1-9
qiúsài	球賽	球赛	8-1-5
qíwàng	期望	期望	8-1-26
qìwēn	氣溫	气温	3-1-20
qìyèjiā	企業家	企业家	8-2-36
qízhōng	其中	其中	6-2-15
qízhōng kǎo	期中考	期中考	8-1-31
qǔ	娶	娶	11-1-27
quán	全	全	7-2-7
quán	全	全	9-2-34
quàn	勸	劝	12-1-9
quánlì	權利	权利	12-1-29
quánlì	權力	权力	12-2-32
quánmiàn	全面	全面	12-1-19
què	卻	却	8-2-7

R

Pinyin	Traditional Characters	Simplified Characters	Lesson-Dialogue-Number
rèmén	熱門	热门	1-1-26
rénjì guānxì	人際關係	人际关系	10-2-33
rěn bú zhù	忍不住	忍不住	7-1-40
rénkǒu	人口	人口	11-1-20
rénmài	人脈	人脉	12-2-22
rénmín	人民	人民	11-2-9
rènqí	任期	任期	12-1-35
rénqíngwèi	人情味	人情味	4-1-2
rènzhēn	認真	认真	8-2-16

Pinyin	Traditional Characters	Simplified Characters	Lesson-Dialogue-Number
rènzì	認字	认字	8-2-26
rèzhōng	熱衷	热衷	12-1-7
Rìshì	日式	日式	11-2-26
Rìwén	日文	日文	8-2-44
ruòshì	弱勢	弱势	12-2-23

S

Pinyin	Traditional Characters	Simplified Characters	Lesson-Dialogue-Number
sāi	塞	塞	5-2-3
sāichē	塞車	塞车	5-1-4
sànbù	散步	散步	7-1-34
sèqíng	色情	色情	5-1-21
shā shíjiān	殺時間	杀时间	5-1-31
shài gān	曬乾	晒干	11-2-38
shāng	傷	伤	10-1-9
shàng	上	上	4-2-3
shāngjī	商機	商机	9-2-15
shāngkǒu	傷口	伤口	10-1-26
shāngliáng	商量	商量	12-2-21
shāngpǐn	商品	商品	2-1-4
shāngrén	商人	商人	5-2-19
shàngxiàn	上線	上线	5-1-5
shāngyè	商業	商业	11-1-6
shāo	燒	烧	11-1-10
shāobǐng	燒餅	烧饼	11-2-4
shǎoshù	少數	少数	11-1-15
shèhuì	社會	社会	3-2-26
shén	神	神	3-2-11
shēn	深	深	11-2-28
shēnbiān	身邊	身边	7-2-18
shēng	生	生	7-1-28
shěng	省	省	2-1-6
shēnqǐng	申請	申请	1-2-18
shènzhì	甚至	甚至	11-1-13
shì	事	事	1-1-31
shì chuān	試穿	试穿	2-1-30
shícái	食材	食材	6-2-3
shìchǎng	市場	市场	5-2-22
shídài	時代	时代	7-2-11
shīfù	師傅	师傅	6-2-16
shìjí	市集	市集	6-2-2
shíjì	實際	实际	3-1-12

Pinyin	Traditional Characters	Simplified Characters	Lesson-Dialogue-Number
shìjì	世紀	世纪	11-1-4
shìjiè miànbāo dàsài	世界麵包大賽	世界面包大赛	8-2-45
shíqī shìjì chū	十七世紀初	十七世纪初	11-1-40
shíqī shìjì mò	十七世紀末	十七世纪末	11-1-42
shìyè	事業	事业	12-2-25
shīyèlǜ	失業率	失业率	8-1-13
shóu	熟	熟	6-1-20
shòu bù liǎo	受不了	受不了	3-1-35
shòu dào	受到	受到	3-1-34
shòu huānyíng	受歡迎	受欢迎	5-1-26
shōuchéng	收成	收成	3-2-22
shōurù	收入	收入	6-1-13
shòushāng	受傷	受伤	10-1-3
shǒushù	手術	手术	10-1-20
shǒuxù	手續	手续	1-2-17
shuākǎ	刷卡	刷卡	2-1-18
shūcài	蔬菜	蔬菜	6-1-5
shuǐjiān bāo	水煎包	水煎包	4-1-35
shuōmíng	說明	说明	1-1-14
shuòshì	碩士	硕士	8-2-5
shúshu	叔叔	叔叔	9-2-25
shǔyī shǔ'èr	數一數二	数一数二	10-2-32
sīlì	私立	私立	1-2-2
sòng	送	送	7-1-23
sōuxún	搜尋	搜寻	9-1-15
suàn le	算了	算了	5-1-25
sùdù	速度	速度	4-2-18
suíbiàn	隨便	随便	6-1-3
suíshí	隨時	随时	9-1-14
suízhe	隨著	随着	6-2-28
sūnzi	孫子	孙子	11-1-23

T

Pinyin	Traditional Characters	Simplified Characters	Lesson-Dialogue-Number
tā	牠	牠	7-1-13
tā	它	它	5-2-2
(Tái) jīn	（台）斤	（台）斤	9-2-24
tánxìng	彈性	弹性	8-2-12
tānzi	攤子	摊子	11-2-10
tào	套	套	11-2-3
tián	填	填	1-2-14

Pinyin	Traditional Characters	Simplified Characters	Lesson-Dialogue-Number
tián	田	田	6-1-22
tiāndēng	天燈	天灯	4-1-4
tiánměi	甜美	甜美	5-2-8
tiānrán	天然	天然	6-1-9
tiào	跳	跳	5-1-16
tiáojiàn	條件	条件	6-1-25
tíchū	提出	提出	12-2-34
tígāo	提高	提高	9-2-20
tīnghuà	聽話	听话	8-1-12
tōngguò	通過	通过	8-2-3
tóngjū	同居	同居	7-2-20
tòngkǔ	痛苦	痛苦	1-2-5
tóngshì	同事	同事	4-2-1
tóufǎ	頭髮	头发	11-1-12
tóunǎo	頭腦	头脑	12-2-6
tóupiào	投票	投票	12-1-1
tóupiàoquán	投票權	投票权	12-1-27
tuángòu	團購	团购	9-2-32
tuánjù	團聚	团聚	3-2-27
tǔdì	土地	土地	6-2-8
tuì	退	退	2-1-25
tuīchē	推車	推车	7-1-25
tuīchū	推出	推出	5-2-35
tuījiàn xìn	推薦信	推荐信	1-2-21
tuīxiāo	推銷	推销	6-2-14
tuīxiāoyuán	推銷員	推销员	12-1-40
tuìxiū	退休	退休	12-2-24
tuōdiào	脫掉	脱掉	5-2-33

W

Pinyin	Traditional Characters	Simplified Characters	Lesson-Dialogue-Number
wàibiǎo	外表	外表	10-2-11
wàikē	外科	外科	10-2-20
wàitào	外套	外套	2-1-2
wàiyǔ	外語	外语	1-2-12
wǎng gòu	網購	网购	9-1-28
wànglái	旺來	旺来	9-2-36
wánměi	完美	完美	12-1-37
wànyī	萬一	万一	9-1-23
wánzhěng	完整	完整	7-2-31

Pinyin	Traditional Characters	Simplified Characters	Lesson-Dialogue-Number
wèi	為	为	12-1-32
wéi zhěngxíng	微整型	微整型	10-2-31
wéixiǎn	危險	危险	10-1-22
wèizēng tāng	味噌湯	味噌汤	11-2-41
wèizi	位子	位子	1-1-16
wénchóng	蚊蟲	蚊虫	3-2-13
wěndìng	穩定	稳定	3-1-5
wēndù	溫度	温度	3-1-9
wēnxīn	溫馨	温馨	3-2-31
wēnyì	瘟疫	瘟疫	3-2-17
wénzhāng	文章	文章	6-2-13
Wú Bǎochūn	吳寶春	吴宝春	8-2-42
wúliáo	無聊	无聊	4-1-20
Wǔyuètiān	五月天	五月天	5-1-24
wūzi	屋子	屋子	6-1-15

X

Pinyin	Traditional Characters	Simplified Characters	Lesson-Dialogue-Number
xǐ'ài	喜愛	喜爱	9-2-13
xià	下	下	9-1-12
xià juéxīn	下決心	下决心	7-2-35
xià yí bù	下一步	下一步	12-2-38
xià yí tiào	嚇一跳	吓一跳	2-2-23
xiàbān	下班	下班	7-2-4
xiànchǎng	現場	现场	5-1-15
xiànfǎ	憲法	宪法	12-1-26
xiāngbāo	香包	香包	3-2-15
xiāngchǔ	相處	相处	7-1-27
xiǎngshòu	享受	享受	7-2-17
xiǎngxiàng	想像	想象	5-2-26
xiāngxìn	相信	相信	11-1-28
xiànjīn	現金	现金	2-1-19
xiànmù	羨慕	羨慕	1-1-19
xiānshēng	先生	先生	7-2-3
xiǎo shíhòu	小時候	小时候	8-2-47
xiāofèi	消費	消费	6-2-30
xiǎonóng	小農	小农	6-2-1
xiāoshī	消失	消失	6-2-32
xiǎotí dàzuò	小題大作	小题大作	5-2-34
xiàowài jiāoxué	校外教學	校外教学	4-1-33

Pinyin	Traditional Characters	Simplified Characters	Lesson-Dialogue-Number
xǐbǐng	喜餅	喜饼	9-2-12
xiětǒng	血統	血统	11-1-21
xíguàn	習慣	习惯	4-2-13
xíng	行	行	1-1-22
xīngfèn	興奮	兴奋	5-1-10
xìngfú	幸福	幸福	7-1-37
xìngkuī	幸虧	幸亏	3-1-6
xíngxiàng	形象	形象	12-2-20
xíngxiāo	行銷	行销	9-2-31
Xīnjiāpō	新加坡	新加坡	8-2-43
xīnkǔ	辛苦	辛苦	6-1-11
xīnqíng	心情	心情	5-1-23
xìnrèn	信任	信任	6-2-9
xīnshǎng	欣賞	欣赏	4-2-23
xīnshēng	新生	新生	1-1-6
xīnxiān	新鮮	新鲜	3-1-17
xīnxíng	新型	新型	5-2-23
xìnyòng	信用	信用	9-1-22
xiónghuáng jiǔ	雄黃酒	雄黄酒	3-2-34
xiū	修	修	8-1-17
xiūjià	休假	休假	10-2-3
xiūkè	修課	修课	8-1-19
xiūlǐ	修理	修理	2-2-18
xiūxián	休閒	休闲	6-2-27
xiūxué	休學	休学	1-1-20
xīyǐn	吸引	吸引	5-2-16
xǐzǎo	洗澡	洗澡	7-1-15
xuǎnjǔ	選舉	选举	12-1-28
xuǎnmín	選民	选民	12-1-36
xuǎnzé	選擇	选择	9-1-27
xuǎnzé	選擇	选择	2-1-9
xǔduō	許多	许多	6-2-23
xuéfēn	學分	学分	8-1-16
xuélì	學歷	学历	8-2-9
xuéshùjiè	學術界	学术界	12-2-1
xuétú	學徒	学徒	8-2-22
xuéxí	學習	学习	8-2-28
xùnhào	訊號	讯号	4-1-6

Pinyin	Traditional Characters	Simplified Characters	Lesson-Dialogue-Number
Y			
yālì	壓力	压力	1-1-13
yán	嚴	严	1-1-7
yǎnchànghuì	演唱會	演唱会	5-1-3
yǎng	養	养	7-1-16
yǎngjiā	養家	养家	7-2-23
yángmáo	羊毛	羊毛	2-1-14
yàngzi	樣子	样子	2-1-10
yānhuǒ	煙火	烟火	4-1-22
yǎo	咬	咬	7-1-18
yàomìng	要命	要命	10-1-17
yèjǐng	夜景	夜景	4-2-7
yěxǔ	也許	也许	12-2-30
yéye	爺爺	爷爷	7-1-2
yì	億	亿	8-2-33
yì fāngmiàn	一方面	一方面	6-2-34
yí zhèn zi	一陣子	一阵子	12-2-37
yìbān	一般	一般	2-1-3
yìbān	一般	一般	10-2-16
yìbān láishuō	一般來說	一般来说	2-1-29
yíhàn	遺憾	遗憾	8-1-24
yǐjí	以及	以及	11-2-23
yìjiàn	意見	意见	7-1-32
yīliáo	醫療	医疗	10-2-28
yīměi	醫美	医美	10-2-1
yímín	移民	移民	3-2-2
yìmó yíyàng	一模一樣	一模一样	5-2-31
yīncǐ	因此	因此	7-2-30
yǐnèi	以內	以内	9-1-25
yīnghuā	櫻花	樱花	3-1-18
yǐngxiǎng	影響	影响	3-1-4
yíngyè	營業	营业	4-2-6
yǐnqǐ	引起	引起	8-2-11
yǐnshí	飲食	饮食	11-2-27
yìnxiàng	印象	印象	5-2-28
yìshù	藝術	艺术	8-2-30
yìtí	議題	议题	12-1-14
yǐwài	以外	以外	1-1-10

Pinyin	Traditional Characters	Simplified Characters	Lesson-Dialogue-Number
yìwù	義務	义务	12-2-27
yíxiàng	一向	一向	10-2-15
yīxué xì	醫學系	医学系	8-1-35
yīyuàn	醫院	医院	7-1-31
yīzhì	醫治	医治	10-2-14
yònggōng	用功	用功	1-1-21
yóu	由	由	12-1-17
yǒu dàolǐ	有道理	有道理	12-1-41
yóuqí	尤其	尤其	2-2-12
yǒushàn	友善	友善	6-2-6
yóutiáo	油條	油条	11-2-5
yóuxì	遊戲	游戏	5-2-29
yóuxíng	遊行	游行	12-1-5
yóuyú	由於	由于	6-2-22
yòuzi	柚子	柚子	3-2-29
yuán	圓	圆	3-2-25
yuánjià	原價	原价	2-1-17
yuánlái	原來	原来	1-1-24
yuànwàng	願望	愿望	4-1-5
yuánxiāo	元宵	元宵	4-1-7
Yuánxiāo jié	元宵節	元宵节	4-1-31
yuányīn	原因	原因	8-2-38
yuèbǐng	月餅	月饼	3-2-28
yuèliàng	月亮	月亮	3-2-24
yuètuán	樂團	乐团	5-1-8
yuèzūxíng	月租型	月租型	2-2-6
yùfù kǎ	預付卡	预付卡	2-2-20
yǔjì	雨季	雨季	3-1-26
yùqí	預期	预期	12-2-17

Z

Pinyin	Traditional Characters	Simplified Characters	Lesson-Dialogue-Number
zāng	髒	脏	7-1-14
zēngjiā	增加	增加	10-2-9
zěnme huíshì	怎麼回事	怎么回事	8-1-29
zérèn	責任	责任	7-2-24
zhǎi	窄	窄	4-2-19
zhāi xiàlái	摘下來	摘下来	6-1-27
zháipèi	宅配	宅配	9-1-11
zhàn	占	占	9-2-5

Pinyin	Traditional Characters	Simplified Characters	Lesson-Dialogue-Number
zhǎng	長	长	6-1-19
zhǎngdà	長大	长大	6-2-18
zhàngdān	帳單	帐单	2-2-7
zhànshí	暫時	暂时	12-2-18
zhànzhēng	戰爭	战争	11-2-14
zhǎo huí	找回	找回	10-2-35
zhào X guāng	照 X 光	照 X 光	10-1-32
zhàogù	照顧	照顾	6-1-23
zhāopái	招牌	招牌	4-1-12
zhékòu	折扣	折扣	2-1-5
zhèndòng	震動	震动	5-1-18
zhěng	整	整	5-1-17
Zhèng Chénggōng	鄭成功	郑成功	11-1-34
zhèngcè	政策	政策	12-2-3
zhèngdǎng	政黨	政党	12-1-23
zhèngfǔ	政府	政府	9-2-17
zhěngxíng	整型	整型	10-2-8
zhěngyè	整夜	整夜	8-1-1
zhèngzhì	政治	政治	12-1-6
zhèngzhìjiè	政治界	政治界	12-2-31
zhēnzhèng	真正	真正	7-1-36
zhèyàng xiàqù	這樣下去	这样下去	1-1-34
zhī	隻	只	7-1-10
zhíchǎng	職場	职场	10-2-5
zhīchí	支持	支持	6-2-12
zhīchídù	支持度	支持度	12-2-14
zhìdù	制度	制度	8-2-14
zhìhuìxíng shǒujī	智慧型手機	智慧型手机	5-1-30
zhímín tǒngzhì	殖民統治	殖民统治	11-2-40
zhīmíng	知名	知名	9-2-21
zhǐtòng	止痛	止痛	10-1-19
zhíwèi	職位	职位	12-1-34
zhīyīn	知音	知音	5-2-25
zhìyú	至於	至于	10-1-23
zhòng	種	种	6-1-4
zhōngjiānshāng	中間商	中间商	9-1-9
zhōngjiān xuǎnmín	中間選民	中间选民	12-2-36

Pinyin	Traditional Characters	Simplified Characters	Lesson-Dialogue-Number
zhǒnglèi	種類	种类	4-1-24
Zhōngnán Měizhōu	中南美洲	中南美洲	11-1-36
Zhōngqiū jié	中秋節	中秋节	3-2-33
zhòngshì	重視	重视	4-2-10
Zhōngshì	中式	中式	11-2-2
zhōngyú	終於	终于	8-2-32
zhōu	粥	粥	4-2-15
zhōunián qìng	週年慶	周年庆	2-1-28
zhuǎn	轉	转	1-1-23
zhuàn	賺	赚	4-1-14
zhuàng	撞	撞	10-1-4
zhuàng dǎo	撞倒	撞倒	10-1-30
zhuàngshān	撞衫	撞衫	5-2-1
zhuàngyuán	狀元	状元	8-1-27
zhuānjiā	專家	专家	12-1-18
zhuānxīn	專心	专心	8-1-18
zhǔfù	主婦	主妇	11-2-20
zhuī	追	追	7-2-13
zhǔjiǎo	主角	主角	5-2-7
zhǔrén	主人	主人	7-1-26
zhǔyào	主要	主要	10-2-17
zhùyuàn	住院	住院	10-1-1
zìdòng	自動	自动	2-2-16
zìrán	自然	自然	6-2-25
zìxìn	自信	自信	10-2-10
zìyóu	自由	自由	7-2-14
zǔchéng	組成	组成	7-2-28
zuìjiā	最佳	最佳	12-1-39
zūnjìng	尊敬	尊敬	10-2-25
zūnshǒu	遵守	遵守	10-1-5
zuò bú dòng	做不動	做不动	6-1-28
zuòfǎ	做法	做法	3-2-18
zuòyòng	作用	作用	3-2-20
zūshū diàn	租書店	租书店	5-1-28
zǔxiān	祖先	祖先	3-2-1

英 - 中 Vocabulary Index (English-Chinese)

English definition	Traditional Characters	Simplified Characters	Lesson-Dialogue-Number
20% , literally 2/10	兩成	两成	9-1-30

A

English definition	Traditional Characters	Simplified Characters	Lesson-Dialogue-Number
a while, a short duration of time	一陣子	一阵子	12-2-37
to be able to manage everything	忙得過來	忙得过来	6-1-30
academia, the academic fields or circles	學術界	学术界	12-2-1
to accept	接受	接受	7-2-27
to accept (application), to admit	錄取	录取	8-2-39
in accordance with, according to	根據	根据	3-2-4
to account for	占	占	9-2-5
accounting, an accountant	會計	会计	1-1-25
actively, to take it upon oneself to, take the initiative to	積極	积极	12-1-38
actual	實際	实际	3-1-12
actually	其實	其实	8-1-9
to adopt	領養	领养	7-1-9
adversely impacting somebody so that they...	害	害	5-2-11
(I am) afraid that, probably	恐怕	恐怕	1-1-29
after	經過	经过	8-2-31
after all	到底	到底	11-1-3
after discount	打完折	打完折	2-1-31
to be against	反對	反对	1-2-9
agricultural product	農產品	农产品	9-2-2
agriculture	農業	农业	3-2-6
air	空氣	空气	3-1-3
air conditioning	冷氣	冷气	3-1-30
Alien Resident Certificate (ARC in Taiwan)	居留證	居留证	2-2-5
all night	整夜	整夜	8-1-1
to be all right	行	行	1-1-22
almost	幾乎	几乎	3-1-22
along with, with the happening of	隨著	随着	6-2-28
ambulance	救護車	救护车	10-1-31
an American-born Chinese	李文彥	李文彦	6-1-1
amongst	當中	当中	3-2-3
ancestor	祖先	祖先	3-2-1
in ancient times	古時候	古时候	3-2-35
ancient, antiquated	古老	古老	4-2-8
and, as well as	以及	以及	11-2-23
anniversary	週年慶	周年庆	2-1-28
another, additional	另	另	10-2-23

English definition	Traditional Characters	Simplified Characters	Lesson-Dialogue-Number
anti-nuclear	反核	反核	12-1-4
anytime	隨時	随时	9-1-14
apologetic	抱歉	抱歉	12-1-2
to appear	出現	出现	9-2-22
appearance, exterior	外表	外表	10-2-11
appearance, looks	樣子	样子	2-1-10
to apply cosmetics	化妝	化妆	5-2-30
to apply for	申請	申请	1-2-18
to appreciate, to enjoy	欣賞	欣赏	4-2-23
apprentice	學徒	学徒	8-2-22
to approach	接近	接近	6-2-24
approval rating	支持度	支持度	12-2-14
arbitrarily, without rhyme or reason	亂	乱	7-1-17
army, military	軍隊	军队	11-1-9
to arrange	安排	安排	7-2-16
art	藝術	艺术	8-2-30
article	文章	文章	6-2-13
as far as possible, do one's best	盡可能	尽可能	12-2-39
as one pleases oneself, to act freely	隨便	随便	6-1-3
as to	至於	至于	10-1-23
to attract, to draw	吸引	吸引	5-2-16
attractive	迷人	迷人	10-2-4
to audit	旁聽	旁听	1-1-17
aunt (mother's sisters)	阿姨	阿姨	7-2-2
authentic	道地	道地	4-2-14
automatically	自動	自动	2-2-16
average	平均	平均	10-2-27
to avoid	避免	避免	5-2-17

B

English definition	Traditional Characters	Simplified Characters	Lesson-Dialogue-Number
bag	包包	包包	5-2-18
to bake	烘焙	烘焙	8-2-27
The Bakery World Cup	世界麵包大賽	世界面包大赛	8-2-45
ball game	球賽	球赛	8-1-5
(music) band	樂團	乐团	5-1-8
barely, nearly, almost	差一點	差一点	1-1-33
to bark	叫	叫	7-1-5
based on	根據	根据	3-2-4
bazaar	市集	市集	6-2-2
to bear (a burden, responsibility)	負擔	负担	7-2-22

322

English definition	Traditional Characters	Simplified Characters	Lesson-Dialogue-Number
beautiful	美麗	美丽	4-2-24
beauty salon	美容院	美容院	7-1-24
because of	由於	由于	6-2-22
to become	變成	变成	6-2-26
to become	成為	成为	8-2-35
to become	滿	满	12-1-25
been the case before	曾經	曾经	9-2-4
behind the times, passé	落伍	落伍	5-2-24
to believe	相信	相信	11-1-28
bell-bottom pants	喇叭褲	喇叭裤	5-2-27
below zero	零下	零下	3-1-10
benefit	利益	利益	11-1-7
the very best, the best possible	最佳	最佳	12-1-39
to be beyond the limits of endurance	忍不住	忍不住	7-1-40
bill	帳單	账单	2-2-7
to bite	咬	咬	7-1-18
black	黑	黑	6-1-26
black tea (lit. red tea)	紅茶	红茶	4-1-29
to blame	怪	怪	10-2-29
to be blazing hot	出大太陽	出大太阳	3-1-32
blood, bloodline	血統	血统	11-1-21
book rental store	租書店	租书店	5-1-28
boring, dull	無聊	无聊	4-1-20
to be born	出生	出生	8-2-18
bosom buddy, confidant	知音	知音	5-2-25
brain, mind	頭腦	头脑	12-2-6
branch store, branch office	分店	分店	8-2-37
brand	牌子	牌子	2-1-7
to break up (said of romantic relationships)	分手	分手	7-1-20
to build (Classical Chinese)	建	建	11-1-1
to build, to erect	蓋	盖	4-2-21
to burn	燒	烧	11-1-10
to burn the midnight oil	熬夜	熬夜	1-1-27
business	商業	商业	11-1-6
business opportunity	商機	商机	9-2-15
business, career	事業	事业	12-2-25
businessperson	商人	商人	5-2-19
but	卻	却	8-2-7
by (a doer)	由	由	12-1-17
by one's side	身邊	身边	7-2-18

English definition	Traditional Characters	Simplified Characters	Lesson-Dialogue-Number
C			
can't stand it	受不了	受不了	3-1-35
candidate	候選人	候选人	12-1-42
cash	現金	现金	2-1-19
category	種類	种类	4-1-24
catty, a unit of measure in Taiwan, equivalent to 600 grams	（台）斤	（台）斤	9-2-24
to cause	引起	引起	8-2-11
to cause, to do	弄	弄	2-1-24
Central and South America	中南美洲	中南美洲	11-1-36
century	世紀	世纪	11-1-4
champion, championship	冠軍	冠军	8-2-1
change	變化	变化	3-1-19
to undergo change	改變	改变	8-2-13
to change to	換成	换成	2-2-21
charming	迷人	迷人	10-2-4
to chase	追	追	7-2-13
to cheat, to swindle	騙	骗	2-2-13
cherry blossom	櫻花	樱花	3-1-18
Chiang Kai-Shek, 1887-1975	蔣介石	蒋介石	11-2-29
chicken fillet	雞排	鸡排	4-1-27
Chihkan Tower, a.k.a. Fort Provintia (stronghold built by the Dutch, in Tainan, in the 17th century)	赤崁樓	赤崁楼	4-2-26
in one's childhood	小時候	小时候	8-2-47
the Chinese Civil War (i.e., between the Kuomintang and the Communists), 1927-1937, 1945-1950	國共內戰	国共内战	11-2-30
Chinese-style	中式	中式	11-2-2
choices	選擇	选择	2-1-9
to choose	選擇	选择	9-1-27
city walls, defensive walls	城牆	城墙	11-1-11
civil servant	公務員	公务员	8-1-10
civil war	內戰	内战	11-2-8
class, i.e., the students(not the classroom or the course)	班	班	1-1-5
clay oven sesame seed biscuits, like Indian 'nan'	燒餅	烧饼	11-2-4
clear(ly)	清楚	清楚	1-1-15
climate	氣候	气候	6-1-18
close (as of familial relationship)	親	亲	7-1-1

English definition	Traditional Characters	Simplified Characters	Lesson-Dialogue-Number
clothing, garments	服裝	服装	5-2-13
coat, jacket	外套	外套	2-1-2
colleague, coworker	同事	同事	4-2-1
to colonise and rule	殖民統治	殖民统治	11-2-40
to come close to	接近	接近	6-2-24
comic (book) exhibition	漫畫展	漫画展	5-1-32
comics	漫畫	漫画	5-1-19
commerce	商業	商业	11-1-6
commodities	商品	商品	2-1-4
common	普遍	普遍	9-1-26
common	普通	普通	10-2-12
companion	伴	伴	7-2-19
to compare prices, price comparison	比價	比价	9-1-18
to compete against	競爭	竞争	9-2-8
competitive edge	競爭力	竞争力	10-2-6
complete, integral	完整	完整	7-2-31
completely	全	全	7-2-7
to comply with	遵守	遵守	10-1-5
compost	堆肥	堆肥	6-1-10
comprehensively	全面	全面	12-1-19
to concentrate	專心	专心	8-1-18
concert	演唱會	演唱会	5-1-3
to confer, consult with	商量	商量	12-2-21
Confucian Temple	孔廟	孔庙	4-1-32
congee, watery rice	粥	粥	4-2-15
to consider, view as, regard	當成	当成	7-1-39
to constitute	占	占	9-2-5
constitution	憲法	宪法	12-1-26
to be a consumer	消費	消费	6-2-30
content	內容	内容	5-1-20
continual, incessant	不斷	不断	11-2-15
to continue, to pick up where something left off	接著	接着	11-2-13
contrary to assumption (followed by a negative statement)	並	并	2-2-8
cooking class	烹飪課	烹饪课	11-2-37
cool	涼快	凉快	3-1-27
correct, check (homework)	改	改	7-2-5
cosmetic surgery	醫美	医美	10-2-1
costs	成本	成本	9-2-6
Could it be that...?, Is it that...?	難道	难道	12-1-24
cousin (older male cousin, from a female lineage)	表哥	表哥	6-1-2
to go crazy, to be insane	瘋	疯	8-1-21
credibility	信用	信用	9-1-22
(academic) credits	學分	学分	8-1-16
crowded with	擠滿	挤满	5-1-27

English definition	Traditional Characters	Simplified Characters	Lesson-Dialogue-Number
customer	顧客	顾客	2-2-11
customer service center	客服中心	客服中心	2-2-24
customer, client	客戶	客户	9-1-2
customs	風俗	风俗	4-2-12
cute	可愛	可爱	7-1-11

D

English definition	Traditional Characters	Simplified Characters	Lesson-Dialogue-Number
daikon cakes	蘿蔔糕	萝卜糕	11-2-36
daikon radish	蘿蔔	萝卜	11-2-12
danger	危險	危险	10-1-22
danzai noodles (special dish from Tainan)	擔仔麵	担仔面	4-1-11
to dare	敢	敢	6-1-24
dark	黑	黑	6-1-26
to deal with	辦	办	1-2-16
to deal with, handle, tackle	處理	处理	12-1-22
to decrease	減少	减少	6-1-7
deep	深	深	11-2-28
deep-fried dough sticks	油條	油条	11-2-5
to defeat	打敗	打败	11-1-41
to be defeated	打輸	打输	11-2-34
degree	度	度	3-1-8
dehumidifier	除濕機	除湿机	3-1-25
delicacies, delicious foods	美食	美食	4-2-2
delicious	美味	美味	11-2-24
democratic	民主	民主	12-1-11
demonstration, rally	遊行	游行	12-1-5
(academic) department	科系	科系	1-2-6
department of medicine	醫學系	医学系	8-1-35
department of surgery	外科	外科	10-2-20
to depend on	靠	靠	7-2-8
desserts	點心	点心	11-2-25
to die, pass away (honorific)	過世	过世	7-1-8
diet	飲食	饮食	11-2-27
to differ	差	差	3-1-21
difficult	困難	困难	11-2-18
diligent in	努力	努力	8-1-28
diligent, conscientious (as a student)	用功	用功	1-1-21
dining table	餐桌	餐桌	11-2-1
dirty	髒	脏	7-1-14
disadvantaged (lit. weak power)	弱勢	弱势	12-2-23
to disappear	消失	消失	6-2-32
discount	折扣	折扣	2-1-5
to be discriminating in, to be discerning, meticulous	講究	讲究	4-2-16
dispute	糾紛	纠纷	2-2-2
diverse, diversified	多元	多元	7-2-1

English definition	Traditional Characters	Simplified Characters	Lesson-Dialogue-Number
to do one's best to	盡量	尽量	6-2-5
to do something impetuously	動不動就	动不动就	10-2-34
dog	狗	狗	7-1-4
to donate	捐	捐	12-2-26
to donate	捐出	捐出	12-2-41
a "drag"	煩	烦	8-1-11
the Dragon Boat Festival (the 5th day of the 5th month)	端午節	端午节	3-2-32
dream, ideals (not during sleep)	夢想	梦想	8-2-34
dried daikon	蘿蔔乾	萝卜干	11-2-42
to drive away	趕走	赶走	3-2-36
dry	乾	干	3-1-23
due to	由於	由于	6-2-22

E

English definition	Traditional Characters	Simplified Characters	Lesson-Dialogue-Number
early 17th century	十七世紀初	十七世纪初	11-1-40
to earn	賺	赚	4-1-14
earnest, serious	認真	认真	8-2-16
the East District (of Taipei)	東區	东区	4-1-21
education	教育	教育	12-2-9
educational background	學歷	学历	8-2-9
effect	作用	作用	3-2-20
an egg wrap	蛋餅	蛋饼	11-2-33
election	選舉	选举	12-1-28
electorate	選民	选民	12-1-36
electronics	電子	电子	5-2-21
EMBA (Executive Master of Business Administration)	EMBA（高級管理人員工商管理碩士）	EMBA（高级管理人员工商管理硕士）	8-2-46
emergency room	急診室	急诊室	10-1-8
to emigrate	移民	移民	3-2-2
to place emphasis on, to lay stress on, to value	重視	重视	4-2-10
to be enamored with, be into, be enchanted by	迷	迷	5-1-11
to encourage	鼓勵	鼓励	8-2-41
to engage in politics	從政	从政	12-2-2
to engage in warfare	打仗	打仗	11-1-14
to be engaged in, work in (a field of work)	從事	从事	10-2-13
to enjoy	享受	享受	7-2-17
enthusiastic about	熱衷	热衷	12-1-7
entire	整	整	5-1-17
entire	全	全	9-2-34
entirely	全	全	7-2-7
entrepreneur	企業家	企业家	8-2-36
to envy	羨慕	羡慕	1-1-19

English definition	Traditional Characters	Simplified Characters	Lesson-Dialogue-Number
especially, in particular	尤其	尤其	2-2-12
to establish	建立	建立	7-1-33
to establish, set up	成立	成立	9-1-5
ethnic group	民族	民族	3-2-23
even, even to the point of	甚至	甚至	11-1-13
to be exaggerated	誇張	夸张	8-1-22
to exceed	超過	超过	10-2-21
except, other than	以外	以外	1-1-10
to exchange	換	换	2-1-26
excited	興奮	兴奋	5-1-10
to be excited	激動	激动	8-1-6
expectation	預期	预期	12-2-17
expectations	期望	期望	8-1-26
experience tough times	吃苦	吃苦	8-2-23
expert	專家	专家	12-1-18
explanation	說明	说明	1-1-14
explanation	解釋	解释	2-2-10
to export	出口	出口	9-2-3
to express	表達	表达	12-1-12
express delivery	宅配	宅配	9-1-11

F

English definition	Traditional Characters	Simplified Characters	Lesson-Dialogue-Number
face	臉	脸	10-1-2
to fail a course	當	当	1-1-28
fair	公平	公平	8-2-17
to fall down	跌倒	跌倒	7-1-38
family	家庭	家庭	7-1-35
a famous baker from Taiwan	吳寶春	吴宝春	8-2-42
farmer	農人	农人	3-2-7
farmer	農夫	农夫	6-1-6
farming village	農村	农村	6-2-17
fashion design	服裝設計	服装设计	8-1-34
father	父親	父亲	8-2-20
father-in-law (of a female)	公公	公公	7-2-6
to feel	摸	摸	2-1-11
to feel	感覺	感觉	3-1-11
feeling; a feeling of...	感覺	感觉	4-1-26
female person's name	美真	美真	7-2-32
female person's name	愛林	爱林	10-2-30
field trip, class excursion	校外教學	校外教学	4-1-33
field, plot of land, paddy	田	田	6-1-22
to fill out (a form)	填	填	1-2-14
filling (of pastries etc.)	內餡	内馅	9-2-10
(X-ray) film	片子	片子	10-1-11
finally	終於	终于	8-2-32
fireworks	煙火	烟火	4-1-22
flatland	平原	平原	11-1-19
flavor	口味	口味	9-2-26

English definition	Traditional Characters	Simplified Characters	Lesson-Dialogue-Number
flexibility	彈性	弹性	8-2-12
to focus on	專心	专心	8-1-18
to follow	遵守	遵守	10-1-5
fond of	喜愛	喜爱	9-2-13
food	飲食	饮食	11-2-27
food materials	食材	食材	6-2-3
for	為	为	12-1-32
to forbid	禁止	禁止	11-1-26
foreign language	外語	外语	1-2-12
forget it; let it be!	算了	算了	5-1-25
a form	表	表	1-2-15
to form	組成	组成	7-2-28
Fort Santo Domingo, lit. red-hair city	紅毛城	红毛城	11-1-30
fortunately	幸虧	幸亏	3-1-6
foundation, fundamentals	基礎	基础	8-2-15
to fracture, break a bone	骨折	骨折	10-1-10
fragrant sachet	香包	香包	3-2-15
free	自由	自由	7-2-14
fresh	新鮮	新鲜	3-1-17
friendly	友善	友善	6-2-6
frugal	節儉	节俭	11-2-19
funds	經費	经费	12-2-28
further	進一步	进一步	11-2-43
future, prospects	前途	前途	12-1-8

G

English definition	Traditional Characters	Simplified Characters	Lesson-Dialogue-Number
gains	利益	利益	11-1-7
game	遊戲	游戏	5-2-29
general	將軍	将军	11-1-17
general, most	一般	一般	10-2-16
generally speaking	一般來說	一般来说	2-1-29
generally; in general	一般	一般	2-1-3
to generate	引起	引起	8-2-11
genetically modified	基因改造	基因改造	6-1-29
to get along (with), to spend time together	相處	相处	7-1-27
to get off work	下班	下班	7-2-4
to get-together	團聚	团聚	3-2-27
to give birth, to bear	生	生	7-1-28
to give up	放棄	放弃	1-2-7
to go after someone trying to establish a relationship of love	追	追	7-2-13
to go shopping	購物	购物	2-2-1
to go up to	上	上	4-2-3
gods, divinities	神	神	3-2-11
good luck	好運	好运	9-2-9
goods	商品	商品	2-1-4

English definition	Traditional Characters	Simplified Characters	Lesson-Dialogue-Number
government	政府	政府	9-2-17
government posts	公職	公职	8-1-8
graduation exhibition	畢業展	毕业展	8-1-33
grandma (father's side)	奶奶	奶奶	7-1-7
grandma, older woman (Taiwanese)	阿嬤	阿嬤	9-1-8
grandpa (father's side)	爺爺	爷爷	7-1-2
grandson	孫子	孙子	11-1-23
to group buy (for cheaper prices)	團購	团购	9-2-32
to grow	長	长	6-1-19
to grow (plants)	種	种	6-1-4
to grow up	長大	长大	6-2-18

H

English definition	Traditional Characters	Simplified Characters	Lesson-Dialogue-Number
habit	習慣	习惯	4-2-13
hair	頭髮	头发	11-1-12
the Hakka people, a branch of Han	客家人	客家人	11-2-31
to handle	安排	安排	7-2-16
Han-ethnic Chinese	漢人	汉人	11-1-33
to hang	掛	挂	3-2-16
happiness, blessing	幸福	幸福	7-1-37
hard-to-come-by	難得	难得	3-2-8
harvest	收成	收成	3-2-22
to have a hole	破洞	破洞	2-1-22
have always	一向	一向	10-2-15
to have an automobile accident	出車禍	出车祸	10-1-28
to have one's eyes opened	大開眼界	大开眼界	8-2-48
to have/undergo a surgery	動手術	动手术	10-1-33
to heal, cure	醫治	医治	10-2-14
to help	幫助	帮助	6-2-19
to hide, to go into hiding	躲	躲	3-1-7
high level, advanced	高級	高级	8-2-4
highly popular	熱門	热门	1-1-26
historical site	古蹟	古迹	4-2-9
historically	古時候	古时候	3-2-35
history	歷史	历史	4-2-11
to hit, beat, smack, slap	打	打	7-1-19
to hit, collide	撞	撞	10-1-4
to hold	舉辦	举办	9-2-18
to hold (a conference, exhibition)	舉行	举行	8-1-23
holiday	假日	假日	9-1-6
hometown	老家	老家	12-2-19
to honor, to pay homage to	拜	拜	3-2-10
to be hospitable, kind, friendly	人情味	人情味	4-1-2
hospital	醫院	医院	7-1-31
hospital bed	病床	病床	10-1-16
to be hospitalized	住院	住院	10-1-1
hotpot	火鍋	火锅	3-1-15

English definition	Traditional Characters	Simplified Characters	Lesson-Dialogue-Number
house	屋子	屋子	6-1-15
housewife	主婦	主妇	11-2-20
humid	潮濕	潮湿	3-1-28
100 million	億	亿	8-2-33
husband	先生	先生	7-2-3

I

English definition	Traditional Characters	Simplified Characters	Lesson-Dialogue-Number
ideal, aspired	理想	理想	1-2-3
ideals, aspirations	理想	理想	4-1-17
identical	一模一樣	一模一样	5-2-31
if it goes on like this	這樣下去	这样下去	1-1-34
image	形象	形象	12-2-20
to imagine	想像	想象	5-2-26
to immigrate	移民	移民	3-2-2
impression	印象	印象	5-2-28
to improve	改善	改善	9-2-29
to be in a hurry	趕時間	赶时间	10-1-29
in case	萬一	万一	9-1-23
in fact	其實	其实	8-1-9
in season	當季	当季	5-2-4
in the areas of (an issue)	方面	方面	12-2-10
in the end	到底	到底	11-1-3
to be in turmoil, be in chaos	亂	乱	7-2-25
to include	包括	包括	2-2-9
income	收入	收入	6-1-13
to increase	增加	增加	10-2-9
to increase, to elevate	提高	提高	9-2-20
independent	獨立	独立	7-2-15
to indicate	表示	表示	12-1-30
inferior to	不如	不如	5-1-14
influence	影響	影响	3-1-4
ingredients	食材	食材	6-2-3
to inject, give a shot	打針	打针	10-1-18
to be injured	受傷	受伤	10-1-3
injury	傷	伤	10-1-9
instructions	說明	说明	1-1-14
intensive course	密集班	密集班	8-1-32
interjection for realization of something important, oh no, yikes	哎呀	哎呀	10-1-27
an interjection indicating the speaker's agreement	嗯	嗯	7-1-6
interpersonal relations	人際關係	人际关系	10-2-33
interview	面試	面试	8-2-6
to introduce, to roll out (products)	推出	推出	5-2-35
investigation	調查	调查	10-2-7
issue	議題	议题	12-1-14
issue, matter, event, thing	事	事	1-1-31
it	它	它	5-2-2

English definition	Traditional Characters	Simplified Characters	Lesson-Dialogue-Number
it (animals)	牠	牠	7-1-13
by itself, on its own	自動	自动	2-2-16

J

English definition	Traditional Characters	Simplified Characters	Lesson-Dialogue-Number
jam	塞車	塞车	5-1-4
Japanese language or writing	日文	日文	8-2-44
Japanese last name: Lingmu (Japanese: Suzuki)	鈴木	铃木	4-2-25
Japanese-style	日式	日式	11-2-26
to joke, to kid	開玩笑	开玩笑	6-1-31
to jump	跳	跳	5-1-16
junior middle school	國中	国中	8-2-8
just now	剛剛	刚刚	4-1-18

K

English definition	Traditional Characters	Simplified Characters	Lesson-Dialogue-Number
to kill pain (lit. stop pain)	止痛	止痛	10-1-19
to kill time	殺時間	杀时间	5-1-31
to knock down, knock over	撞倒	撞倒	10-1-30
Koxinga, 國姓爺, 1624-1662, who ruled Taiwan against the Manchu sovereignty	鄭成功	郑成功	11-1-34

L

English definition	Traditional Characters	Simplified Characters	Lesson-Dialogue-Number
lamb's wool	羊毛	羊毛	2-1-14
lamp	燈	灯	8-1-3
land	土地	土地	6-2-8
the Lantern Festival (15th day of the 1st month)	元宵節	元宵节	4-1-31
to be late (in arrival)	遲到	迟到	1-1-32
late 17th century	十七世紀末	十七世纪末	11-1-42
leading role, leading actor	主角	主角	5-2-7
to learn characters	認字	认字	8-2-26
to leave behind	留下來	留下来	4-2-27
leisure	休閒	休闲	6-2-27
a letter of recommendation	推薦信	推荐信	1-2-21
light	燈	灯	8-1-3
light blue	淺藍色	浅蓝色	5-2-32
to listen, to obey	聽話	听话	8-1-12
to live together (as a couple), to cohabit	同居	同居	7-2-20
live; lit. on-site	現場	现场	5-1-15
livelihood depends on the whims of nature	看天吃飯	看天吃饭	6-1-32
lively, bubbly, vivacious	活潑	活泼	1-2-11
local	當地	当地	4-1-13
to log in	上線	上线	5-1-5
lonely	孤單	孤单	7-1-12
to lose	弄丟	弄丢	2-1-32

English definition	Traditional Characters	Simplified Characters	Lesson-Dialogue-Number
to lose an election	落選	落选	12-2-15
to love	愛	爱	4-1-1
the lunar calendar (lit. the agricultural calendar)	農曆	农历	3-2-5
lyrics	歌詞	歌词	5-1-12

M

English definition	Traditional Characters	Simplified Characters	Lesson-Dialogue-Number
to mail	寄	寄	5-2-9
main	主要	主要	10-2-17
a major, usually international, competition	大賽	大赛	8-2-2
to make (friends)	交	交	4-1-16
to make a mountain out of a molehill, to make a big deal of nothing	小題大作	小题大作	5-2-34
to make up one's mind (to do something)	下決心	下决心	7-2-35
to make up	化妝	化妆	5-2-30
male	男性	男性	11-1-25
male person's name	家華	家华	7-2-33
a man from Honduras	安德思	安德思	1-1-1
a man from Japan	高橋健太	高桥健太	3-1-2
many	許多	许多	6-2-23
market	市場	市场	5-2-22
market	市集	市集	6-2-2
to market	行銷	行销	9-2-31
master (of a trade)	師傅	师傅	6-2-16
master, owner	主人	主人	7-1-26
master's degree	碩士	硕士	8-2-5
to match	合	合	1-2-4
Mayday (name of a Taiwanese rock band)	五月天	五月天	5-1-24
to mean	表示	表示	12-1-30
verbal measure word for a duration of action	頓	顿	2-2-14
measure word for a stretch, swath (of land)	片	片	6-1-21
measure word for academic courses	門	门	8-1-14
measure word for animals	隻	只	7-1-10
measure word for the duration of a meal	頓	顿	4-2-17
the media	媒體	媒体	5-2-14
medical treatment, health care	醫療	医疗	10-2-28
menu	菜單	菜单	11-2-11
merely	而已	而已	12-1-10
method, way of doing something	做法	做法	3-2-18
method, ways	方式	方式	5-2-15
micro-cosmetic surgery, plastic surgery, face contouring	微整型	微整型	10-2-31

English definition	Traditional Characters	Simplified Characters	Lesson-Dialogue-Number
the Mid-Autumn Moon Festival (the 15th day of the 8th month)	中秋節	中秋节	3-2-33
middleman, reseller	中間商	中间商	9-1-9
mid-term exam	期中考	期中考	8-1-31
to migrate	遷移	迁移	11-2-16
to mildew	發霉	发霉	3-1-24
military service member	軍人	军人	11-1-18
Ming Dynasty, 1368-1644	明朝	明朝	11-1-35
minor (in college)	輔系	辅系	8-1-20
minority, a few	少數	少数	11-1-15
miso soup (Japanese food)	味噌湯	味噌汤	11-2-41
to miss (an opportunity)	錯過	错过	4-2-5
a monthly plan	月租型	月租型	2-2-6
mood	心情	心情	5-1-23
moon	月亮	月亮	3-2-24
moon cake (shaped like the moon)	月餅	月饼	3-2-28
moral	道德	道德	7-2-29
moreover	並且	并且	9-2-30
mosquitoes and other insects	蚊蟲	蚊虫	3-2-13
mostly, in the majority of cases	多半	多半	11-2-17
mother	母親	母亲	8-2-21
mouthful	口	口	4-1-28
to be moved	感動	感动	4-1-10
mover and shaker, popular and influential person	風雲人物	风云人物	7-2-34
murderous, horrible	要命	要命	10-1-17
must, to have to	必須	必须	9-1-21

N

English definition	Traditional Characters	Simplified Characters	Lesson-Dialogue-Number
narrow	窄	窄	4-2-19
national pension (scheme)	國民年金	国民年金	12-2-35
natural	天然	天然	6-1-9
nature	自然	自然	6-2-25
neighbor	鄰居	邻居	7-1-3
net congestion	塞車	塞车	5-1-4
network of people, contacts	人脈	人脉	12-2-22
new student	新生	新生	1-1-6
new style	新型	新型	5-2-23
the next step (in doing things)	下一步	下一步	12-2-38
night view	夜景	夜景	4-2-7
no matter, regardless of	不管	不管	1-2-8
it's no wonder, no wonder	難怪	难怪	3-1-13
nobility, aristocrat	貴族	贵族	7-2-10
not be in time for, not make it on time	來不及	来不及	5-1-33
not merely	既	既	9-1-13
nuclear power	核能	核能	12-1-15

English definition	Traditional Characters	Simplified Characters	Lesson-Dialogue-Number
O			
to obey	遵守	遵守	10-1-5
to be obsessed with	迷	迷	5-1-11
to obtain	得到	得到	12-2-11
of	當中	当中	3-2-3
of these, of which, amongst which	其中	其中	6-2-15
to offer a discount	打折	打折	2-1-16
to offer convenience	方便	方便	9-1-3
Oh no! Oh boy!	唉	唉	5-1-2
old-fashioned	落伍	落伍	5-2-24
on the one hand	一方面	一方面	6-2-34
on the other hand	而	而	4-1-15
once	曾經	曾经	9-2-4
one of the top or best in..., leading…	數一數二	数一数二	10-2-32
to go online	上線	上线	5-1-5
online shopping	網購	网购	9-1-28
only	而已	而已	12-1-10
only child (girl)	獨生女	独生女	1-2-1
to open for business, in operation (businesses)	營業	营业	4-2-6
to open up land for farming	開墾	开垦	11-1-16
to operate (a business)	經營	经营	9-1-10
operation	手術	手术	10-1-20
opinion	意見	意见	7-1-32
opinion	看法	看法	12-2-8
to oppose	反對	反对	1-2-9
oral test	口試	口试	1-1-8
an order (trading)	訂單	订单	9-1-1
to order, place an order	訂購	订购	9-1-4
ordinary	普通	普通	10-2-12
to organize	舉辦	举办	9-2-18
original price	原價	原价	2-1-17
originally	原來	原来	1-1-24
out of luck, down on one's luck	倒楣	倒楣	5-1-7
P			
packed with	擠滿	挤满	5-1-27
a pain in the neck	煩	烦	8-1-11
painful	痛苦	痛苦	1-2-5
to pan fry	煎	煎	11-2-21
pan-fried pork bun	水煎包	水煎包	4-1-35
(body) part, location	部位	部位	10-1-24
to pass	通過	通过	8-2-3
passionate	推薦信	推荐信	1-2-21
about	熱衷	热衷	12-1-7
patience	耐心	耐心	4-1-9
patient	病人	病人	10-1-13

English definition	Traditional Characters	Simplified Characters	Lesson-Dialogue-Number
pattern for indicating percentages or fractions	X 分之 Y	X 分之 Y	8-2-49
pay	待遇	待遇	10-2-18
to pay a fee	繳費	缴费	2-2-19
percentage of votes received	得票率	得票率	12-2-16
perfect	完美	完美	12-1-37
perhaps	也許	也许	12-2-30
period, time of	時代	时代	7-2-11
personality	個性	个性	1-2-10
to persuade, to urge	勸	劝	12-1-9
pesticide	農藥	农药	6-1-8
pestilence	瘟疫	瘟疫	3-2-17
pet	寵物	宠物	7-1-29
pineapple	鳳梨	菠萝	9-2-1
pineapple farmer	鳳梨農	菠萝农	9-2-40
pineapple shortcake	鳳梨酥	凤梨酥	9-2-38
Pingxi, a town in northern Taiwan	平溪	平溪	4-1-30
to place (an order)	下	下	9-1-12
place of origin	產地	产地	6-2-4
plague	瘟疫	瘟疫	3-2-17
plains	平原	平原	11-1-19
plastic surgery	整型	整型	10-2-8
please (lit. allow me to trouble you)	麻煩	麻烦	2-1-20
to pluck, to pick (e.g., fruit from a tree)	摘下來	摘下来	6-1-27
points	分	分	1-1-18
police	警察	警察	10-1-21
policy	政策	政策	12-2-3
political party	政黨	政党	12-1-23
politics	政治	政治	12-1-6
pomelo	柚子	柚子	3-2-29
poor	窮	穷	8-2-19
popular	流行	流行	5-1-1
popular	受歡迎	受欢迎	5-1-26
population	人口	人口	11-1-20
pornographic; obscene	色情	色情	5-1-21
position	地位	地位	6-1-12
position, job	職位	职位	12-1-34
power	權力	权力	12-2-32
power plant	電廠	电厂	12-1-16
prepaid SIM card	預付卡	预付卡	2-2-20
to present offerings to gods or ancestors	拜拜	拜拜	3-2-12
pressure	壓力	压力	1-1-13
price	價錢	价钱	4-1-25
price	價格	价格	9-2-7
primary	主要	主要	10-2-17
private	私立	私立	1-2-2

English definition	Traditional Characters	Simplified Characters	Lesson-Dialogue-Number
to have problems	出問題	出问题	6-2-33
procedures	手續	手续	1-2-17
to produce	出產	出产	6-2-21
product	產品	产品	5-2-20
production value, output	產值	产值	9-2-19
profit	利潤	利润	6-1-14
to promote, to market	推銷	推销	6-2-14
to propose	提出	提出	12-2-34
public	公共	公共	12-1-13
public will, popular opinion	民意	民意	12-1-20
public; government-run	公立	公立	10-2-19
publishing company	出版社	出版社	12-2-40
to purchase	購買	购买	9-2-28
to purchase things	消費	消费	6-2-30
purse	包包	包包	5-2-18

Q

English definition	Traditional Characters	Simplified Characters	Lesson-Dialogue-Number
Qing Dynasty, 1644-1911	清朝	清朝	11-1-37
quality	品質	品质	2-1-8
quiet	安靜	安静	6-2-31
to quit, resign	辭	辞	12-2-5
to quit, resign	辭掉	辞掉	12-2-33

R

English definition	Traditional Characters	Simplified Characters	Lesson-Dialogue-Number
rainy season	雨季	雨季	3-1-26
to raise, bring up, train, educate (one's children)	教養	教养	7-2-26
to raise, to keep	養	养	7-1-16
rare	難得	难得	3-2-8
rather	而	而	4-1-15
real	真正	真正	7-1-36
realgar liquor, a wine seasoned with realgar, a type of arsenic, and is traditionally considered to be an antidote to other poisons	雄黃酒	雄黄酒	3-2-34
reason	原因	原因	8-2-38
reasonable	合理	合理	10-2-2
to rebuild	重建	重建	11-1-2
receipt	發票	发票	2-1-23
to receive, to be, to get	受到	受到	3-1-34
to recover	恢復	恢复	10-1-25
to rediscover, to retrieve	找回	找回	10-2-35
to reduce	減少	减少	6-1-7
to reduce	減輕	减轻	7-1-22
to reflect	反映	反映	12-1-31
reforms	改革	改革	12-2-7
refrigerator (lit. ice box)	冰箱	冰箱	9-1-16
regarding	至於	至于	10-1-23

English definition	Traditional Characters	Simplified Characters	Lesson-Dialogue-Number
regretful (that something undesirable happened), a pity, a shame	遺憾	遗憾	8-1-24
to reject	拒絕	拒绝	8-2-10
to relax	放鬆	放松	5-1-22
to release	放	放	4-1-3
to rely on	靠	靠	7-2-8
to repair	修理	修理	2-2-18
report	報告	报告	1-1-12
report card, transcripts	成績單	成绩单	1-2-19
to report to (or call) the police	報警	报警	10-1-7
to represent	代表	代表	9-2-16
representative	代表	代表	12-1-21
to resolve oneself	下決心	下决心	7-2-35
to respect, respectful of	尊敬	尊敬	10-2-25
responsibility	責任	责任	7-2-24
as a result	結果	结果	9-2-27
retail outlet	門市	门市	2-2-4
to retire	退休	退休	12-2-24
to return (purchases)	退	退	2-1-25
to reunite; reunion of family members	團聚	团聚	3-2-27
rice rolls with various fillings	飯糰	饭团	11-2-6
right	權利	权利	12-1-29
right to vote, suffrage	投票權	投票权	12-1-27
to be ripe, to ripen	熟	熟	6-1-20
risk	風險	风险	9-1-19
roadside stand	攤子	摊子	11-2-10
round	圓	圆	3-2-25
rules, regulations	規則	规则	10-1-6
to run	跑	跑	6-2-11
to run (a business)	經營	经营	9-1-10
run for (an office)	競選	竞选	12-2-29
to run into	碰到	碰到	4-1-34

S

English definition	Traditional Characters	Simplified Characters	Lesson-Dialogue-Number
sad	難過	难过	5-1-13
salesperson	推銷員	推销员	12-1-40
salesperson, store employee, clerk	店員	店员	2-1-12
satisfied	滿意	满意	9-1-24
to save, to put away	省	省	2-1-6
seafood	海鮮	海鲜	3-1-16
to search	搜尋	搜寻	9-1-15
season	季節	季节	3-1-14
seat, place	位子	位子	1-1-16
second (place)	第二位	第二位	9-2-39
secondhand book	二手書	二手书	12-2-42

English definition	Traditional Characters	Simplified Characters	Lesson-Dialogue-Number
self-confidence	自信	自信	10-2-10
to sell	販賣	贩卖	9-1-7
seller	賣家	卖家	9-1-20
to send, dispatch	派	派	11-1-8
a sentence-final particle meaning 'in that case'	嘍	喽	11-1-22
to serve	服務	服务	12-1-33
to serve a successive term	連任	连任	12-2-12
set of (books, clothes, equipment etc.)	套	套	11-2-3
to set up a family, to marry (from the male's perspective)	成家	成家	7-2-21
to set up a vendor's stall	擺攤子	摆摊子	11-2-35
to shake	震動	震动	5-1-18
shocked, startled, taken aback	嚇一跳	吓一跳	2-2-23
shop around and you won't get ripped off (lit. Compare products at three stores and you won't be cheated.)	貨比三家不吃虧	货比三家不吃亏	9-1-29
short	短	短	2-1-13
to shout	喊	喊	8-1-7
shouting	大喊大叫	大喊大叫	8-1-30
to sightsee	觀光	观光	6-2-29
to sign	簽名	签名	2-1-21
signal (data connection)	訊號	讯号	4-1-6
since, given that...	既然	既然	5-2-12
to sing	唱	唱	5-1-9
Singapore	新加坡	新加坡	8-2-43
to be single	單身	单身	7-1-30
single parent	單親	单亲	7-2-9
to sit in (on a class)	旁聽	旁听	1-1-17
situation	情況	情况	10-1-14
skills	技術	技术	8-2-29
sky lantern	天燈	天灯	4-1-4
small farmer	小農	小农	6-2-1
smartphone	智慧型手機	智慧型手机	5-1-30
snacks, dessert (served with tea)	茶點	茶点	9-2-14
so	因此	因此	7-2-30
society	社會	社会	3-2-26
to be a soldier, to do military service	當兵	当兵	8-2-25
solution	辦法	办法	2-2-15
some other day	改天	改天	4-1-19
somewhat	多少	多少	3-2-19
son	兒子	儿子	8-1-25
sorry	抱歉	抱歉	12-1-2

English definition	Traditional Characters	Simplified Characters	Lesson-Dialogue-Number
Southern Min dialect, i.e., Taiwanese	閩南語	闽南语	9-2-35
the Southern Min people, also called Hokkien	閩南人	闽南人	11-2-32
Southern Min sound for pineapple, lit. "abundance comes"	旺來	旺来	9-2-36
soy milk	豆漿	豆浆	11-2-7
speaking skills	口才	口才	1-1-30
specialist	專家	专家	12-1-18
species	品種	品种	6-1-17
speed	速度	速度	4-2-18
to spend the holiday in some manner	過節	过节	3-2-37
splendid, brilliant as (of a performance)	精彩	精彩	11-1-29
stable	穩定	稳定	3-1-5
stable	安定	安定	12-2-4
(school) to start	開學	开学	1-1-4
starting from...	起	起	2-1-1
to starve to death (an exaggeration)	餓死了	饿死了	3-1-36
status	地位	地位	6-1-12
to stay in a hospital	住院	住院	10-1-1
to stay up all night	熬夜	熬夜	1-1-27
to stay, to remain	待	待	4-2-22
to steep (tea) to soak oneself in, i.e., to bath in	泡	泡	4-2-4
stepmother's face, i.e., stern and cruel look	後母臉	后母脸	3-1-37
to stir up	引起	引起	8-2-11
store manager	店長	店长	2-1-27
store sign	招牌	招牌	4-1-12
storefront	店面	店面	9-2-33
story	故事	故事	3-2-30
street	街道	街道	4-2-20
stress	壓力	压力	1-1-13
strict, stern	嚴	严	1-1-7
stroller	推車	推车	7-1-25
strong	強	强	7-2-12
to study	讀書	读书	8-1-15
to study	學習	学习	8-2-28
to stuff, cram, squeeze (into)	塞	塞	5-2-3
stuffy	悶	闷	3-1-29
style (of clothes)	款式	款式	5-2-5
to succeed	成功	成功	5-1-6
successful	成功	成功	8-2-40
to sue, bring suit against	告	告	10-2-26
to suffer a loss	吃虧	吃亏	9-1-17
suggestion	意見	意见	7-1-32

English definition	Traditional Characters	Simplified Characters	Lesson-Dialogue-Number
to sun dry	曬乾	晒干	11-2-38
superstition	迷信	迷信	3-2-21
to support	支持	支持	6-2-12
to support one's family	養家	养家	7-2-23
to have surgery	開刀	开刀	10-1-12
surgery	手術	手术	10-1-20
survey	調查	调查	10-2-7
sweet and cute, lovely	甜美	甜美	5-2-8
sweet sticky rice dumplings	元宵	元宵	4-1-7
swing voters	中間選民	中间选民	12-2-36
to swipe, i.e., use a credit card	刷卡	刷卡	2-1-18
system	制度	制度	8-2-14

T

English definition	Traditional Characters	Simplified Characters	Lesson-Dialogue-Number
tablet computer	平板電腦	平板电脑	5-1-29
to take (courses)	修	修	8-1-17
to take a bath	洗澡	洗澡	7-1-15
to take a break from school	休學	休学	1-1-20
to take a class	修課	修课	8-1-19
to take a walk	散步	散步	7-1-34
to take a woman in marriage	娶	娶	11-1-27
to take an X-ray	照 X 光	照 X 光	10-1-32
to take care of	照顧	照顾	6-1-23
to take off (clothing)	脫掉	脱掉	5-2-33
to take time off	休假	休假	10-2-3
to take to	送	送	7-1-23
to tally with	合	合	1-2-4
Tamsui	淡水	淡水	11-1-32
technology	科技	科技	9-2-23
telecommunications	電信	电信	2-2-3
temperature	溫度	温度	3-1-9
temperature (weather)	氣溫	气温	3-1-20
temporarily, for the time being	暫時	暂时	12-2-18
tense	緊張	紧张	7-1-21
term of office	任期	任期	12-1-35
term, tenure of elected office	屆	届	12-2-13
terms, conditions, (here) good qualities (in a prospective spouse)	條件	条件	6-1-25
territory (of a nation)	領土	领土	11-1-24
to test into	考上	考上	1-2-20
the East, the Orient	東方	东方	11-1-31
the Netherlands (lit. Holland)	荷蘭	荷兰	3-1-31
the people	人民	人民	11-2-9
the Qing Empire	大清帝國	大清帝国	11-1-38
there is a leader in every industry	行行出狀元	行行出狀元	8-1-36

English definition	Traditional Characters	Simplified Characters	Lesson-Dialogue-Number
there's no way, there's nothing that can be done	沒辦法	没办法	1-1-35
there's some truth (to what you are saying)	有道理	有道理	12-1-41
therefore	因此	因此	7-2-30
times, -fold	倍	倍	10-2-22
Tokyo	東京	东京	9-2-37
tomato	番茄	番茄	6-1-16
top-ranking in a public exam (originally the person with the highest marks on the imperial test)	狀元	状元	8-1-27
to touch	摸	摸	2-1-11
to be touched	感動	感动	4-1-10
tough, hard, bitter (life, work, etc.)	辛苦	辛苦	6-1-11
to tour	觀光	观光	6-2-29
trade	貿易	贸易	11-1-5
to transfer (to a different major)	轉	转	1-1-23
to treat	對待	对待	6-2-7
to treat as, to serve as	當做	当做	9-2-11
true, genuine	真正	真正	7-1-36
to trust	信任	信任	6-2-9
to try on (garments)	試穿	试穿	2-1-30
to turn off, to shut down	關機	关机	2-2-17
to turn on, to power on	開	开	8-1-2
one's turn, it's up to	輪到	轮到	11-1-39
TV series	連續劇	连续剧	5-2-6
type	種類	种类	4-1-24

U

English definition	Traditional Characters	Simplified Characters	Lesson-Dialogue-Number
to be unable to physically function due to old age	做不動	做不动	6-1-28
uncle (father's younger brother)	叔叔	叔叔	9-2-25
to understand	明白	明白	8-2-24
unemployment rate	失業率	失业率	8-1-13
unexpectedly, counter to assumption	居然	居然	5-2-10
unlimited data (lit. all you can eat)	吃到飽	吃到饱	2-2-22
up to	由	由	12-1-17
urgent	緊急	紧急	10-1-15

V

English definition	Traditional Characters	Simplified Characters	Lesson-Dialogue-Number
values	價值觀	价值观	10-2-24
variety	品種	品种	6-1-17
variety of dishes	菜色	菜色	11-2-22
various types	各種各樣	各种各样	11-2-39
vegetable	蔬菜	蔬菜	6-1-5
vendor's stall	攤子	摊子	11-2-10
to venerate ancestors	祭祖	祭祖	3-2-9

English definition	Traditional Characters	Simplified Characters	Lesson-Dialogue-Number
verbal, oral	口頭	口头	1-1-11
to vibrate	震動	震动	5-1-18
video game	電玩	电玩	8-1-4
view	看法	看法	12-2-8
to pay someone a visit	拜訪	拜访	6-2-20
Visiting (it) is a must!!	非去不可	非去不可	4-2-29
to volunteer, on a voluntary basis, to do something gratis	義務	义务	12-2-27
to vote	投票	投票	12-1-1
voters	選民	选民	12-1-36

W

English definition	Traditional Characters	Simplified Characters	Lesson-Dialogue-Number
wall	牆	墙	4-1-8
war	戰爭	战争	11-2-14
"wardrobe clash", more than one person unintentionally wearing duplicate garments	撞衫	撞衫	5-2-1
warm	暖和	暖和	2-1-15
warm, heart-warming	溫馨	温馨	3-2-31
to wear (items other than those that cover the torso, legs, or feet, mostly ornamental items.)	戴	戴	3-2-14
wedding-announcement pastries	喜餅	喜饼	9-2-12
welcome in the (solar) New Year (lit. span the years)	跨年	跨年	4-1-23
well known, renowned	知名	知名	9-2-21
well-received; well-liked	受歡迎	受欢迎	5-1-26
What's wrong?	怎麼回事	怎么回事	8-1-29
whole	整	整	5-1-17
whole	完整	完整	7-2-31
widespread	普遍	普遍	9-1-26
to be windy (lit. blow wind)	颱風	刮风	3-1-33
wish	願望	愿望	4-1-5
within	以內	以内	9-1-25
a woman from Indonesia	羅珊蒂	罗珊蒂	1-1-2
a woman from Taiwan	何雅婷	何雅婷	1-1-3
a woman from the Netherlands	陳敏萱	陈敏萱	3-1-1
wooden; made from wood	木造	木造	4-2-28
workplace	職場	职场	10-2-5
the world of politics	政治界	政治界	12-2-31
to worry about, to fret over with	擔心	担心	1-2-13
would rather	寧可	宁可	6-2-10
wound	傷口	伤口	10-1-26
written test	筆試	笔试	1-1-9
to go wrong	出問題	出问题	6-2-33

English definition	Traditional Characters	Simplified Characters	Lesson-Dialogue-Number

Y

to yell	喊	喊	8-1-7
to yell, yelling	大喊大叫	大喊大叫	8-1-30
yet	卻	却	8-2-7
younger female cousin	表妹	表妹	12-1-3

Linking Chinese

當代中文課程 3 課本

策　　劃	國立臺灣師範大學國語教學中心		出 版 者	聯經出版事業股份有限公司
主　　編	鄧守信		發 行 人	林載爵
顧　　問	Claudia Ross、白建華、陳雅芬		社　　長	羅國俊
審　　查	姚道中、葉德明、劉　珣		總 經 理	陳芝宇
編寫教師	王瓊淑、盧翠英、盧德昭		副總編輯	陳逸華

執行編輯	張莉萍、張雯雯、張黛琪、蔡如珮
英文翻譯	James Friesen、施行一、范大龍、畢永峨、蔣宜臻
校　　對	張莉萍、張雯雯、張黛琪、連詩儀、陳怡靜、蔡如珮
編輯助理	林家彤、張瑜庭、梁詩韻、許雅晴、喬愛淳、蔡佳恩
技術支援	李昆璟
插　　畫	林欣穎、桂沐設計、張榮傑、黃奕穎
封面設計	桂沐設計
內文排版	楊佩菱
錄　　音	王育偉、吳霈蓁、李世揚、許伯琴、Michael Tennant
錄音後製	純粹錄音後製公司

叢書主編	李　芃
地　　址	新北市汐止區大同路一段 369 號 1 樓
聯絡電話	(02)86925588 轉 5317
郵政劃撥	帳戶第 0100559-3 號
郵撥電話	(02)23620308
印 刷 者	文聯彩色製版印刷有限公司

2016 年 6 月初版・2020 年 2 月初版第六刷
版權所有　・　翻印必究
Printed in Taiwan.

ISBN	978-957-08-4737-6　(平裝)
GPN	1010500768
定　　價	900 元

著作財產權人　國立臺灣師範大學
地址：臺北市和平東路一段 162 號
電話：886-2-7734-5130
網址：http://mtc.ntnu.edu.tw/
E-mail：mtcbook613@gmail.com

感謝

〈倔強〉3DNA LIVE 版 音樂提供／相信音樂
（詞・曲／五月天阿信、演唱人／五月天、OP／認真工作室、SP／相信音樂國際股份有限公司）

王力生、王雪妮、何瑞章、林欣穎、林雅惠、陳建宏、陳韋誠、黃奕穎、楊凌雁、羅翊晨
協助拍攝本教材及試用教材期間使用之相關照片

聯合報、艋舺龍山寺
授權提供本教材之相關照片

（以上依姓氏或單位名稱筆畫順序排列）

國家圖書館出版品預行編目資料

當代中文課程 3 課本 ／ 國立臺灣師範大學
國語教學中心策劃 . 初版 . 新北市 . 聯經 . 2016年6月
360面；21×28公分 . (Linking Chinese)
ISBN　978-957-08-4737-6（平裝）
［2020年2月初版第六刷］

802.88　　　　　　　　　　　　　105007618